Accidentally Cricket

Accidentally Cricket

Alan Haselhurst

The Professional and Higher Partnership Ltd

ISBN 978-1-907076-00-8
First published 2009 by The Professional and Higher Partnership Ltd
4 The Links, Cambridge Road, Newmarket, Suffolk, CB8 0TG

www.professionalandhigher.com

Credits
Cartoons: Hoby (www.hobycartoons.com)
Editorial management, text design and typesetting:
The Running Head Limited (www.therunninghead.com)
Cover design: Richard Carr, Carrdesignstudio (www.carrstudio.co.uk)
Printing and binding: MPG Books Group, Bodmin and King's Lynn

Contents

For Essex County Cricket Club

– in grateful thanks for allowing me to be a member of
the Committee for twelve years and for the
friendship and insights it has brought.

Acknowledgements

Six years have passed since the publication of *Incidentally Cricket*. Since then people (I won't say exactly how many) have asked when a further account of the activities of the Outcasts Cricket Club might be expected.

Well, of course, it had to be compiled and I was experiencing a big increase in the demands of the day job. I also needed a new publisher, Queen Anne Press having exited the scene. The prospect of finally securing a successor spurred my efforts to complete this latest volume. I am most grateful to Anthony Haynes for coming to my aid and to John Blundell who made the introduction.

Anthony has given me a great deal of useful guidance, not least about my excessive use of adverbs. His scrutiny has hopefully helped to make *Accidentally Cricket* a better read. Before he came into the picture my long suffering Parliamentary Assistants, notably Tom Lockton, made useful comments and criticism. In the end, though, responsibility is mine. I apologise in advance for any mistakes which have survived the checking process. As to the final product, it is meant to be a bit of fun with something for ardent cricket lovers and less ardent cricket lovers alike.

Once again the slog of converting my longhand scribbles into text on the computer fell to my wife, Angela. I cannot thank her enough for the skill, patience and hard work which she contributed. The family connection is extended by a set of illustrations from my cartoonist son, David (Hoby). They are a far cry from his political cartoon strips which are acquiring a growing reputation. My thanks go to him as well.

I freely make the customary disclaimer that the characters who feature in this book bear no relation to any persons living or dead and any resemblance is strictly accidental. There is, however, one possible exception to this, for I have come under heavy pressure from my distinguished American friend to have a presence in this novel beyond the acknowledgements page. If he recognises himself in what I have written, I shall strenuously deny it!

My publisher and I (I like that) would like the sales of this book to do more than cover its costs. We propose to donate a small percentage of the revenue to the Lord's Taverners.

Encouraged by Anthony Haynes and excited by the launch of *Accidentally Cricket*, a fifth book is now in my mind and already spilling on to paper. The most I can tell you at this stage is that *Unusually Cricket* begins with the words 'France was a mistake.' The rest is up to your imagination – and mine.

Members of the Outcasts Cricket Club

Rashid Ali
Colin Banks
Ray Burrill
Phil Cole
Charlie Colson
Dean Faulds
John Furness
Richard Furness
Winston Jenkins
Toby Lederwood
Kevin Newton
Harry Northwood
Jon Palmer
David Pelham
Nigel Redman
Tom Redman
Greg Roberts
Basil Smith
Stewart Thorogood
Alan Birch (in absentia)
Tim Jackson (in absentia)
Simon Crossley (Scorer)
Syd Breakwell (Umpire)

Prelude

THE CELL DOOR CLANGED SHUT. The prisoner was on his own. Not for the first time he gave vent to his feelings in a torrent of bad language. 'Shut up', came the rejoinder from outside – not for the first time. The prisoner continued to curse, but silently. He was not used to this. Yet these cramped and grey surroundings looked like being his home for the best part of the next ten years. How in God's name had he got himself into this mess? It was a question he had asked many times over, but only to himself. The answer would continue to haunt him.

His slide from a life of luxury to bare existence in a grim box which passed for twenty-first-century prison conditions had begun with a phone call. It had come at a far from ideal moment. Although the answering machine was switched on, so was the loudspeaker. Ever the opportunist, he had conducted his partner of the afternoon with such speed from door to couch to bed that not only was the speaker unmuted, but the door was open. His caller's voice came through loud and clear. It was a distinct distraction from his current activity. The situation might have been salvaged if the style of the female caller had not been suggestive of an intimacy which had never occurred. The well-modulated voice and choice of language eventually irritated his companion to the point of interruption. With as much dignity as she could muster after earlier consuming (most of) a bottle of a rather good New Zealand Sauvignon Blanc and (the greater half of) a bottle of a particularly fine vintage of Châteauneuf-du-Pape, chased by two (large) Armagnacs, she left. He was furious. A lunch at the Savoy Grill and all for nothing.

He calmed down before ringing Caroline, who had announced herself as a friend of Margot (his brother's wife's sister). The invocation of the lovely Margot was the only reason why he felt obliged to make the call, for otherwise he would have left the grand-sounding Caroline Bingley-Adams to stew. His obligation stemmed from the day of his brother's wedding when he and Margot had found an irregular way of passing the time. He had not wanted knowledge of this to get back to his brother or sister-in-law as Margot had hinted it might if she could not call on him from time to time for little favours. It had been bad enough, he remembered, not being in the right place at the right time to make his best man's speech. (How could he have been, in view of what had happened to his trousers?) No, he suspected trouble if he did not contact Caroline as requested. The exact reason for her enquiry had been withheld. He reflected later that had she only been succinct and to the point his afternoon might not have been ruined.

The point, however, had taken some reaching when finally he spoke to his sister-in-law's friend. To begin with, most of the speaking had not been done by him. Effusive was an inadequate epithet for the flow of words which greeted him. It was made only just tolerable by the amount of flattery with which it was embellished. Slowly the request began to take shape. There was to be a cricket match with a team of celebrities. At least that was Caroline's idea. She (or more likely Daddy, who was increasingly mentioned) had access to celebrities, but they would not commit unless it was a significant charity occasion. Caroline was not sure what might be a sufficient charity that would have fresh appeal. And then she had spoken to Margot, who did know someone who was well connected with charities. (He groaned inwardly.) Hence the call.

Could he help? Wasn't he just *the* expert in putting charity events together? It would be super if she could have his advice, better still his involvement. If he was on board, she would have no difficulty in assembling a super team of cricketing celebs. They would raise lots of money. Daddy would get lots of sponsors. It would be a really super day. Having had his own envisaged super day disintegrated by this bloody woman's intervention, he was of a mind to deliver an emphatic negative. Just before he could open his mouth to deliver his crushing reply, she mentioned the venue.

Helmerstead Hall in Hertfordshire was a veritable jewel in the crown of English rurality. Now owned by a scion of the musical theatre, it had been restored to the highest excellence of its seventeenth-century founders. Not untypically of giants of the entertainment industry the new owner was a cricket devotee and therefore a grateful recipient of one main feature of the legacy of his predecessor. The New Zealand media magnate, Sir Blain Rough, had not had sufficient time to fulfil his aim of adding English squirearchy to his portfolio. During his brief ownership of Helmerstead Hall, the bequest of a distant cousin, he had given priority to the establishment of a cricket venue. He had believed (with possible justification) that this was the key to acceptance in British society. A huge sum of money had therefore been committed to the transformation of a conveniently flat area of land adjacent to the Hall to a cricket ground. Sir Blain was unable to reap the full harvest of his investment due to sudden business vicissitudes and his own even more sudden demise – accredited to heart disease, but in reality stemming from a disease which afflicts a lower part of the human frame.

It was well known that to achieve the most productive atmosphere for money-raising the right venue was crucial. People, the prisoner had reckoned, would come from far and wide to get a glimpse inside Helmerstead Hall. Would that be allowed as part of the package? Caroline Bingley-Adams assured him that it would. Despite his initial reluctance the prisoner had found himself becoming interested. Proximity to wealth had always fascinated him; proximity to great wealth was a compelling attraction. It had been his happy experience that it had usually led to part of the wealth rubbing off on him. His charities, imaginative in their conception, were a most effective cover for his own enrichment. Suddenly he recognised, as Caroline Bingley-Adams bubbled on, an opportunity for a major advancement of his interests. It would be a sweet way of doing her down although she need never know. He allowed himself to be invited to lunch. There was no way in which he was going to undertake any expenditure on his own part.

In the event he would not have been seriously out of pocket. Caroline had suggested a super little salad bar in a shopping mall which was in easy reach of both of them. It had turned out to be a very vegetarian salad bar. There was not even a nut to be had. Neither was it licensed. There was not even the bonus for him of finding his host overwhelmingly attractive. He told himself that he might have been able to compromise had it not been for that voice. She talked so much that few of the dreary mixed leaves left her plate. She enthused about the project, expressed her confidence that it would be an absolutely super event and thanked him so many times for his co-operation that he felt nauseous. But, he had to admit, she knew her stuff and when he finally took his leave of her he was close to being convinced that there was going to be a super profit in it – for him.

A few weeks later he informed her that he had chosen TRANSECT as the nominated charity. He sent her leaflets which explained that it operated in deepest Africa, remotest South America, furthest Asia and other far-flung places. It brought water, fuel, power, transport and culture to some of the most deprived peoples of the world. The leaflets were mainly pictorial and short on detail. A balance sheet was supplied showing that the charity had been in existence for three years, but was now desperately in need of expansion if its 'innovative concept' was to bring its undoubted benefits to the relief of millions. The list of trustees, headed by the Most Honourable Sebastian Umjumbe, the greatest living ambassador of the Third World, was an impressive roll-call of the influential of five continents. It was all utterly convincing. Yet it was at the same time all utterly bogus. Nevertheless in a mere three weeks the great charity organiser had put in place a network to support this pretence. Any cursory enquiry would have been met by a plausible response. He was good; he had done it all before.

So where had it all gone wrong? It was a mistake – he knew that now – to have had his arm twisted and to have taken part in the match. He cursed Caroline Bingley-Adams, but as his mind went over the events of that day for the umpteenth time, he reserved his loudest and longest profanities for the Outcasts Cricket Club. 'SHUT UP' came the chorus again.

A winter's tale

IN A BAR IN THE SMALL COMMUNITY of McCrory in the South Island of New Zealand, the young man lingered. His team-mates had long since departed, some to their wives. His home was a hostel and he was in no hurry to return to it. Perhaps it might not be necessary. He glanced towards the fair-headed girl in the corner who was poring over what looked like a ledger. He had worked out that she must be the daughter of the bar owner. He knew that she was not ignoring him even though she pretended she was. She had been at the match earlier and he was quite sure that she had not been ignoring him there either. How could she have done? Had he not been man of the match? However, by now it was not her love of cricket that he wished to put to the test.

What a great trip so far it had been. He looked back to the months of work he had done to finance his travels: those months on the market stall selling vegetables and learning to fix the scales; in the evenings the taxi work, which had had its perks. He had flown to Bangkok, as he had thought, well flush. By the time he had traversed Thailand and Malaysia it had taken only two days in Singapore to realise that he was broke. There are ways of making money in Singapore and he had discovered them. By the time the restrictions on his air ticket allowed him to move on to Australia he was in funds again and had recorded some unforgettable Asian experiences.

The opportunities to play cricket in Australia and New Zealand had abounded, and with them opportunities of a different kind. Aussie girls certainly liked their cricket – and their cricketers, if they played with the flair of the visiting Englishman. His good looks and – untypically for an Englishman – total lack of inhibition contributed to almost instant acclimatisation, although he found it wise to keep moving on. He did not wish all his deeds to go before him. In Sydney they almost did, but his departure for New Zealand had in the end been orderly. In both North and South Islands he had been able to continue a travelling life which combined pleasure with pleasure.

As he waited for the fair-headed girl to finish what she was doing and put the ledger away, he reflected on what a fantastic time he had had. Yet it could not go on indefinitely. As that thought entered his mind his hand went almost subconsciously to the back pocket of his jeans and extracted the by now crumpled email. It had been sent by his brother and it was the last sentence which stood out. 'If you do take the job, it'd mean you could play for the Outcasts this summer.' Yes, thought Richard Furness, it would indeed.

Richard Furness was unaware during his passage through Australia that two of the Outcasts' biggest hell-raisers were also on the same continent. That they were thousands of miles away in Western Australia probably explained why no tales about them had filtered through to the club cricket world he had inhabited. He had received no forewarning from his brother that any of the Outcasts would be in Australia. Perhaps it was because Charlie Colson and David Pelham themselves had had very little forewarning.

As with so many of the scrapes in which members of the Outcasts Cricket Club found themselves it had begun in a pub. In truth Charlie Colson and David Pelham were already in a mild state of inebriation when they arrived in the Fur and Feathers public house (nearer Fulham than Earl's Court) at around nine o'clock. Their mood was good. They had watched on television a rugby international in which England had trounced the French. It was not victory alone which had put them in good spirits. It had had the accompaniment of a firkin of a new bitter beer. Its source had been identified by Charlie Colson with his habitual display of initiative and drive where real ale was involved. He had managed with a parade of sketchy credentials to have himself registered as a test drinker. That was how a barrel of Aspelhorner's Original came to rest on the kitchen counter of his flat. It had not taken Charlie long to conclude that it was a very reasonable ale, an opinion with which – after four pints and a memorable England victory – David Pelham was only too ready to concur. The chance location on a satellite channel of recorded highlights of an Australia–New Zealand Test Match of ten-year vintage persuaded them into a fifth pint and a delayed departure for a curry at a restaurant for which Charlie had received a strong recommendation.

After an alcohol-free repast they were feeling thirsty when they crossed the familiar threshold of the Fur and Feathers, the first pub in striking distance of the Delhi Deli. They were quickly at home once they saw pumps labelled with two or three of their favourite beverages. They discovered themselves slightly less at home when it became obvious that apart from the barman who had served them, they were the only ones in the entire bar speaking the English language. Everyone else seemed to be Australian. The second surprise was that some of these Australians were drinking such delicacies as Hoppenhall's Charger Bitter instead of some of the cordials more usually associated with them. Charlie Colson and David Pelham observed this phenomenon with interest.

They must have stared too long or conversed too loudly, because the person closest to them glanced cursorily and said 'OK, mate?' It was a flimsy basis for ongoing conversation and the question, if such it was, did not demand a response. Things might have worked out very differently if Charlie Colson had chosen to ignore the opening. Although his tongue was loose his words were remarkably restrained in view of the fact that his interlocutor presented a provocative image. A sun-tanned complexion and long, curly, blond-flecked hair were complemented by moleskin jeans, a replica gold and green top commemorating a particularly emphatic Ashes victory and, if further emphasis of nationality was required, a bushman's felt hat slung loosely on his shoulders. Charlie Colson's cautious 'So you like real ale?' was taken as an invitation to have another. The round embraced six companions whose backs were suddenly replaced by outstretched arms.

During the obligatory eight rounds which followed, the evening could easily have descended into disarray. Jocular exchanges about the respective cricket prowess of England and Australia can with an ill-judged expression here or there give way to insults or worse. On that evening in the Fur and Feathers the noise level might have gone up as the level of liquid in the glasses fell, but harmony prevailed.

The reason for this near-spontaneous outburst of Anglo-Australian accord in west London was the establishment of mutual respect. Charlie Colson and David Pelham were impressed to find Australians with a taste for real ale. The Australians for their part realised they were in the company of two guys who knew their cricket and who, as the hours passed, were revealed as prodigious boozers. What is more, the two Englishmen took in their stride the whisky chasers which were introduced by one of the Australians after about the second round.

It was unclear how much each of the Australian party had already consumed by the time of their merger with the two Outcasts. However, when they were gathered outside the pub after the eventual expiry of drinking-up time, the pallor of Shane Deebrett reflected the yellow and green of his replica Aussie top. This was to prove in no way a barrier to his further enjoyment of the encounter with his new acquaintances. He vomited into a conveniently vacant section of the gutter, pronounced himself as fit as a flea and suggested that they should all retire to his place.

His place turned out more accurately to be their place. Shane Deebrett, who worked in the Australian High Commission, shared a capacious flat with Bob, Craig and Crapper (which was apparently not his real name). The floor of the living room was a carpet of empty cans through which Shane cut a swathe on his way to what David Pelham could see was a huge refrigerator in the kitchen beyond. 'It's Aussie beer from now on,' he said as he returned with an armful of tinnies, 'but you needn't worry about the Scotch.' David and Charlie looked at one another. If their Outcasts friends could see them now . . . But they couldn't and the situation cried out for diplomacy and tolerance. The whisky had affected their taste buds in any case. So what the heck?

Charlie Colson awoke the next day on the section of living room floor he had made his own. The ripple of cans disturbed his next-door neighbour, Mark, who had mysteriously decided to undress before crashing out. There was a gradual chain (or more nearly can) reaction by which all of the participants in the night's session struggled back to life. It struck Charlie as odd that everyone had slept where they had fallen despite four of them presumably having beds in the place. Quite a night it had obviously been. Charlie's last recollection was his halting effort to name all the left-handed batsmen who had scored centuries for England since World War Two. He had got stuck at thirteen when oblivion, probably mercifully, had overtaken him. David Pelham confided his desperate desires to get to the bathroom and to obtain a recovery pint.

In fact it was over large mugs of black coffee that some of the details of the night came to be filled in. Apparently it had been around 3.30 a.m.

that Charlie and David had agreed to play cricket for three weeks in a team with which Craig was associated. It was called The Chunderers and was based in a small town, Mirabillo Heights, in Western Australia. They had committed to being there next month. Shane was organising their visas. Some highly discounted airline tickets would be supplied by another of their new friends, Billy, who worked for the Australian airline Qantas. All they had to do was arrange leave from work and get fit. In stating the latter requirement Craig was met with much mirth from his fellow countrymen. And when he also said that (no worries) accommodation would be provided there was more merriment.

How Charlie Colson and David Pelham had managed to get themselves into this position became clearer when a reduced company returned to the Fur and Feathers, a pub which fortunately practised all-day opening. There had been farewells to Max, a sports journalist, required by his newspaper to cover a darts tournament (for which the previous evening would have been ideal preparation); and to Bob, who was due on shift as houseman in the accident and emergency department in the hospital down the road (for which the previous evening would probably not have been ideal preparation). Charlie and David found themselves feeling (and appearing) totally at one with this dishevelled, unshaven and noticeably beer-stained crowd. A full recapitulation of the night's proceedings had then taken place.

First it had emerged that not only did Charlie and David talk cricket, but they also played it. This led to mention of the Outcasts. In response to questions Charlie and David garrulously described the club, some of its members and some of their exploits. It seemed that all their new-found companions played cricket at various levels and at various times. None more so than Craig Vishinsky, who had been the co-founder of a cricket club in his home town of Mirabillo Heights. It had first been called the Wanderers, but as they had got into their style and stride it had been decided that the Chunderers was far more distinctive and appropriate. At around three o'clock in the morning Craig had pronounced that Charlie Colson and David Pelham would make ideal Chunderers. This was a judgement to which eighteen other Outcasts could readily have assented had they been available for consultation.

It had taken no more than half an hour after the thought had formed in Craig Vishinsky's mind for Charlie and David to be persuaded to accept an invitation. They would go out to Western Australia as guest players for the Chunderers in a tournament due to take place in the course of the following month. It would be a laugh. However, Craig Vishinsky's brain was not entirely befuddled. He knew that two of his team members would be absent from the tournament through injury – groin strains, which in the case of the two individuals concerned was not a complete surprise. No more than half an hour was required in the light of day to persuade Charlie Colson and David Pelham that imminent departure for Australia was a practical possibility and a certain laugh. The massaging effect of Hoppenhall's Charger Bitter played its part in clinching the argument.

After dispersal from the Fur and Feathers there was much to do before a follow-up meeting a week later. The lesser difficulty faced David Pelham. He had long contemplated a career move. His work for a major national charity had begun to lose the attraction which had taken him in that direction. He had become depressed by the sheer scale of what needed to be done and he had reached the conclusion that he could no longer make a difference. Through a mate he had heard that there might be an opening in the commercial department of a county cricket club. He had been interviewed and was awaiting word. A suitable break seemed to be presenting itself.

Charlie Colson's problem was more complicated – a lot more complicated. Sales of industrial paint were not booming. Pressure on salesmen was therefore intense. Charlie's company had introduced a scheme four months ago to provide incentives for its sales force. Early results had been meagre. Rumour of merger was in the air. Redundancy was the fear. This was not the best atmosphere in which to be requesting time off. Charlie spent the morning of Monday following the experience of his Australian weekend contemplating the approach he might adopt to his Divisional Director. Before reaching a conclusion he had a piece of extraordinary good fortune. There landed on his desk a fax from a company he had been courting for some months. It proposed a significant new contract. Thus armed, Charlie was in a powerful position to request annual leave. His reason also found favour with his Divisional Director, who shared Charlie's interest in cricket. Cautious approval matured into full-hearted enthusiasm after forty-eight hours, for Charlie was then called back to be told that there were two or three contacts in Perth who could usefully be visited on behalf of the company. So that was all right.

The domestics were trickier to resolve. Charlie Colson had been dating Liz Allason for over four years. Theirs was a comfortable relationship which had been neither too distant nor too intense. However, for his part Charlie felt that they had been inching closer together. He had been screwing up courage to suggest that Liz might move in with him. It was hardly seizing the moment to depart for Australia for nearly a month on what was very evidently a laddish trip. Charlie felt himself forced into some serious thinking. Jon and Adrienne Palmer were enjoying their new baby. The Crossleys were expecting another. The riveting thought hit Charlie that he wanted more from life and that he did not want more without Liz. They had to talk.

Their best friends would have been fascinated to have had invisible observer status when Charlie met Liz. It was over dinner at her flat. She had said that she wanted to see him and there was a note to her voice which intrigued Charlie, causing him to wonder whether some snare lay in wait for his carefully planned line of approach. The Chardonnay he had accepted was exceptionally good. He noted that it came from Western Australia and wondered if that was a sign. This was served as an aperitif whilst dinner was still in preparation. That too was different. Most often they went out or had a take-away. Well into the second glass Charlie's courage grew to the extent that he began to recount his experience of the previous weekend. His glass had been filled again before he approached the punch-line.

'Oh!', she said and for a little while nothing more. She sat down twisting her glass in her hand. Charlie picked up the bottle of Chardonnay with a view to refreshing it. Liz shook her head and then Charlie realised that she had been drinking water, not wine. He equally realised that he had emptied his own glass and took steps to remedy that situation while racking his brain as to how best to remedy what now looked to be a seriously awful situation enveloping him. 'Oh!' Liz repeated. She looked utterly crestfallen. 'But', and her voice trailed away. 'But, look, there's more', said Charlie. 'Oh God!' choked Liz, promptly bursting into tears. 'Oh God!' Charlie thought to himself grimly, 'this is going really well.' Barely noticing that his glass was empty again, Charlie went down on one knee and launched his big surprise. He was quite unprepared for hers.

The visit to Western Australia had gone ahead with mixed fortunes. The Signal Hotel in Mirabillo Heights was not one of the world's greatest locations. Situated at the centre of the town it was adjacent to the only set of traffic lights within a hundred miles. These shone more brightly into David Pelham's bedroom at night than they did in the street during the day. This *lumière* was not without *son* as heavy lorries revved their engines or clanked their gears as they negotiated the intersection. The bathroom was so far from being ensuite that it required mounting two flights of stairs. Fortunately there were never many residents during Charlie and David's stay. They worked out that the bar was nearer than the bathroom. It was large and well equipped – unlike the bathroom. The food was plentiful and good. Combined with the liquid hospitality it amounted to a serious handicap to fitness.

There had been eight matches in all. Like many more exalted tourists before them, Charlie and David had found it hard to adjust to Australian conditions. The pitches on which the Chunderers played offered more extreme variation than any simple contrast between the Sydney Cricket Ground and the WACA in Perth. At first Charlie Colson's gentle in-swingers were greeted by bush cricketers with much the same enthusiasm displayed by the Outcasts' regular opponents. For self-respect he had to concentrate on accuracy. By the end of the tour he was achieving an analysis more in the nature of 2-30 than the 1-70 with which he had started. The same lesson had to be learned by David Pelham, whose off-spinners came up against fewer left-handed batsmen than he would have liked. In the end he managed to obliterate the memory of a horrendous mauling when he had gone for 100 off eight overs by cleaning up on a dodgy pitch with 7-15 and bowling the Chunderers to a big win at Dunces Creek.

Batting had been easier, but that was a relative term. It took Charlie and David a while to accustom themselves both to the light and then to the bounce. Against bowling which was not often better than their own they fared better (that too was a relative term) as match followed match. Their finest hour came appropriately in the climactic game. A team called the Hoppers from the neighbouring but distant township of Runts Mill had piled up an immense total of 352 during which even the greatly improved Englishmen had not been entirely spared. What was euphemistically called tea stretched to the best part of an hour, leaving the Chunderers forty-five overs or until sundown to get the runs. After fifteen overs this prospect, never bright, had dimmed. A score of 75-6 was not a good platform from which to launch a final assault. There would be at least eighteen occasional cricketers back in the UK who would heavily have backed this opinion on being made aware that the batsmen at the crease, both on nought, were Charlie Colson and David Pelham. Naturally they did not reach the target, but defeat came only after David had notched up a half-century and Charlie had been left not out on 84. The home team drew consolation from the treatment their guest players handed out to the two Runts Mill bowlers who had done the early damage. Clearly tiring, they found themselves up against a pair who were demob happy. The bat was swung almost recklessly, but to tremendous effect. The other visiting bowlers were found to pose no threat at all and for an hour an improbable victory looked to be on the cards. The inspired partnership was broken in the most unfortunate way. David Pelham answered the call for a second run without realising in his and everyone's excitement that it had come not from his batting partner but from Craig Vishinsky on the pavilion steps. On realising his mistake he could not recover his ground and was comfortably run out.

This near-heroic stand put together by the two Poms was given pride of place on the back page of the Mirabillo Heights *Messenger*. Up to that point Charlie Colson and David Pelham had starred only on the front page. They had made a pact before leaving the UK that in the absence of any seriously drinkable beer being available in Australia they would be obliged in the interests of harmony, international diplomacy and sheer mateship to drink the local brew. Tinnies! Their approach was founded in the belief that the beer which came in such receptacles was of a lower order that could be consumed at will. This gave them a head start over most of their Australian hosts. Records tumbled before them: most tinnies in a playing day, most tinnies before start of play, most tinnies in transit before start of play, most tinnies at the crease during an innings, most tinnies during a tea interval, most tinnies whilst fielding and most tinnies between official close of play and official closing time. This last was the most difficult record to authenticate as official closing time was not always recorded.

One record eluded them during their sojourn in Western Australia. The club to which they had been attached had acquired its name for no abstract reason. Chundering was a mark of esteem. Scores were kept as meticulously as runs scored and overs bowled. The Chunderer of the Match award guaranteed the holder free beer until close of play in the following match. The prestigious Chunderer of the Season award was chosen with all the deliberation associated at a higher level with the Young Player of the Year citation. With their dismissive view of the potency of Aussie ales there was no danger of either Charlie Colson or David Pelham being in the frame. However, following a riotous send-off, necessary monopolistic occupation of one of the toilets on the aircraft which carried them back from Perth to London would have earned some plaudits from the mates they had left behind.

When the memo landed on his desk, Kevin Newton had to pinch himself. His few years in local government work so far had offered variety and a fair number of challenges. But in sterner moments of assessment he had to admit that nothing he had done could be rated other than humdrum or routine. Understandably the content of the memo took some digesting. Barbados. A two-week seminar: building better communities. Two volunteers required. There had to be a catch. Well, there was, but it was not necessarily to his disadvantage. It had been decided high up in the chain of command that London's representatives should be chosen from his borough. High up within the borough organisation it was decided that this was a low priority. The chief executive consulted his senior colleagues, and it was the boss of Kevin's department, Len Hutton, who was deputed to select.

The process of selection would not have passed any test of fairness or objectivity, but it was brilliant in outcome. Len Hutton's parents were Bajans. Their first child was born during the England (or then MCC) tour of the West Indies with the great Yorkshireman, Len Hutton, as captain. Being keen cricket followers and having aspirations that their child might one day improve himself by moving to Britain, Mr and Mrs Hutton optimistically named their son Leonard. Young Len inherited his parents' love of cricket and likewise his father's inability to master the rudiments of the game. He did fulfil their ambition that he would study and work in Britain, where he had done modestly well for himself. Noting the small print in the prospectus for the seminar, Len Hutton realised that first amongst equals should be anyone in his division who was an active cricketer. That left two people: Kevin Newton and Toby Lederwood. So off they went.

The programme for the seminar was not overloaded. Nor could it be said that the standard of participants would have merited more intensive sessions. Clearly other organisations had similarly given the event low priority. Rigour was conspicuously lacking; free time was not. Most of it was unregulated apart, that is, from periods allocated to cricket. Those running the seminar had evidently felt that a mini-tournament on the local cricket ground would put an indispensable West Indian stamp on proceedings. Kevin Newton had been eager to enter into the spirit of the event. He had continued his winter coaching sessions, having already become (by the standards of the Outcasts Cricket Club) a sensationally improved batsman. His wicket-keeping skills had remained uncertain, varying, his friends maintained, according to the length of his hair. This theory would require further exploration when, after three days in Barbados, Kevin decided to shave his head.

Kevin Newton had always been sensitive to tonsorial fashion. Seeing so many West Indian men with shaved heads and influenced by his surroundings he had decided to take the plunge or, more appropriately in this case, the cut. The cheery barber who had executed the order assured his customer that it would make him a star with the ladies. It was unclear to Kevin at the time whether this was the gratuitous offering of an observed phenomenon or a pitch for the sale of some gentlemen's requisites. However, within less than twenty-four hours the barber's prophecy was proved accurate – at least in the singular sense. Kevin and Toby met Gloria at the first of the cricket matches with which the seminar was liberally imbued. She was of mixed blood and stunningly beautiful. How Kevin made 27 runs that day he would never know. His mind was entirely on other things (and not on building better communities). His distraction was evidenced by two dropped catches whilst fielding in the deep. As Toby observed afterwards it was as well that he had not been behind the stumps.

Kevin Newton learned two important things from his visit to Barbados (three if you include the fact that a newly shaven head burns badly in the sun). He very much wanted to marry Gloria Lockwood. From the moment they met the priority for the rest of Kevin's stay on the island was not with building better communities, but with building a better relationship with this fabulous woman. She seemed keen to join the project. As days passed, their friendship and intimacy grew. Gloria even liked cricket. This inspired Kevin to rather greater performances on the field of play than in the workshops of the seminar. The chance of this being a mere holiday romance evaporated on news that Gloria, a high-flying young solicitor, had decided to take up a job offer from a firm in London. Meeting Kevin had finally swayed her into leaving Barbados.

The second prize which Kevin took from Barbados was the knowledge that Toby Lederwood would be an excellent recruit to the Outcasts. A left-handed bat with a long reach, he put in a couple of good performances, dealing particularly well with some fierce if erratic fast bowling. He also looked a useful left-arm spinner. Perhaps of greatest importance was his knowledge and consumption of real ale. This was a quality Kevin learned at second hand, because these prime beverages were not available in Barbados. He and Toby had agreed that it was diplomatic to go native and consume rum in its many manifestations. In the process each had respected the other's capacity. The bond of friendship between them was further reinforced by Kevin's reliance on Toby to produce a comprehensive report on the seminar for their employers. Toby had at least attended all of the sessions in workshop and plenary, whilst Kevin's attendance had declined from the point of his becoming acquainted with Gloria Lockwood.

So it could be said that Richard Furness, Charlie Colson, David Pelham, Kevin Newton and Toby Lederwood (Outcasts members and new recruit) had wintered well. During their various sojourns overseas all had heard casual mention of a charity linked to cricket. They had not given it a thought. Eventually they would.

At about the time when Charlie Colson and David Pelham were still in residence at the Signal Hotel in Mirabillo Heights, WA, there was a gathering of two elderly ladies in the state of Oklahoma, USA. Geraldine Rogers and Margaret Hamersteen had recently been blessed with rich widowhood. Geraldine's husband had been big in oil, Margaret's enormous in the vice industry. The late Mr Rogers had had a streak of meanness deeper than the Grand Canyon. His life with Geraldine had been at best austere. What he had refused to spend during his lifetime amounted by his death to millions of dollars. His will made only token provision for their two sons as he had made sure that both of them married the daughters of extremely rich businessmen. Why look after them yourself in adult life, he had reasoned, when others carefully selected could do it for you? When the sudden and generally unexpected onset of a massive heart attack had finally removed Mr Rogers from the control of his empire, a large amount of money had been put at his wife's disposal. As she was already seventy-eight years of age she was determined to waste no time in spending it.

This was an outlook shared by Margaret Hamersteen, who was also a septuagenarian. Her resolve to enjoy her inheritance was fuelled by the resentment she harboured for the humiliations the late Mr Hamersteen had heaped upon her. His money had been made through exploitation of the worst weaknesses and predilections of mankind. Like all good salesmen he had believed in testing for himself the standard of the services his business enterprises offered. If this was not enough, he had been a serial philanderer. Unable to conceive a child with Mrs Hamersteen, he had had no such problem with the other women in his life. For all of them he had plentifully provided on condition that he need have no further contact with them. Nor in material terms had he neglected his wife. She was able to live in a magnificently appointed mansion surrounded by objects of fine art. For most of her married life she had also been surrounded by an ageing mother and a physically handicapped sister. Her love for them absorbed her hours and shielded her from the scorn or pity of her neighbours. Her husband's wealth freely given enabled her to ensure that her dependants had the highest possible quality of life.

After the death of her mother and sister, Margaret Hamersteen was left to brood about her existence. Her mood was severely jolted by a television documentary which presented a very painful exposé of her husband's life. She had, of course, known its general nature. She had never wanted to know the particulars. Suddenly they were paraded before her in lurid detail. The programme had climaxed with the revelation that her elderly and increasingly arthritic spouse was apparently squiring a very young aspiring starlet. So young, the programme hinted salaciously, as to prompt the question as to whether she was of legal age. At that moment Margaret Hamersteen felt the last drop of tolerance drain away from her.

Not many nights later when alone in bed in her part of the house, Margaret Hamersteen was awoken by a commotion which by its racket did not suggest an intruder. On investigation she discovered her husband, clearly intoxicated, nearing the top of the long winding staircase with his arm around that girl, who from her continuous giggling also seemed to be intoxicated. When confronted by his wife Mr Hamersteen's free hand was reaching towards the topmost banister rail. Whether through shock or an arthritic spasm, he stumbled. His wife could have reached out to catch him, but she didn't. Her husband overbalanced and fell backwards. His weight combined with his female appendage ensured a good momentum for the downward plunge. He bumped from stair to stair with increasing

speed before lying motionless on the floor of the grand hall. The girl's fate was less pleasant. At one point she appeared to bounce and thereafter took an aerial route before becoming impaled on the sharply pointed ornamental spike which crowned the bottom banister rail.

Margaret Hamersteen had looked on impassively before returning to bed. She needed to read three more pages of James Thurber to put her back in a mood for sleep. She dreamed of the inheritance she knew would be hers – after she had had time to overcome her grief.

Grief was long gone when she first met Geraldine Rogers. It was at the beauty parlour in which they both had need for heavy investment. They sympathised over each other's position (but not for long) and realised that they had ambitions in common. Not least was their desire to travel, an indulgence their husbands had denied. As companions Geraldine and Margaret felt that they could overcome their handicaps of age and inexperience. They agreed to meet regularly in each other's houses to investigate the prospects over a few drinks. They were soon knee-deep in holiday brochures (and bottles). In the end they decided that Europe sounded like a nice country. It could be combined with a cruise. At a much later stage in proceedings and just in time, someone told them of the need for passports. With that hiccup overcome they were off. It would be quite a trip.

During the winter the Outcasts had suffered attrition. Their longest-standing (and oldest) member, Alan Birch, had decided on a career move. Goaded too far by the regulatory excesses of the National Health Service he finally made up his mind to quit pharmacy in favour of his other great interest in life – food. He and his wife, Margaret, had estimated that there was a more stimulating living to be had catering for the culinary tastes of the British – in Spain. They had acquired a restaurant with rooms in the lively, often rumbustious resort of Los Asbos and planned to make it a gourmet paradise in the sunshine paradise of the Costa Blanca. Thus Alan Birch would no longer be available on Saturday afternoons to play cricket in villages in Essex, although in his new location he would not be short of the company of both Essex man and woman in generous numbers. Since its formation, Alan was the first member to leave the Outcasts Cricket Club. His departure was soon followed by another.

Whether opening or batting in the middle order, Alan Birch had often given stability to the Outcasts' batting – although stability was strictly a relative term. No such claim could be made about Tim Jackson. He was the original rabbit, rarely contributing with the bat. But in a way his loss threatened to be a greater disappointment. Tim was the supreme party-maker. If there was a party within fifty miles of where the Outcasts were playing, Tim could usually be relied on to sniff it out. Similarly, through the winter months he fed the Outcasts' social programme. No one was likely to reproduce this talent. The only consolation for his friends was that his absence was only for one year. He had been offered a secondment to one of the most prestigious art galleries in the United States, and he was Washington-bound. The memory of his leaving party would linger throughout the season. It had lasted twenty-four hours. Coming the day after Alan Birch's bash it had left the normally resilient Outcasts a touch below their best when Monday morning came (and, for several, went). But, apart from giving a party, Tim Jackson also left a present behind him which was to have an unexpected bonus.

Some other Outcasts were not known for being regularly available for selection. Tom and Nigel Redman, besides having to run a bookshop which traded on Saturdays, had a mother who possessed a powerful belief in the fragility of her health. This placed heavy demands on her sons, not to mention her doctor, health visitor, district nurse, physiotherapist and the National Health Service in general. In purely analytical terms there was not a trace of illness or incapacity about her, but she had spent many a cheerful year in denial. Her condition had magically been transformed when she had been persuaded to visit family relatives in Australia, but her northern hemispheric state had reasserted itself immediately on her return. Thereby convinced that Australia was the better place for their mother, Tom and Nigel Redman were engrossed in the concoction of a formula to get her there once again. This exercise in itself acted as a distraction from the greater priority that is properly cricket.

Basil Smith, chartered accountant and off-spinner, was another who had played less often for the Outcasts than he would have liked. In his case the distraction was his wife. Jane Smith subscribed to the view that after five days of labour in confined office space, her husband was entitled to rest and recreation over the weekend. She preferred that this took the form of social intercourse with members of her family, which was large, or concerts or mini-breaks in expensive hotels. As Basil had prospered in his accountancy work, his wife's attitude had been reinforced. With no children to divert them Jane saw more money as opening the way to an ever more intense routine of culture and comfort. Basil loved his wife dearly, but found himself in something of a rearguard action to preserve his cricket slots. Jane was not above planning surprises, and this had sometimes wrecked Basil's carefully laid plans. He had begun to realise that the only hope of prolonging his cricket career was to persuade his wife that they should have fertility treatment.

To make matters worse the Outcasts' most recent recruit, Harry Northwood, had finally decided that he should go to university. What had tilted the balance in this direction was his identification of a degree course with a heavy sporting content. It did not possess the rigour his father would have liked to see in his son's higher education. Nor was the selected university to be found in the higher echelons of such institutions, but it had the merit in Harry's eyes of putting him in striking distance of some of the venues on the Outcasts' fixture list.

Early season

THERE WAS A COLLECTIVE SIGH OF RELIEF amongst the Outcasts gathered in the Sink and Plumber for a pre-season team talk (and drink) when John Furness announced that his brother, who had notoriously played once before with the Outcasts,* was available as a full-time member of the club. Kevin Newton strongly recommended the enrolment of Toby Leder-wood, and this too was greeted with acclamation. The chances of being able to take the field with a full side for every match were thus enhanced.

Early-season experience did nothing to dim the hopes – at least in that respect. Early-season performance was another matter. In Outcasts' circles it was always considered a minor triumph if the team turned up at the appointed place with a full complement. This would usually guarantee a satisfactory number of rounds being bought before, during and after the game. Successful deeds on the field of play were a bonus. Almost sensation-ally the Outcasts' first game of the season against Snidswell yielded a handsome bonus. Nearly always the Outcasts found it hard to win the first match. When Snidswell were the first of the season's opponents, the Out-casts never won. A change in fortune owed something to a virulent bout of food poisoning which had struck members of the Snidswell team on the eve of the match. The likely cause was the veal, ham and egg pie which had been on sale in the Mariners' Rest. This was vigorously denied by the land-lord of this otherwise splendid public house, but suspicion lingered over the provenance of the egg.

At very short notice six schoolboys had had to be drafted into the team. Most of them were of immature years and it said a lot for their pluck and determination that they helped to restrict the Outcasts' winning margin

* *Occasionally Cricket* (1999).

to a mere 20 runs. The Outcasts had batted first and found run-scoring easy against a side robbed of three-quarters of its bowling strength. Regular openers, Jon Palmer (a dad of a few months' standing) and Stewart Thorogood (an aspiring politician who had been aspiring for some while without success), scored sixty for the first wicket before both were deceived by what looked suspiciously like donkey drops bowled by a lanky fourteen-year-old who wore a baseball cap and a ring through his left nostril.

Their replacements, Dean Faulds (a technical engineer) and Rashid Ali (the team solicitor and, until the arrival of Toby Lederwood, the only left-handed batsman in the side) were not so easily fooled. The youth was struck for three sixes in one over and four in the next. This led to his removal from the attack and he did nothing of consequence in the remainder of the game. Dean Faulds and Rashid Ali took the score past the 150 mark before their partnership was broken in an unfortunate manner. Spurred into a second run by a loud cry of 'Yes' from the pavilion end, Rashid Ali was half way down the pitch before realising that Dean Faulds had not moved. His involuntary yell was actually in response to a message telegraphed from the pavilion by Winston Jenkins (well-built, Welsh-born, black banker) announcing that they had successfully backed a 25-1 outsider in the 2.30 pm at Pontefract. Rashid Ali was less successful in trying to recover his ground.

Winston Jenkins' temporary triumph over the bookies was not to be matched by any batting heroics. Whether through over-concentration on his winnings or distraction over his unintended contribution to Rashid Ali's demise, Winston's innings was a desultory affair. A few nicks and prods produced one nick too many, which was safely pouched by the wicket-keeper. His replacement was Phil Cole (an NHS administrator with claims to be an all-rounder). He was the supreme Nicker and Prodder in the Outcasts' side whilst Dean Faulds was not. Unfortunately for the momentum of the innings Dean Faulds was the next man to go. Heaving a cross-batted swing against a short ball, he missed. Although the ball would have comfortably passed over the stumps with a foot or more to spare, the umpire thought differently and accepted the young bowler's falsetto appeal.

Harry Northwood unexpectedly filled the number seven spot in the batting order. He had declared himself available for the game, but thought he would be late. Accordingly he was assigned the role of twelfth man. However, in the event he was on time and it was Ray Burrill (recently qualified veterinary surgeon) who failed to appear. So Harry played and Ray, who had dallied too long on a visit to his girlfriend, was mortified to find himself on the subs' bench when eventually he had arrived. This late switch cut the Outcasts' bowling strength without measurably adding to the batting. Harry, usually a pugnacious and effective batsman, had been vilely drunk the previous evening with some of his pals from uni and it was little short of a miracle that he had turned up ahead of Ray Burrill. Still feeling the effects of a heavy night, Harry at the crease was little more than the nicker and prodder who was his partner. The Outcasts' innings limped along until during the last three overs it ended in a blaze of glory.

The final flourish was unexpectedly provided by Tom Redman and Colin Banks. Thirty-two runs were added in an unbroken last wicket stand. Every aspect of it could fairly be described as unexpected. It had, of course, depended on the removal of the usually cautious Phil Cole and the unusually lethargic Harry Northwood. With few overs left Phil Cole had sensed the need for urgency but not for quite the stroke he played. Snidswell's captain had been persuaded to toss the ball to another of his young substitutes. The persuasion had come from the boy's father. Believing at that stage of the Outcasts' innings it probably did not matter, the captain indulged his team-mate, who also happened to be his bank manager. The decision had a dramatic and possibly decisive effect on the outcome of the game.

The boy bowled simple medium pace with the advantage of straightness. He could not have known that Phil Cole would choose his first delivery to try to change the pace of his innings. An unaccustomed full swing of the bat sent the ball high in the air. So far did it travel skywards that almost any member of the fielding side could have got into position to catch it. Nine people quickly eliminated themselves from the running, but there remained a closely contested play-off between bowler and wicket-keeper, made more intense by virtue of the latter being the bank manager and therefore the boy's father. Everyone watching could see that the rivalry was keen. The captain's one attempt to impose himself was ignored. It turned out that this was the boy's first wicket at this level of cricket and he had no intention of giving his father any share in it. It was finally so achieved only after the somewhat unconventional call of 'Lay off, you bastard.'

The batsmen had crossed. Harry Northwood had the strike. At the other end was John Furness (who worked in the family garden centre and was elder brother to Richard). John was not the strongest contributor to the playing strength of the Outcasts. A batting position of eighth for someone who did not bowl told its own story. More particularly, it gave a guide to the prowess of those who were due to follow, although, as was to be shown, there is an exception to every rule. Harry Northwood played two identical balls from the young bowler with exemplary aplomb, thought he had his measure, swung lazily at the next, was struck on the pad and obliged to depart LBW. Family resentment obviously still simmered, for the wicket-keeper took no part in the appeal. Tom Redman took a single off the first ball he faced, leaving John Furness to play the remaining ball of the over. Whether by chance or intention this 'did a bit'. John Furness, drawn into the shot, only succeeded in edging to the wicket-keeper. Paternal feathers were smoothed.

The partnership between Tom Redman and Greg Roberts (retail banking consultant) being stillborn, the Outcasts' innings looked to be on the verge of extinction when Colin Banks (estate agent, fast bowler and eternal romantic optimist) arrived in the middle. Colin, who entirely wrongly fancied himself as a lusty hitter, egged on Tom, who batted too infrequently to have any form, to join him in having 'a bit of a dip'. Incredibly it came off and mostly at the expense of the bank manager's son, whose second and third overs went some way to extinguishing the pleasure of the first. The precious runs scored proved to be in excess of the margin of victory.

If he had been indecisive at one point in the Outcasts' innings the Snidswell captain knew exactly what he was doing when it came to what was formally known as the tea interval. He was familiar with the Outcasts by now, and on becoming aware of the decimation of his team he had planned a diversionary tactic. There would not be the usual tea in the pavilion; instead the teams would take a break at the nearby Mariners' Rest. The Snidswell captain's hope was that this would lead to an injudicious amount of beer consumption by the visitors. The principal beer sold at the Mariners' Rest was a real ale of the finest quality: Dunderwell's Thickhead Ale. Its name referred strictly to the appearance of the beer when properly drawn from the pump, for it was well known that generous consumption never usually led to morning-after effects. Short-term effects on the field of play were, the Snidswell captain hoped, another matter.

How long the interval between innings could be drawn out was something requiring delicate judgement. The Outcasts were mostly ready to enjoy the unexpectedly early access to Dunderwell's Thickhead Ale. However, after the third (and in some cases fourth) round the umpires became somewhat testy. What finally caused the Snidswell captain to declare the interval closed was a warning that the young substitute members of his team, brassed off by their exclusion from the licensed premises, might very well abandon the game. Such was the general air of rowdiness in the saloon bar of the Mariners' Rest that he hoped that his strategy would bear fruit. The first six overs of the Snidswell innings bolstered his optimism.

The Outcasts, who rotated their captaincy, had Winston Jenkins in charge for this match. Winston had not had a great match with the bat, but as an all-rounder he could always hope that failure in one discipline could be compensated by success in the other. Moreover he had a cricket brain when he chose to engage it. After Colin Banks and Stewart Thorogood had each sent down three wayward overs studded with no-balls and wides, Winston Jenkins reappraised the situation. It was apparent that the cutting edge of his leading strike bowlers had been blunted by the extended sojourn in the Mariners' Rest. Whilst this had not prevented a couple of wickets being taken (Colin Banks had managed two deliveries which were straight and fast) far too many runs had been squandered. The natural replacements were himself and Phil Cole. They had not practised abstinence whilst in the Mariners' Rest, but bowling at no more than (and in Phil Cole's case much less than) medium pace they seemed less handicapped in achieving accuracy – or a degree of it. Penetration was another matter, and the Snidswell innings began to build.

Winston Jenkins knew that he had to get more overs out of Colin Banks and Stewart Thorogood, but their state of health necessitated their re-introduction to the attack being postponed as long as possible. Yet with the combination of Phil Cole and himself not working, his options were limited – more limited than they need have been, Winston Jenkins reflected, had Ray Burrill got to the match on time. (The Snidswell captain had politely declined to accept a late substitution.) That left Tom Redman (a highly speculative call) and Greg Roberts (a desperate one). Tom Redman bowled leg-spin. What Greg Roberts bowled defied generic description. On his day, for a club bowler and very occasional cricketer, Tom Redman was quite a respectable leg-spinner. This type of bowler more than any other needed solid practice. Getting away from the demands of his mother was achieved sufficiently infrequently to deny him this. When he began to bowl in any game neither he nor his captain knew exactly what to expect.

What the Snidswell batsman with 47 to his name did not expect third ball after he had knocked two long-hops for four apiece was a perfectly pitched topspinner which hurried on to him straight and low. Not even the Outcasts' genial but erratic travelling umpire Syd Breakwell (ex-policeman) could be faulted for allowing the appeal. It was as plumb an LBW as one could wish to achieve. Any thought Tom Redman might have had of passing this off as a carefully crafted ploy was dispelled when 10 runs were taken from the three remaining balls of the over. Nevertheless Winston Jenkins did not regard a return of one wicket for 18 runs as fatal to the cause.

After seven more overs of Phil Cole and Tom Redman in tandem, the captain was inclined to revise his judgement. The new batsman, his Snidswell opposite number, had a partner who appeared well settled. Together they pushed the score on at what must for the home side have been a gratifying rate. This partnership represented the last of the adults. The Snidswell captain's tactic had been to put his team regulars in the first five places in the order. Most of them were batsmen or had pretensions to bat. The youngsters followed. So much was now apparent to Winston Jenkins. By taking one more wicket he thought that there might be a chance of complete breakthrough. But how to get it? It took no more than a cursory glance at Colin Banks and Stewart Thorogood to persuade Winston that he must urge further effort from Phil Cole and Tom Redman and be ready to play a captain's role himself. He went into an exclusive huddle with them. Luck, it seemed, was with him.

It came with the third ball of Tom Redman's last permissible over. The first and second balls could fairly be described as dross and were punished as such by the Snidswell captain. The next delivery was in all truth no better than its predecessors. It was short of a length and wide. The Snidswell captain was intent on meting out more punishment. Dean Faulds, fielding surprisingly and dangerously close at a sort of square cover, instinctively turned his back as the batsman shaped to play his shot. The ball struck Dean Faulds so hard that it ricocheted in an upward direction, giving Harry Northwood at deep point time to rush over and make the catch. A much larger, more inclusive huddle of jubilant Outcast players then took place. It took a few moments to appreciate that one member of the side was not a participant. Dean Faulds lay writhing on the ground.

When the game resumed, a beanpole of a young man was at the crease and Dean Faulds was in the pavilion. The injured fielder was receiving attention (treatment would have been too strong a word) from Sophie, the wife of the Outcasts' scorer, Simon Crossley. On this occasion she was the nearest thing to a nurse available. Between his 'I'll never walk again' and her 'It's only a bruise' there was scope for compromise, but for a while Dean Faulds was left feeling very sorry for himself. So was the beanpole.

Given two balls left in his spell, a better bowler than Tom Redman would have quickly disposed of the new batsman. There was every appearance of it needing only a straight ball. Tiring, perhaps unused to bowling his full allocation off the reel or lacking fitness in this early season encounter, or feeling the effects of the between-innings break in the Mariners' Rest, Tom was unable to dispense the necessary prescription. Both deliveries were wide, short and inviting. The beanpole lunged at each one without moving his feet and consequently without contact. His efforts earned a frown from his senior partner and an immediate recall for Colin Banks and Stewart Thorogood. Their appetite had been whetted by what they had seen. A spring had belatedly returned to their step.

And so it was. Bowling as fast as they were able and occasionally straight, Colin Banks and Stewart Thorogood mopped up the rest of the Snidswell innings. They were too quick for the makeshift young players in the team. Except one. Coming in at number eleven was the smallest of the schoolboy substitutes. After he had taken guard and crouched over his bat there seemed scarcely any gap between the top of his pads and the peak of his helmet. Colin Banks licked his lips, but soon he was licking his wounds. The young boy – he was aged twelve – could handle a bat. For all that there appeared a lack of proportion about him there was no lack of harmony in the way he moved to meet the ball. After two defensive strokes he demonstrated maturity beyond his years by recognising a half-volley for what it was and caressing it to the boundary. Some rather lustier blows followed as he treated the Outcasts' bowling at its true worth. It finally took an inspirational outswinger from Stewart Thorogood to get the wicket of the middle order batsman, leaving the young tyro undefeated. In the Mariners' Rest afterwards they discovered that he knew how to handle a pint as well as a bat.

It was at about the time of the match between Snidswell and the Outcasts that Geraldine Rogers and Margaret Hamersteen were embarked on the high seas. They had chosen the SS *Pink Princess* because it was the only vessel which offered a cruise across the Atlantic and through the Mediterranean. The final destination was Istanbul. From this furthest point of Europe the two ladies planned to journey westwards to sample as many delights as possible of 'this old country', as they termed it. In the meantime the journey eastwards held its own delights. In choosing the *Pink Princess* the ladies had thoughts only for its advertised comforts and destination. There was no reason for investigating its ownership. It struck them after boarding that there appeared to be many more male passengers than female. By the time everyone had taken their places in the dining salon for the first time the male majority was shown to be very pronounced. As some tables were multi-occupied it took a little longer to work out that all the couples on board were of the same sex. Not so strange perhaps, Geraldine and Margaret reflected, because that was precisely their situation.

Their fellow passengers were charming and attentive. There was always a nearby hand or arm ready to assist lest either of the elderly pair appeared at risk of stumbling. Geraldine and Margaret were delightfully cosseted. It was on the second afternoon at sea that Julian and George, fashion consultants, asked them whether they would be interested in a game of bridge. The ladies exchanged glances, neither at first being sure whether the other played. They agreed to give it a go whilst protesting their inexperience and hoping that they would not make a mess of it. Geraldine and Margaret readily assented to George's suggestion that there should be a token money element 'just to keep us honest'. It was after all just for fun. Five cents a point was adjudged to be about right. After two rubbers in which Geraldine and Margaret had carried all before them the amount was doubled, and so roughly were the ladies' winnings. They agreed to reconvene after dinner when the stakes were raised to 50 cents a point. At a quarter to midnight with Geraldine and Margaret still going strong, re-invigorated rather than dulled by two large brandies, Julian professed to being a little weary and proposed an adjournment to the next day. The ladies thanked the men for a 'most entertaining' evening. They gratefully accepted an escort back to their cabin. It was fortunate that Margaret carried a capacious handbag which spared them the embarrassment of walking from the scene with large wads of dollar notes in their hands.

Back in the Starlight Lounge where the one-sided encounter had taken place, views were exchanged between Julian and George and a circle of other passengers who had been drawn in as observers. Such a run of luck, it was concluded, could not last for ever. The ladies would surely be there for the taking well before the end of the voyage. If Julian and George had ideas of further rubbers of bridge in mind, one of the other passengers who had followed the play had formed a different plan. Edward, an actor whose best days were behind him, kept his thoughts to himself. Change of game, change of atmosphere, change of tempo – that was his formula. In a word, poker was the answer. Could he put the right sort of school together and could he entice the two old biddies into it? In the end it did not require much of his fading charm.

It was over a mid-morning coffee that Edward waylaid Geraldine and Margaret. Employing one of his smarmiest smiles from which sincerity and warmth had long drained, he suggested drinks in his cabin after dinner and possibly, if they were interested, a hand of cards. The ladies accepted with alacrity and declared what fun it would be. Edward shared his cabin with an ambitious but untalented actor who was thirty years his junior. Adam possessed eager charm and a bad gambling habit. During breakfast Edward had trawled the ship's restaurant for poker players and found two oil rig workers who claimed to be veterans. At Edward's behest Adam arranged drapes around the cabin and fixed the lighting so that the character of a gambling den could be adopted at the flick of a switch. To this carefully staged venue Geraldine and Margaret came – and went four hours later ten thousand dollars richer.

In their second match of the season the Outcasts found reality re-asserting itself. Chipping Figworth was a new fixture. The Outcasts found it hard to maintain a constant fixture list. Not all their hosts were in sympathy with their approach to cricket. Sometimes those who were could still nevertheless be affronted by some outrage perpetrated singly or collectively by the visitors from south-west London. The Outcasts were at risk of their name going before them, but some village sides refused to believe the enormity of the tales told and it might take a few seasons before they were stripped of their simple trust. So before playing a club for the first time the Outcasts had come to appreciate the wisdom of restraint before and, if at all possible, during a match. It was extremely unfortunate therefore that the evening before the Chipping Figworth game was Charlie Colson's stag night.

It was an unusual stag night, taking place as it did several weeks after Charlie's wedding. Charlie's proposal coincided with an admission by Liz that she was pregnant. Apologies followed as each felt one was due to the other. Then there was laughter which merged into bonding. Afterwards came planning which was swift and decisive. A registry wedding was booked. Charlie's best mate, David Pelham, was sworn to secrecy and engaged as best man/witness. Liz chose a friend from work. The wedding group was as small as that. Liz's parents were dead and her brother was in Canada; Charlie's folks were on safari. For them the news would have to wait. It would probably be no great surprise. But fellow Outcasts were not to be told until a time of Charlie's choosing. To that end involving David Pelham in the secret was a high-risk strategy. The secret remained safe during the sojourn in Australia. However, security came under great strain once Charlie and David were back in Britain and socialising with the rest of the club members in the lead-up to the new cricket season.

Inevitably it was loose talk after hours in the Sink and Plumber, the Outcasts' unofficial headquarters, which caused the news to spread. On that particular evening no more than eight of them had gathered. They had been confronted with a real treat. The landlord had acquired a rare guest beer: Nickelson's Powerhouse Ale. The Outcast members made substantial inroads into the limited stock. Understandably therefore the leak when it came was almost literal. Propelled eventually after the first six pints of the tasty Nickelson brew, John Furness and David Pelham found themselves side by side in the gentlemen's lavatory.

It must have struck John Furness how odd it was that such a notorious consumer as Charlie Colson was missing such a special evening. With tongue loosened, David Pelham let slip a cryptic remark which far from ending the exchange simply provoked a series of more probing questions, their penetration only slightly impaired by slurred speech. Back in the snug bar and during the seventh pint, David Pelham's defence mechanism finally crumbled. A flash of light passed through the fog which had begun to envelop John Furness' mind. Suddenly he saw a thread connecting David Pelham's responses. 'He's only bloody well got hitched, hasn't he?' Despite the word 'hitched' being mangled in pronunciation, David Pelham shrank from telling an outright lie. Thus eight Outcasts came to share the secret. That was more than enough to ensure that the knowledge was club-wide by the following morning (to be accurate, by twenty-five minutes past ten o'clock). Outcasts were not easily denied a celebration. That could come later. First there had to be a stag night. By nine minutes past eleven o'clock on the same morning, preparation was already under way.

Arguably there was a lack of co-ordination between Greg Roberts, who, in Tim Jackson's absence in Washington, had taken on the mantle of Social Secretary (strictly on probation) and Winston Jenkins, the Fixtures Secretary. It was nevertheless short notice on the part of Chipping Figworth Cricket Club to request the postponement of the Outcasts' visit by one week. Being keen to oblige a club new to the Outcasts' list of fixtures, Winston Jenkins, consulting only that list (still in unfinished form) readily agreed. That was how Charlie Colson's stag night came to take place on the eve of the match against Chipping Figworth. Quite apart from this unfortunate juxtaposition, Winston Jenkins would have done well to enquire as to the precise reason for the fixture's postponement.

On taking charge of the organisation of the stag night, Greg Roberts' first and strategic decision was not to hold it at the Sink and Plumber. For the otherwise tolerant landlord of their default establishment, he sensed that it might be a binge too far. In any case the snug at the Sink and Plumber lacked space for an augmented gathering. His choice alighted on the Dusty Dray. This was not the product of his own researches; it was a tip from his flat-mate, Colin Banks, who had heard from someone in his office that a friend had spoken well of it. Greg and Colin made the journey to northwest London and were well pleased with what they saw, heard and tasted. Rumour that the landlord and his wife (who was Italian) were flexible and tolerant when it came to parties of the kind envisaged was not unfounded.

43

Armed with the guarantee that never fewer than five fine ales were on draught and that buckets of spaghetti bolognese could be made available at a modest price, Greg and Colin had come away with a firm booking.

It was a great pub and a great night. Every Outcast was present with only one exception. Alan Birch had flown in from Spain on a ticket that had cost him £5.99. He spent several multiples of that first in airline extras and then in celebration of Charlie Colson's retreat from bachelorhood. Tim Jackson was the absentee, being unable to find a sufficiently low-price ticket to cross the Atlantic. Ever a man of extravagant taste and unwilling to fly long distances in the back of the aircraft, Tim could not justify the cost of a business class fare. Instead he sent a fraction of the ticket price by way of a donation to the kitty. It earned him one toast whilst the other partygoers still remembered. Numbers were boosted by some of Charlie's friends from outside cricket, none of whom had the staying power to outlast his friends from inside the cricket circle.

No Outcast left before midnight, but most had gone by dawn. 'After all,' Kevin Newton was heard to murmur, 'there is a match today.' Charlie's other friends could not maintain the pace, possibly by dint of failure to take on board spaghetti bolognese and real ale in the right proportion. The last one of them staggered out soon after midnight whilst the Outcasts partied on. The bridegroom, if such was the appropriate title, was declared officially legless at thirty-seven minutes past three in the morning. Others fell beside him. Last to lie down on the bar floor was John Furness, which was a pity as he was the designated captain for the match later that day. Of the fifteen Outcasts who had declared their availability to play against Chipping Figworth, only nine got to their beds with varying degrees of lateness that early morning. The only thing that could be said about the other six was that their whereabouts were known.

The first attempt to rescue the situation was begun by Rashid Ali at around ten o'clock. Never the leading imbiber of the group, Rash had managed seven hours' sleep not without interruption, but it helped him to be thinking straight when he finally forced himself out of bed. After two large mugs of black coffee he commenced a roll-call. Starting with the easy ones he found that Syd Breakwell, who had been the first to leave after midnight, would be reporting fit for umpiring duty. Simon Crossley was up and about, albeit with a sore head, and did not doubt his ability to sit quietly and keep the score. Rashid Ali wondered which person was his best option to call next. Those with partners, flat-mates or family suggested themselves. But, logically if not perhaps hopefully, he felt he should try first the captain for the day.

Attempting to reach John Furness at his flat yielded Rashid Ali no reward and plenty of cause for concern. The worry deepened after Amanda Sutton, Stewart Thorogood's partner, had informed him (gaily) that Stewart had not returned home and that she imagined that he was 'probably in some nightclub somewhere' and the news from Jane Smith (imparted frostily) that Basil had returned home 'in a dreadful condition' and would be going 'nowhere today'. The phone at the Redmans' bookshop was answered by Tom, who was not down to play that day. He told Rash that Nigel was sleeping it off, but 'would probably be OK'. If that marked a step forward, Rash soon felt that he was several paces back after achieving no replies at all from Phil Cole, Winston Jenkins and Dean Faulds. Nor was there any comfort from the parental home of Harry Northwood. His mother (resignedly) said to Rash that she presumed Harry was in bed, because his door was locked with a sign saying 'Bugger off', which had not been there yesterday.

Adrienne Palmer had slightly better news depending on how it was interpreted. Jon was in the bathroom, but she did not know whether this was a prelude to getting up or going to bed. He had been there 'some time'. It took five minutes for Greg Roberts to answer the phone. Ever conscientious, he assured Rash that he would be ready for the game, but to Rash's ear he sounded far from ready. Greg's limited ability on the cricket field could not bear much diminution from external factors. Rash did not gain massive assurance from Ray Burrill, who answered the phone soon enough, but complained of feeling dreadful. Kevin Newton swore at him for being disturbed, but acknowledged that he would 'just about make it'. Toby Lederwood was left until last. He sounded surprisingly chirpy in comparison. Perhaps being the Outcasts' newest recruit made him aware of his obligation although, Rashid Ali reflected after he had put the phone down, it had not appeared to stint his consumption at the Dusty Dray.

After this round of calls it was plain to Rashid Ali that the Outcasts were well short of fielding a team. For an inaugural fixture this was especially embarrassing. Then and there Rash would have cancelled the game, but as he had not been directly involved in the arrangements he realised that he did not know whom at Chipping Figworth to contact. He mused over a third mug of black coffee how best to get out of this mess. And then his phone rang. Before picking it up he would not readily have guessed the identity of his caller. 'This is your captain speaking.'

Rashid Ali was not slow in guessing where the call was coming from. There was a clink of glasses in the background. After a night on the floor of the Dusty Dray, John Furness sounded surprisingly rational if hardly energetic. He was able to account for the whereabouts of Phil Cole, Winston Jenkins and Dean Faulds, but was reticent about their stage of health. Caution was understandable as two of them were still unconscious. Dean Faulds' condition was scarcely better as he had fallen asleep in the confined environment of a cubicle in the gents' lavatory and so far had articulated nothing more than groans. John Furness reported that before crashing out he thought he had seen the erstwhile bridegroom leaving the pub with his arm around the shoulders of Stewart Thorogood (but it could have been the other way round). There had never been any thought of Charlie Colson taking part in the match against Chipping Figworth, but Stewart Thorogood, unless located, would be missed. Piecing together such information as they had been able to assemble, Rashid Ali and John Furness took the joint decision to go ahead with the fixture. As far as the logistics of the exercise were concerned much would depend on Arthur.

For some years the Outcasts had frequently relied for transport to matches on an outfit called Executive Sporting Coachways, operated by a chancer by the name of Bill Blimp. It had been very much an on/off relationship in that Bill Blimp had not always been in possession of a vehicle that was roadworthy even by his loose standards. A series of blunders and misjudgements had finally spelt ruin for the would-be transport entrepreneur. After a short spell in one of Her Majesty's custodial institutions (his choice of solicitor had been as ill-judged as several of his business ventures) Bill Blimp had been obliged to find a new way of eking out an existence. The search was prolonged. The Outcasts – not without a measure of relief – were themselves obliged to look for a suitable alternative. Their search had been less prolonged. It had ended providentially in the latter part of the previous season. The result was Arthur.

The first contact had occurred neither at a cricket ground nor a pub, which made the eventual outcome all the more remarkable. A friend of the temporarily absent Tim Jackson was mounting an art exhibition on the premises of a local dealer. As it was due to take place after Tim's departure for Washington he had passed on his two complimentary preview tickets to

Alan and Margaret Birch, who were not due to leave until a fortnight after him. So it was that Alan Birch found himself with a glass (of what he had to concede was a better Chilean Chardonnay than he would have expected to have been served on such an occasion) in one hand and a stick, which had previously supported a diminutive sausage in the other. The consumer was looking around for a receptacle wherein or whereon he would divest himself of the stick. He had edged towards a freestanding object and was trying to decide whether in his present surroundings it was a utilitarian waste bin or a valuable artefact when a voice interrupted his deliberation. 'All it lacks is the archetypal village cricket match.' Momentarily puzzled as to how the words related to the object of his consideration, Alan Birch turned to find their source.

In front of a rural English landscape painting stood a man who on first appearance might have passed for a foreign spy. He was in his late forties, had dark close-cropped hair, a short black beard and slightly sharp features. The fact that a black leather jacket, worn denims and maroon shirt were complemented by an MCC tie did not immediately destroy the image. 'Don't you think', the man continued when he saw that he had gained Alan Birch's attention, 'some cricketers in the foreground would have set it off rather better?' Snapping the sausage-less stick in two and thrusting it into his pocket, Alan Birch found himself drawn into a long, stimulating discussion not about art, landscapes or otherwise, but cricket. Little did he realise at that moment that Tim had unwittingly performed one of his greatest services for the Outcasts, for this was Arthur.

However, the Outcasts were not mentioned until their second meeting, an engagement prompted by Arthur. He had phoned the next day and suggested 'a spot of supper', and while Alan Birch was thinking about that and wondering whether there was time before they left for Spain, he added, 'at Flemms'. Alan Birch thought no longer and reached eagerly for his diary. Angela Flemms, with the training (and more) of a well-known TV chef behind her, had burst upon the culinary scene and taken it by storm. Hers became the place to eat for anyone with pretensions to gastronomy – and Alan Birch had plenty of those. The following Wednesday was proposed. 'Will we be able to get a table so soon'? asked Alan, for he had heard that the restaurant had a long waiting list. 'Oh, yes', said Arthur. And so it proved. Over a dream of a meal when other matters of cricket moment had been exhausted, Arthur was given an account of the Outcasts Cricket

Club. The tale had become steadily less sanitised as the evening progressed. As a clear sign of his disinterest, it was Arthur himself who queried how the Outcasts managed for transport if their cricketing expeditions were inextricably linked with 'a spot of refreshment'. A potted history of the Outcasts' relationship with Executive Sporting Coachways had spanned two rounds of Cognac. 'So', concluded Alan Birch, 'we've been left with a bit of a problem.' To which Arthur had replied, 'I may be able to help.'

A week later at the Sink and Plumber Arthur had got to know most of the Outcasts and some at least of their little ways. The meeting went on into the early hours of the morning, which was one of the more pronounced of the Outcasts' little ways. There had seemed much to celebrate. Arthur explained that he had taken early retirement. Without actually saying so he left the impression that this had been on medical grounds. He was largely a free agent. He 'helped out' with a few projects. His wife's profession (he hinted that it was fashion-orientated) took her out of Britain for much of the summer. His daughters had left home pursuing their own careers. He was a cricket enthusiast and he had another minor hobby: he kept a small collection of vintage coaches. To raised eyebrows (their owners had a mental image of two vintage coaches of recent memory*) he quickly added that he had just acquired an ex-Green Line single decker which was in excellent working order. Weekly trips to cricket grounds in the Home Counties would help to keep it that way. He apologised if it might not offer the comfort to which the Outcasts were accustomed, but his further disclaimers were drowned in a chorus of enthusiastic acceptance speeches, of which 'have another pint' was the most insistent.

Arthur had become happily and loosely attached to the Outcasts as their transport contractor. He asked for nothing more than his fuel costs. He enjoyed the outings and had volunteered for the responsibility of collecting team members before the matches and delivering them afterwards. There were one or two days when he was not available, but he promised to do his best to accommodate all match days in his diary if he was given sufficient notice. Once the season ended the Outcasts saw nothing of him, but he was back on duty when the season began. He had excused himself from the stag night on the grounds that he was entertaining his daughter and one of her business colleagues. Fortunately when contacted by Rashid

* *Incidentally Cricket* (2003).

Ali he was in a position to start early. With a mixture of determination and charm he managed to coax the necessary number of players on to the coach, to collect kit as instructed and to make a final pick-up at the Dusty Dray. So by a remarkable effort the Outcasts fulfilled their commitment to be in Chipping Figworth for a prompt start.

There was also a prompt finish. The game was all over in two minutes short of the hour. The Chipping Figworth captain, having had an early sight of the pitch, had decided that it was a belter. If he won the toss he would bat first. One look at the Outcasts on their arrival prompted a change of mind. He did win the toss and invited the visitors to bat. The Outcasts' innings lasted eleven overs and four balls. It yielded 17 runs of which 6 were extras. The final total represented something of a recovery, as there were only two runs on the board when the seventh wicket fell. The quality of the Outcasts' bowling did not exceed that of their batting, but this time there was no recovery. Chipping Figworth's opening batsmen knocked off the runs in two overs.

By timely improvisation the tea interval (although, if one wished to be pedantic, this was no longer an accurate description) was brought forward. It turned out to be of longer duration than the match. However, in the somewhat strained atmosphere which prevailed, the Outcasts did not feel that they could spin out proceedings until opening time at the Figworth Arms. Midst apologies Winston Jenkins attempted to resurrect respectability by muttering a reference to the team being affected by a bout of food poisoning (the words 'goat' and 'curry' were thrown in for verisimilitude), and the Outcasts withdrew with no certainty that the fixture would be renewed. The lie proved to be ill-chosen. In the rush to have sandwiches ready in time, one of the ladies in charge had imperfectly defrosted the prawns. Sadly, Winston Jenkins and those of his team-mates who had feasted on them in preference to the cheese and pickle alternative ended the day in as poor a shape as they had been twenty-four hours earlier.

It was only in the cold light of Sunday morning that Rashid Ali realised that his pre-match calculations with John Furness had completely failed to take account of the whereabouts of the latter's brother. Missing the match, not to mention the prawn sandwiches, had not been the sole piece of luck enjoyed by Richard Furness. In the course of Friday evening at the Dusty Dray, his concentration on drinking plentifully the health of Charlie Colson had only begun to waver after establishing eye contact with a striking brunette who had appeared behind the bar. It had not taken long for contact to develop beyond the merely ocular. After the landlord had for the sake of form called last orders, he turned to the barmaid and said to her, 'You can go to bed now, love, if you like.' She did and she was not unaccompanied. Not for Richard Furness the floor of the bar or overnight confinement in the gents' lavatory, but whether he obtained more rest was another matter. By the time he came downstairs the following day for breakfast, cooked by the landlord's wife without a blink and with all the trimmings, any possibility of his participation in the match at Chipping Figworth had long since become academic as the players by then were on their way home.

Geraldine Rogers and Margaret Hamersteen disembarked from the SS *Pink Princess* wealthier women than when they had boarded. In every game of chance into which they had been invited or lured they had invariably come out on top. Gradually other passengers had begun to disengage from the company of the two elderly ladies, looking for their pleasures elsewhere. Conscious of their accumulated good fortune the captain invited Geraldine Rogers and Margaret Hamersteen to join him at his table for dinner on the evening prior to the ship berthing at Istanbul. This was not done without an eye to the main chance. He spent most of the meal persuading them to attend the gala party in the ship's casino. There he thought (no, he knew) the odds would favour the house. The shipping line might as well have its share of what the ladies had so far netted. When he waved them farewell at half past eleven the following morning he regretted his intervention. No doubt it had been a pure fluke, but Margaret Hamersteen insisted that the seven of spades had always been her favourite card.

After such a humiliating experience most cricket teams might be expected to carry out a post mortem. The Outcasts conformed to this practice only in part. Having no match on the Saturday after the encounter with Chipping Figworth Cricket Club, most of them turned up at the Sink and Plumber for a 'net'. By five o'clock a number of conclusions had been reached. There was general agreement that in future care would have to be taken when arranging the dates of post-wedding stag nights. Tighter parameters would need to be applied. It was also felt that Arthur should be prevailed on to make his bus available at the conclusion of such events despite the inherent difficulty of predicting when the end might come.

There was absolute clarity about establishing a rule that in any match which did take place on the day after a stag night, whether held pre- or post-wedding, no runs other than boundaries should be taken during the first ten overs. In the debacle at Chipping Figworth no fewer than four players in the Outcasts' team had been run out. They had either not heard the call of their partner or been too lethargic to cover the statutory distance in the time available.

No part of these wise deliberations was pertinent to the Outcasts' next match against a bunch of like-minded cricketers who called themselves the Dregs of Essex (they always drank everything to the last drop). Played on a placid pitch at a school ground on the edge of a picturesque market town, whose principal asset in the eyes of both teams was not its market but its brewery, it proved to be a run feast. The Outcasts narrowly lost, but not before five of their batsmen had recorded half-centuries. There was encouragement too in the form of Richard Furness, who demonstrated the benefits of his Antipodean experience by bowling ten overs for 21 runs and three wickets and by collecting a couple of phone numbers confided to him (separately) by two extremely attractive (and possibly gullible) young women spectators. Neither performance was matched by any other member of the bowling attack. With many fine pints consumed afterwards in the warmest camaraderie with their opponents, the Outcasts (who narrowly won in terms of quantity) felt that their equilibrium had been restored.

It was around this time that Amanda Sutton first heard of a prestigious charity cricket match which was to be played at a luxurious venue in Hertfordshire. Attending a work-related seminar she found herself attached during a coffee break to Caroline Bingley-Adams. Conversation it hardly was. Most of the talking was done by Caroline. To a large extent Amanda let it wash over her head whilst her mind concentrated on which restaurant Stewart should be persuaded to choose to take her to for a meal at the end of this high pressure day. It was hearing the word 'cricket' which broke this chain of thought. It was not so much the mention of her partner's great sporting pastime which grabbed her attention but more the improbability of this languid, talkative lady having so much to say about it. Amanda listened long enough to pick up the essentials and recognise that the event in which Caroline was involved would be 'super' and 'fantastic'. If only out of polite recognition Amanda did chance to say that her partner played cricket and, she admitted later, she might, in a break in the flow of words pouring from the mouth of Caroline Bingley-Adams, have let slip the name of the club for which he played. 'Careless talk' and all that.

In contrast to life on board ship Istanbul was a great disappointment to the travelling duo from Oklahoma. The attraction of any historic city can dim for visitors when they are confined to their hotel bedroom and, more often, its ensuite bathroom. Geraldine Rogers and Margaret Hamersteen, having done most of what their guidebook advised, were already looking forward to moving on when, following a candle-lit dinner at a restaurant perched high above the Bosphorus, they began to feel very unwell. Diners in half-light cannot always distinguish what is on the plate before them. The situation of Geraldine Rogers and Margaret Hamersteen was compounded by their not being sure what exactly had been meant to be on their plates. Being in adventurous mood they had all too readily succumbed to the charm of an engaging and handsome waiter who had directed them to the most exotic dishes on the restaurant's menu. As neither the printed words nor the waiter's broken English had offered any enlightenment the ladies had plunged on regardless. Washed down by generous amounts of German wines, their meal had seemed quite palatable at the time, albeit in an anonymous way. At a later time in the middle of the night the verdict had been different. Not even the ministrations of an engaging and handsome hotel doctor – when finally he had arrived – had brought much comfort. His English was far more badly broken than that of his waiter compatriot. The two ladies had in desperation devoured within eight hours the contents of the two bottles of mixture he had left with them. This had been unwise and unavailing. Their stay was of necessity extended. Their disappointment was shared by the hotel manager, who had other guests scheduled to occupy the room; guests, moreover, more capable of consuming the hotel's other services than the stricken Americans.

The Outcasts' fourth match was an exercise in futility. The match manager and captain for the game against Rainmere was Colin Banks. Although everyone had to take their turn, the nomination of Colin was never greeted without anxiety. His reputation for unreliability had not been lightly won. On one occasion his team selection had taken place over a period of weeks and either side of a tempestuously passionate relationship with a raven-headed divorcee. He emerged with an unclear idea both as to his amorous prowess and the names of the team-mates he had engaged. Nine players were never sufficient to beat a competitive club like Haleshaw, whose captain had rubbed salt into the wound by stonily refusing the use of local substitutes.

Another more distant 'triumph' of Colin also lingered in the memory. The village of Arne in west Essex could usually be relied on to provide an agreeable outing. Its excellent pub, the Black Ball, was situated at no greater distance from the clubhouse than the wicket from the boundary. The members of Arne Cricket Club enjoyed their ale as much (or almost as much) as the Outcasts. Colin had had thirteen players lined up for the trip and it was eagerly anticipated. Not to have to drive was an essential pre-condition of the outing. It had come as a severe jolt to Colin to be told by Bill Blimp, proprietor of Executive Sporting Coachways, then in the early stages of his dealings with the Outcasts, that his only vehicle was unroadworthy. At a later time this was not a word which formed part of Bill Blimp's vocabulary, but at the outset of a contractual relationship he was at pains to pass himself off as a model of road safety consciousness. In his desperation Colin Banks pressed Bill Blimp over the exact nature of the problem. The answer was a dodgy radiator (Bill Blimp, in grim anticipation of the vehicle's frailties, held back on the dodgy clutch and the dodgy brake linings). Colin Banks pooh-poohed this minor defect and urged Bill Blimp not to let him down. Bill Blimp struggled with his conscience for as long as it took for Colin Banks to come up with the offer of an extra thirty quid.

At first Colin Banks thought that they had run into fog on the journey to Arne, but had quickly been forced to admit to himself that it was indeed a cloud of steam from an overheated radiator. The clutch grated in sympathy, but the brakes held – eventually. The team was four miles from its destination when the coach finally halted. Some athletes can cover this distance inside twenty minutes, but the generic term 'athletes' did not cover members of the Outcasts Cricket Club, with or without kit to carry. By the time the team had hauled itself through the gate of the Arne cricket ground over an hour and a half late for the start of the match, the players looked anything but athletic. To have covered the distance in this time owed a great deal to there being no pub of any description between the location of the breakdown and the cricket ground. Having been profuse in his apologies, Colin had completely forgotten to propose that in the circumstances the length of the match should be curtailed. It was not until the tea interval (by which time it was established that Bill Blimp's coach would be covering no further miles that day) that the logistics of the return journey to London were discussed. The last train from the nearest station left at eight o'clock. The home team sportingly offered to drive the visitors there after the match had concluded. There was little time to spare and none of what there was could be spared for a visit to the Black Ball. Winning by two wickets was in the circumstances little consolation for the Outcasts.

For the trip to Rainmere Arthur, exceptionally, was not available. When asked he had said cryptically that he was best man at a divorce. Responding to quizzical looks, he had added no more than 'Long-term commitment, sorry, can't let them down.' Colin Banks was at pains to reassure his friends, now used to the certainty and reliability associated with Arthur's new regime, that he would 'sort it'. When it came to the day of travel his team-mates had ample cause to question his judgement. In the car park of the Sink and Plumber Colin's own sports coupe was the only recognisable vehicle. No one gave any thought to the truck alongside it until Greg Roberts waved from the driver's cab. It was an open truck, down the sides of which were bales of straw by way of seating. Hoops straddled across its width suggested that a cover had at one time been in place, but no longer. 'Don't worry,' said Colin, noticing disapproving looks, 'it's not going to rain', but it was a more immediate and present discomfort that was earning the scowls.

'I suppose you know what you're doing?' queried Kevin Newton with distaste written all over his face. Colin explained that this conveyance was the best he had been able to come up with at short notice and that it would be a bit of fun. Greg was to be congratulated for once again taking the pledge (a reference to last season's visit to Doredell) and volunteering to be driver. Kevin suppressed a demand to see whether Greg's driving licence covered this type of vehicle. Colin said that he would lead the mini-convoy. With an air of superiority he explained that he had recently equipped his car with a satellite navigation system that was 'quite simply state of the art'. It would deliver them infallibly to Rainmere. Given a fair chance it might have done, but there were handicaps put in the way of its processing efficiency.

Colin had not taken the precaution of pre-programming his system. It was not until he had jumped into the driver's seat ready for the off that he pressed the buttons necessary to set the route. He was confounded to discover that the key words 'Rainmere' and 'Hertfordshire' gave him several options. Apart from Little Rainmere and Great Rainmere he was offered

Rainmere End, Copping Rainmere and Rainmere-on-the-Hill. Having bragged about his satellite navigator, Colin was not disposed at this early stage to consult his colleagues to see if anyone could supply greater precision. Accordingly he selected Great Rainmere because it sounded the most important of the Rainmeres and therefore the place where the cricket club was most likely to be located. He also gambled that all these villages formed a coherent cluster. One of his assumptions was wrong.

The slightly unusual nature of the convoy persuaded Colin Banks not to travel the motorway route his navigation system recommended as he thought that they might attract the attention of police patrols. This meant that the system was soon thrown into a continuous frenzy of re-calculation which thrust the driver into a battle between instruction and instinct. The procession was already running late when it encountered an obstacle the satellite had not been able to foretell. With Great Rainmere not more than a mile away and a church steeple in sight, the road ahead was closed due, a large sign said, to the installation of mains drainage. What might have been eagerly anticipated by the good folk of Rainmere was not so well greeted by the Outcasts' party. It was no comfort to be informed by the self-same sign that the work was being undertaken by virtue of European Union funding.

There was no alternative but to do an about-turn. This seemed to put the satellite navigation system into a strop. Its recalculation insisted that the sports coupe should undo its latest manoeuvre and maintain its frontal assault on Great Rainmere. As Colin Banks refused to obey this instruction the system relapsed into a long sequence of re-programming which finally told him that he was forty-seven miles from home. Then it froze. After circling to the west Colin found a signpost which directed him to the Rainmeres. He congratulated himself on recovering the situation so quickly and took the indicated road. His hopes wilted on reaching a village sign for Rainmere Rishton. To him this had all of the surprise and none of the thrill of the astronomer who discovers that Jupiter has an extra moon. His navigation system unchivalrously did not register the discovery.

In the middle of what seemed no more than a tiny hamlet the road divided. A signpost stood at the fork with doubtless the historic mission of guiding the traveller to whichever of the Rainmeres held his interest. Unfortunately its mission had not survived into contemporary life as both its arms were missing. So too was any manifestation of human life. With faint encouragement from the direction of the dashboard and reliance on his own gut feeling, Colin Banks chose to aim right. At the next junction there were not even the remains of a signpost. Colin chose the road which appeared wider and in possession of a substantial tarmacadam surface complete with a white-painted centre line. He went left – and wrong. Appearance had been truly deceptive. The road narrowed significantly and tufts of grass began to punctuate the hard surface. An urgent blast of horn behind him forced Colin to realise that the passenger lorry could physically proceed no further along this route. More time was lost in reversing cautiously back to the junction. The earlier rejected option looked as though it could be of dubious width, but obligingly it exceeded expectation and the Outcasts were able to make progress until at last a village gateway sign proclaimed Great Rainmere. Destination achieved, even the satellite navigation system concurred.

It did not prove, however, to be journey's end. The ground on which Rainmere Cricket Club played was not after all in the village of Great Rainmere. This information was acquired at the bar of the village hostelry outside which stood a particularly arresting inn sign indicating that it was called the Rope. The first Outcast across the threshold claimed that he had only entered in search of information. The second and third wanted to use the toilet. The fourth and fifth, who had merely drifted in their wake, had time to notice that the Rope's guest bitter that week was Mackay and Brewster's Topps – quite a rarity so far south. Within seconds two pints had been served and word passed to those still outside. So chilled were they by their al fresco ride that they needed no second bidding to decant into the pub, leaving Colin and Greg to exchange anxious glances.

In all thirty-five minutes passed before the Outcasts were on their way again. Another ten were lost when it was realised that David Pelham was not aboard. Having managed to cram two pints into the stopover he had been in the lavatory when the journey recommenced. At least the lead driver was now possessed with reliable local knowledge as to the exact whereabouts of the cricket ground. Against expectation it was actually at Rainmere-on-the-Hill. Despite being deep in rural Hertfordshire it was not the prettiest of grounds, its setting not improved by a distinct slope. Nor could it be said that the home team was in the prettiest of moods, having been kept waiting so long. Most of their displeasure had been vented on the unfortunate Simon Crossley and Syd Breakwell, who, having travelled together and sensibly, were the Outcasts' only visible representatives when the match was due to begin. They had been left proffering excuses which, as the time ticked by, required ever more vivid imagination.

If the trip to date had not been a perfect joy, what followed did nothing to improve the Outcasts' day. The Rainmere captain won the toss and said with a determined gleam in his eye that he would bat. And bat he did. Opening the innings he tucked into the bowling of Colin Banks, whose day's experience seemed to have diminished his enthusiasm. At the other end, bowling uphill, Winston Jenkins fared no better. Nor when it was their turn did Phil Cole, Charlie Colson, Ray Burrill and David Pelham (especially not David Pelham). The only wicket before the rain came fell to Greg Roberts, whose very occasional nondescript assortment produced (accidentally) a leg-break which the Rainmere captain was expecting no more than Colin Banks a change in the weather. With Rainmere on 181-1 after twenty-three overs the players left the field. After a quiet tea lacking in bonhomie the rain looked as unrelenting as the Rainmere batting. When the home captain approached Colin Banks and suggested that they should call it a day and have a beer, his offer was enthusiastically embraced. Once again Colin Banks' judgement proved to be at fault. After his team had changed and showered they were confronted by the sight of cans being unpacked from a supermarket crate.

Simon Crossley and Syd Breakwell were able to get away, the former muttering that he had to get back to wife and family. Several sets of eyes followed enviously, the two spare seats in Simon's car being in mind. As the rain outside pounded on the open truck and with the future of this new fixture hanging in the balance, the players knew that they were trapped. With, apart from the drivers, one notorious exception (Phil Cole said he was a teetotaller) they sipped the inferior fluid until they spotted the chance to claim that the rain was easing. They had got no further than Great Rainmere before the heavens opened once more. His drenched colleagues would never allow Colin Banks to forget their appalling experience. He wisely forbore from mentioning that on touching the 'home' button on his satellite navigation system it had guided him infallibly back to the Sink and Plumber.

For Geraldine Rogers and Margaret Hamersteen their trip equally had not been a perfect joy. A feeling of mild recovery eventually tempted them to venture down to the hotel lounge. There another temptation was soon to present itself. The only occupant of the lounge was an elderly silver-haired man engrossed in a book. Whether it was the ladies' accent or the title of the gentleman's book, *A History of American Cricket*, which triggered the mutual recognition that they were all US citizens was impossible to say. Introductions naturally followed. He was C. Ramsgate Fishburn. Recently retired from the government service, he was undertaking a major research project for the United States Educational League for Environmental and Sporting Studies. This involved him travelling across Europe, an exercise with which the ladies could make common cause.

The topic of conversation in this chance American reunion was not the nature of C. Ramsgate Fishburn's studies but rather the state of health of the two ladies (Mr Fishburn had noticed their sickly pallor). It transpired that he had a patent remedy: champagne. Not without some difficulty in the middle of an afternoon in a hotel in Istanbul a bottle was produced. Mrs Rogers and Mrs Hamersteen were prevailed upon to drink it. Mr Fishburn limited himself to a single glass. By early evening there was no doubt about it. The ladies felt immeasurably better, even admitting an appetite for dinner, which was to be accompanied by a further bottle of champagne. They were forced to ask themselves why it had taken them so many years of their lives to discover the restorative qualities of this beverage.

The following day they set out to make repairs to a travel schedule which had been severely disrupted by their indisposition. They found that they had well and truly missed the bus. They had selected for their land tour through Europe what had been described as an exclusive luxury coach service. So exclusive was this mode of travel that departures from Istanbul took place only once a fortnight. In the tourist centre where their enquiries were being pursued the agent on duty possessed language skills unequal to the task of explaining to Geraldine Rogers and Margaret Hamersteen any alternative means of leaving Istanbul in the manner and style to which they had pledged themselves. As they turned away in frustration bordering on despair they were greeted by a young man who had been changing money at an adjacent counter. He had picked up from the one-sided conversation that the ladies were in difficulties and he asked them to explain what their travel plans were. 'Changed', said Geraldine Rogers; 'flexible', said Margaret Hamersteen. 'Well then,' responded the young man, 'how does this strike you?' After a shared bottle of wine at a street café it struck them very well.

The morning encounter led to an afternoon engagement. By two o'clock Geraldine Rogers and Margaret Hamersteen were sitting in a park on the southern fringe of the city surrounded by young men. Their contact at the travel centre had been one of a band of English cricketers who were on a mission to foster cricket amongst the nations of eastern and central Europe. They formed a club which eccentrically (and misleadingly) called itself the Soul of Discretion. Good-looking, well-spoken, charming and attentive; the ladies could not have wanted for more reassuring companions. The deal was that they could have seats on the team coach, which was adequate but not luxurious, stay (they had overbooked) in the team's hotels, which were a few stars less than luxurious, and sightsee or watch cricket as the mood took them.

One thing could be said with some certainty. When the two ladies had left the United States it would never have entered their heads that they would spend any minute part of their holiday watching a game of which they had scarcely heard. So as they settled down to see the Soul of Discretion do battle with the Galatasaray Warriors, they simply weighed the loss of comfort in travel and accommodation against the opportunity to see parts of Europe which in some cases had not been included in their original schedule. However, as the day progressed, another element began to enter the equation. The occasion grew on them – not, it has to be said, the game itself, which they did not understand, but the general ambience. A bottle of wine was produced for them. They had comfortable seats shaded from the sun and were ministered to throughout, very politely, by the players. As millions of people around the world had discovered before them, there were worse ways of spending time. And then finally they were taken out to dinner (fortunately not to a restaurant high above the Bosphorus) at which they ate safely and drank dangerously. Their fortuitously remodelled tour began to hold out very good prospects indeed.

Similarly the Outcasts became more optimistic about their prospects on the evidence of their match against Gradely St Mary. Still shuddering from the Rainmere experience no chances were taken with this next outing. Arthur was back in charge of transport arrangements and Colin Banks was omitted. The day was perfect. So too was the pitch. Batting first, the first five in the Outcasts' order helped themselves, the star performer being Toby Lederwood. It was as well that the Outcasts amassed a total of over

350. Being deprived of their spearhead bowlers, Colin Banks and Stewart Thorogood, the attack lacked penetration. The bowlers did not perform disgracefully badly, but batting was too easy. Within the pre-determined allocation of overs the home side fell short of the Outcasts' total by a margin of 30 runs. Despite capturing only two wickets the Outcasts were the winners. A mighty thirst was then overcome in a pre-determined allocation of hours in the Church Arms.

Victory in the next match was from a cricket point of view more satisfying as it involved an all-round performance in which there was a fair balance between bat, ball and beer, albeit not entirely consecutively. The village of Bracefold had two pubs close to the perimeter of its cricket ground and the Outcasts had always found it hard to judge which was superior. Of necessity tastings had to continue as opportunity arose. With overs needed from Charlie Colson, David Pelham and Richard Furness it was as well for the Outcasts that they fielded first. These three went about their work with rare concentration, their sights being set on an early re-acquaintance with the two excellent ale houses. Their efforts were complemented by fine performances from Jon Palmer, Toby Lederwood, Rashid Ali and Kevin Newton, who between them knocked off the 187 runs needed for victory without Charlie Colson having so much as to poke his head out of the Unicorn's front entrance – although he had taken the precaution of strapping on his pads before entering. The post-match revelry took place at the Lion in deference to the home team's wishes. The Outcasts were ever the gracious winners.

Geraldine Rogers and Margaret Hamersteen had made stately progress with their entourage. So companionable were their English cricketing friends that the two American widows visited more cricket grounds than cathedrals as they toured Bulgaria, Romania, Hungary and Croatia. Finally they arrived in Slovenia where the cricket tour was to end. It was also where they ran into a snag. The modest but decent Hotel Rzadji into which they were booked seemed from outward appearance to be open as usual, but the entrance door, unusually, was locked. On close inspection they found a small notice affixed to the glass. It was printed in Slovene and, had they been able to understand a single word, gave a very good reason why the hotel was not operational. In a *crime passionnel* the owner had shot his wife and chef, a possibility which a band of touring cricketers from England could never have been expected to anticipate. The police had arrested the husband and closed the hotel. Subsequent enquiries by the team in search of alternative accommodation led to the conclusion that all Ljubljana's modest but decent hotels were full.

Just as despair was beginning to set in (a night in the park being no preparation for a cricket match) Geraldine Rogers and Margaret Hamersteen came to the rescue. The two ladies had been conferring aside from their male escorts. At the second attempt they had found a passer-by who spoke good English. What was the finest hotel in Ljubljana was the question they posed. The answer was the Grand, and it was to the Grand that the ladies directed the coach. At the prices charged it was no surprise that the Grand had rooms available sufficient to cater for the pressing need. Geraldine and Margaret had decided that there was no fairer way of expressing their thanks to the members of the Soul of Discretion who had been so kind to them. They booked them two to a room for two nights, themselves taking the bridal suite for one.

In discussion with their cricketing friends the two ladies had made a further change in their travel plans. The cricketers were flying home on the day following their match in Ljubljana. In their hours together they had offered advice to their American companions about how to make the best of their remaining time in Europe. Not unnaturally they pressed the attractions of London and the English countryside (one of them was even heard to mention Wales – doubtless out of respect to the ECB), with Venice and Paris not to be missed en route. A new itinerary reliant on rail had been drawn up and appropriate bookings made, departure from Ljubljana being necessitated on the evening following the cricket match. Much had to be packed into a single day in Slovenia. So, first, it had to be Lake Bled.

More usually in the history of the Outcasts Cricket Club it was the teams they played who were inclined to ponder whether the fixture should be maintained. In the case of Cruddenham, however, it had been the Outcasts' turn to debate the matter. The fixture was only of one year's standing, but the visit to this tiny Essex coastal village had left a very negative impression. After hot debate in the Sink and Plumber it had been decided to renew the fixture for three reasons. The home side promised that this year it would put out its first team; secondly, Toby Lederwood reported that for a very minor detour, if they started early, they could take in lunch at a 'fantastic' curry house and so there would be some benefit from the outing; and, finally, the Outcasts would otherwise face three weeks without cricket, because Little Tetlow had declined to play them 'after last year's unfortunate incident' (Basil Smith's wife had got completely the wrong end of the stick) and Melworth had asked to move their match from early to late summer.

The Outcasts on their own admission were not the most athletic of cricketers, but on their first visit to Cruddenham they had been surprised to be confronted by a team of veterans. Without exception every member of the home team was old enough to be the father of every member of the Outcasts' team and, in some cases, the grandfather. There was a muttered excuse about misunderstanding. Cruddenham claimed to have heard that the Outcasts were an elderly outfit. This was an outrageous fiction. Cruddenham had indeed heard about the Outcasts and what they had heard was absolutely accurate. When therefore an opportunity had come out of the blue to be guests of a local company (a big employer in the area) at the Test Match, Cruddenham's First Eleven had had no pangs of conscience in dumping the Outcasts.

The match which ensued was thoroughly unsatisfactory. There was huge embarrassment when Cruddenham's opening bowler (left-arm fast-medium over the wicket) had to withdraw on account of a defect in his prosthetic limb. For the first fifteen overs, Jon Palmer and Stewart Thorogood were

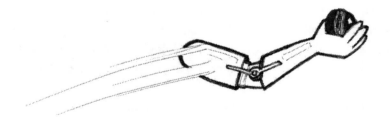

able to do much as they wanted, rattling up 135 runs. This prolific scoring rate was boosted by lack of mobility in the field. It was not so much a matter of the batsmen having to place their shots between fielders; they could as easily place them through fielders. The only loss of momentum in the Outcasts' innings was when Captain (ex-BOAC) Riley was brought into the attack. From appearance portly, five foot nine and probably over seventy, he may at first have instilled over-confidence in the batsmen. Three overs and four wickets later his donkey drops against the dark background of the pavilion were seen for what they were worth. The keener eyes of Harry Northwood and Richard Furness enabled them to reap 80 runs from Captain Riley's remaining overs.

The target of 319 from forty overs was always going to be a challenging target for the Cruddenham seniors with only ten men on whom to rely. Captain Riley had collapsed during the tea interval. It was thought that exhaustion was the cause, as it had been many years since he had had to bowl eight overs off the reel. It was unclear whether he was affected more in mind than body after his mixed experience, but he was carted off to hospital as a precaution. A combination of Colin Banks (looking forward to a hot date with a Swedish masseuse) and Stewart Thorogood (also on a high as he was due to be interviewed the next day for selection as a parliamentary candidate) was too potent for the scratch Cruddenham side. The nine wickets were captured with embarrassing ease, leaving both teams anxious to part company at the close.

It was on the renewed visit to Cruddenham that the Outcasts got their first clue that their recent recruit, Toby Lederwood, had not got a good sense of direction. They had set off early. The very minor detour they took on leaving the main road had yielded no curry house, fantastic or otherwise. The second detour proved to be less minor, but every bit as lacking in Indian restaurants. On the third attempt an ever optimistic Toby Lederwood let out a cry of triumph as the bus rounded a bend and there came in view a sign announcing Restaurant Nazir. 'That's it', he said in a voice which, if they had known him longer and better, would have betrayed lack of conviction. At least, Toby Lederwood rationalised to himself, he had delivered an Indian restaurant and they could not exactly have been two a penny in this remote neck of the woods.

The interior of the Restaurant Nazir bore all the trappings of the early genre of Indian restaurants, but there the likeness ended. There was nothing remotely Asian about the man who came forward to meet the Outcasts. 'What do you want?' could not have been a more ungracious or superfluous greeting. The arrival of fourteen customers in an otherwise empty restaurant should ordinarily have filled the proprietor or manager with delight. However, it was with no sense of joy that the man on being informed of their purpose directed them to one side of the cavernous room. It was more as an afterthought that he produced menus and then promptly disappeared before the question of drinks could be raised.

It was established very early on that this would not be a day which Toby Lederwood would be allowed to forget in a hurry. The menu raised doubts and lowered expectations. It offered a curious selection of which curry seemed to form only a minor part. There was burger this and burger that. Steak, ham and fish all featured. Chips accompanied everything. Not so much as a lettuce leaf indicated any concession to healthy eating. The Outcasts concentrated on the curry section. Choice was restricted to three flavours or strengths: mild, Nazir and 'viagara'. The customer could opt for chicken, rabbit or goat. Not a lot of thought was required; even less when they had been told that mild and viagara were off. Hopes of a good meal faded further when the dour manager shouted through the kitchen door, 'Fourteen chicken Nazirs, Fred.' But memorable it certainly proved.

The Outcasts arrived at their destination with stomachs better described as heavy than full. There had been no skimping in the servings, although it had been hard to tell which parts of the birds they were eating. Nevertheless it had smelled and tasted good. There had been mountains of a rather grey-looking rice, but none of the other usual side dishes. More disappointing was the absence of beer, or at least beer the Outcasts could bring themselves to drink. Whether two or three good pints would have helped or hindered in the situation which was to develop could not be known. What did become clear at an early stage was that fielding first was a mistake. Ray Burrill, whose turn it was to be captain, adhered firmly to the view that it was better to chase a total. There was insufficient in his record to show whether the theory was sound, but in light of what happened on this occasion even he was forced to query the doctrine.

The first indication of anything untoward occurred after it had already become apparent that this might not be the Outcasts' day. The local umpire paired with the Outcasts' own Syd Breakwell was none other than Captain Riley. There were early signs that his experience of the previous year was still smarting. Cruddenham's opening batsman, a muscular young man of giant frame, padded up to the second delivery from Stewart Thorogood and was trapped palpably in front of his stumps. The umpire's verdict, delivered with stentorian emphasis, did not go in favour of the bowler. In his second over Stewart Thorogood induced a thick edge from the other opener and saw it safely pouched by Kevin Newton deputising for Rashid

Ali behind the stumps. However, Captain Riley did not see it the same way and gave the batsman 'not out'. A rank long-hop from Winston Jenkins in the next over was cut wildly and low into the hands of Richard Furness at deep backward point. From square leg Captain Riley intervened to say that the ball had bounced. The fielder's disagreement was only just contained.

Stewart Thorogood was the first to go. After the second ball of his fourth over (the first had been a curiously tame effort which the muscular young man of giant frame had hit back over his head for a one-bound four) Stewart fell to his knees clutching his midriff in obvious distress. 'Severe stomach cramps', he managed to mutter as he was led off the field. In his place Nigel Redman appeared as twelfth man and his over was completed by Phil Cole, not without some expense. During the passage of two more overs everything appeared to be back to normal except, from the Outcasts' point of view, a rapidly increasing total of runs. Then as he completed his opening spell Winston Jenkins took his sweater and his leave. Having returned to his fielding position at deep fine leg he did not stop but accelerated into the pavilion with an audible gasp. This time there was no substitute fielder to take his place.

The scoring rate accelerated and so did the rate of attrition amongst the fielding side, although not before a wicket was captured. The less muscular of the two opening batsmen had been quietly accumulating runs with deft dabs and prods. Aiming a leg glide at a ball from Phil Cole which appeared to be veering in that direction, he moved too far towards the ball and was mortified (as much as Phil Cole was surprised) when the ball broke back and dislodged the off bail. Cruddenham's number three was a stocky young man who radiated confidence with every stride to the wicket. The confidence was rapidly bolstered after lifting a long-hop from Phil Cole over the midwicket boundary. The next ball was also short and was pulled savagely in the same direction only to be brilliantly saved by a full-length dive by Toby Lederwood. Charlie Colson backed up and threw to the keeper, saving two runs. Phil Cole had moved back to his bowling mark before it was realised that Toby Lederwood had not moved at all. There was a short interruption whilst he was carried to the pavilion by Charlie Colson and Jon Palmer. Only Charlie Colson returned.

A side of seven fielders found it hard to staunch the flow of runs. The task was made worse when Dean Faulds succumbed to whatever bug was attacking the Outcasts. His was not a pretty departure. For a while the

Cruddenham batsmen ran amok. Then a measure of control was achieved for the Outcasts in a combination of Ray Burrill bowling off-spin mixed with off-cutters and Richard Furness with his orthodox left-arm spin. Being the youngest members of the side they were perhaps better able to keep at bay the digestive demons which had laid low so many of their team-mates. It was nevertheless an extraordinarily controlled spell of bowling which enabled them in part at least to neutralise the handicap of so many gaps in the field. After half an hour a pale-looking Stewart Thorogood resumed his place in the field whilst making clear to Ray Burrill that there was no question of his doing anything so energetic as bowling. He was the only returnee. The Outcasts captured no more wickets and the Cruddenham innings ended 363 runs to the good.

During the tea interval the Outcasts' dressing-room had the appearance of a field hospital. No one was actually bleeding, but bodies were spread around in various states of discomfort and repose. Those who had stayed in the field throughout the Cruddenham innings without succumbing to the Nazir syndrome were nevertheless feeling weak. Ray Burrill as captain felt obliged to present himself in the main part of the pavilion for tea, but he was joined only by Syd Breakwell and Simon Crossley who had also weathered the storm. Even then they all politely declined the tuna mayonnaise sandwiches and fruit cake, restricting themselves to cautious sips of weak, sweet tea.

In retrospect it was a considerable achievement not only that Stewart Thorogood and Jon Palmer fulfilled their responsibility to open the Outcasts' innings but that all eleven players were able to bat. It was, of course, all in vain. The Outcasts made only 35. Yet it was perhaps an additional achievement that they made the innings last thirty-nine of the forty overs. It had certainly required that length of time for Toby Lederwood to be sufficiently recovered to come to the wicket. The criticism he inevitably attracted from the other members of the team for misdirecting them into culinary disaster was tempered by his courage in going out to bat and the manner of his dismissal. Determined to have the last say, Captain Riley contrived to give him out for obstructing the field.

There was no scope for after-match partying. Even Charlie Colson, who could normally be relied on to sink a minimum of five pints if only to quench his thirst, was off-colour and showing no enthusiasm to hang around. Ray Burrill, conscious of his responsibilities, tried desperately to foster some bonhomie. Anxious as he was to dispel any suggestion of sour grapes, no one was more relieved than Ray when Arthur appeared in the doorway to announce that an accident on the main road would require an extended detour if they were to be back in time for the charity concert. Arthur's capacity for invention had obviously been undiminished by his own uncomfortable afternoon. The retreat was swiftly accomplished, but made no sweeter by what the Outcasts felt were scarcely suppressed vengeful smiles on the faces of their hosts.

The visit of Geraldine Rogers and Margaret Hamersteen to Bled in Slovenia had not been without its own degree of discomfort. Getting there had not been any problem. They had hired a car. It was on arrival that the limitations of the expedition presented themselves. To get the most out of a trip to Lake Bled a certain amount of exertion or, failing that, time is required. Apart from walking by the side of the lake, looking at shops or eating in one of a number of very agreeable places, there are two principal attractions for the tourist. One is to visit the castle and the other is to cross the lake to the island and church in its midst. Game as the two ladies were for most things, rowing across the lake was not a serious option. To be rowed in a vessel which appeared to be a design conflict between a sampan and a gondola could equally not be contemplated if they were to return to Ljubljana in time to watch their friends play cricket. That left the castle, which represented a stiff climb for two elderly women. Though it towered above them Geraldine and Margaret were undaunted. The mission had to be completed. With a deep breath they began their ascent.

'I thought I might see you here' were the words which greeted them when they stumbled finally into the brightness of a courtyard. Seated at a table was a familiar figure. The would-be scholar from America, C. Ramsgate Fishburn, had in front of him a bottle of champagne and, in an apparent display of prescience, three glasses. (From his elevated position he had in fact had forewarning of their proximity.) Once again the ladies were impressed by the remedial qualities of champagne and were further stimulated by the views from the castle ramparts. The conversation accompanying the refreshment was confined to exchanges about countries visited since their last encounter. Nothing was said on either side about how they had spent their time during these visits. It was only when the ladies showed signs of preparing for departure that the word 'cricket' was mentioned.

C. Ramsgate Fishburn became quite animated and pressed the ladies to say more. Their recent adventures were revealed and this seemed to add to his excitement. He expressed interest in attending the cricket match which was next on the ladies' itinerary. Graciously they offered him a seat in their car.

The three Americans spent a pleasant enough afternoon at Valburga, where the cricket was played on a matted wicket in a rented field mowed by its farmer owner. It would be hard to claim that their understanding of the game materially increased. By now Geraldine Rogers and Margaret Hamersteen had seen sufficient of their English friends in action to have gained some idea whether they were winning or losing. Of C. Ramsgate Fishburn not even this could be claimed. Disappointed to find no bar in the periphery of the ground, the elderly scholar laid himself on the grass and fell asleep. The champagne at the castle in Bled had unfortunately not been his first alcoholic intake of the day. After what the two ladies perceived to be an exciting finish in which the Soul of Discretion prevailed they reunited themselves with the cricketers and used their transport for the ten-mile return to Ljubljana. At that point there was no longer any sign of C. Ramsgate Fishburn.

After an early dinner in the Grand Hotel (there had been no tea worthy of the name at the ground used by Ljubljana Cricket Club) the ladies prepared to depart for Venice. They took their leave of their young friends, enjoining them to have a really good time on the last night of their tour. The cricketers were thanked for their companionship and assured that their expenses at the hotel would all be covered. Geraldine Rogers and Margaret Hamersteen were truly grateful for the attention heaped upon them by the young Englishmen. 'Will we ever see each other again?' they asked. 'Why not?' they were told. If they were in England in a fortnight's time, the team would be playing a rather special match. The ladies were given details and urged to fit the event into their schedule. Alas, it was a reunion which would not be consummated.

Charles Brett replaced the cover of the fuse box, picked up the china mug from which he had drunk some welcome tea, came out of the utility room and smiled reassuringly at his hostess. All his clients said that he had a lovely smile. 'I think you'll find that's much better now, Mrs Fergusson. These circuit breakers make life a whole lot easier. You won't have to fiddle with fuse wire any more.' Again he smiled, but this time he was thinking of the size of the invoice he would be submitting – tomorrow, he reckoned, if his wife was up to date with her secretarial duties, and, knowing Beryl, she would be. They ran an efficient operation. It was just one of the reasons why clients queued for his attention, that and his meticulous workmanship. He was also a clean and tidy worker (his freshly laundered white overalls heightened the impression) and this scored heavily against the barely perceived notion that his pace of work was a little on the slow side, not helped by his propensity for tea and a chat. Such informal friendliness went down very well with most of the ladies whose houses he visited, and even the men regarded him as courteous. As Charles Brett went towards his van he turned and treated Mrs Fergusson to a final smile and a wave. Another satisfied customer.

And an observant one. 'Not your usual van, I see, Mr Brett.' The electrician had time to remove from his face the scowl which reference to his transport had caused before responding. ''Fraid not, Mrs Fergusson, the other one finally died on me.' 'Oh, but I didn't think it was so old. It always looked very smart to me.' It had not been so old and it had looked very smart indeed to Charles Brett until his eighteen-year-old son had contrived to drive it into a tree. However, this was not an episode to which he wished to draw attention. The vehicle, fortunately shorn of all his tools and equipment at the time of the accident, had been declared an economic write-off. Always a man to keep a tight lid on his overheads, Charles Brett had been mortified to find that the insurance money left him well short of the cost of a new van. A like-for-like replacement would not be easily found. Then he remembered Martin More Motors.

This establishment on the Yarfield by-pass combined motor repairs, very occasional vehicle sales and assorted fruit and vegetables in a difficult-to-classify general emporium. That is why the presence on its forecourt of a white Transit with a price adhering to its windscreen had stuck in Charles Brett's mind. Under pressure of need he had decided to investigate. 'It was quite fortuitous the way I came by them', said the emporium's proprietor, Ted More (not the motor mechanic his father had been). It transpired that there were two white Transit vans acquired in a distress sale on the sudden closure of an independent school two counties distant to the west. Closer to the van on display Charles Brett could see that roughly painted out was the legend 'St Margaret's School for Enterprising Young Ladies'.

That was how Charles Brett, electrician of Hertfordshire, had been able to mitigate his loss. The Transit was not a year old, the mileage was correspondingly low and the bodywork faultless. Sign-writing to reflect new ownership could wait.

As an electrician Charles Brett was self-taught. He had read the books, obtained some basic qualifications and gained experience. He prepared well, used only the best equipment and aspired to the highest standards of execution. His bills were high, but not extortionate. His workmanship never gave cause for complaint. He had earned himself the topmost accolades from his clients. The reputation he enjoyed was supreme. No one had a word to say against him. That was something which suited Charles Brett very well, because he was also a thief.

Charles Brett was as meticulous a thief as he was electrician. He had tried to learn from what he saw as the mistakes of others. In this activity too he prepared well and aspired to the highest standards of execution. Above all he was not greedy. He did not clean people out. He would usually confine himself to a single object, often one that its owner did not miss for many weeks or months. Sometimes his clients would tell him that something had been taken. Charles Brett would be very solicitous and encourage them to call the police. When they did – as he could very well anticipate – the police seemed uninterested in what seemed a trivial matter. No investigation took place and so there was no chance of two and two being put together.

To Charles Brett his thieving was a bit of a thrill and a modest boost to his income. Whilst he took pride in his skill in being undetected he never boasted about it. He knew the danger of careless talk. So no one knew – except one person, his wife, Beryl. She fenced the stuff. The disposal was discreetly done through car boot sales and other informal channels. The aim was not to make the maximum amount of money but to be quietly successful. It was a very smooth, low-key operation which nevertheless brought in a steady flow of cash. And no one had ever suspected him. His winning smile and when necessary his show of sympathetic concern shielded him from any thought of his complicity. And, of course, he was a very good electrician, and they were like gold-dust.

Never, it is counselled, abandon a winning formula. For many years Charles Brett had stuck limpet-like to that advice. Yet, as the years passed, he found himself being increasingly restless. Correcting electrical faults,

70

installing new systems and detaching possessions from their owners had become so straightforward and relatively unchallenging that he was bored. Did he really want another twenty years of this routine, however profitable it had been? Just as the stand-up comedian sometimes aspires to be a Shakespearean actor, Charles Brett increasingly felt that something bigger and better was within his capability. He began thinking of a better life: Australia with sun, surf and cricket. What ties did he really have? His son looked to be a complete loser, a conclusion at which he had arrived long before his van had been ditched. His daughter, as far as he could tell, was living off immoral earnings. The fact that his wife seemed barely disapproving made him harbour suspicions about whether there was something in her past life of which he was ignorant. There was no love left in his marriage. It was just a business relationship. For Charles Brett life had lost its savour. Continued success in what he had chosen to do no longer seemed enough. He was ready to break out. All that was needed was the final spur.

Towards Helmerstead

THE NEWS FIRST APPEARED as a single line on Ceefax: 'British players cause fracas in Europe'. This could have meant almost anything, but the interested viewer tempted to seek the relevant page for further detail found himself no better informed. The nominated page confusingly and, hopefully, non-sequentially showed only a fruit-cake recipe. In two of Monday's broadsheets there were mini-paragraphs reporting that a group of British sportsmen had been detained for questioning in connection with claims of disorderly behaviour. The British Embassy was said to be requesting details. Diplomatic efforts in that direction were superseded by the tabloid press. On Tuesday bold headlines announced 'Lager louts in Ljubljana' and 'Slovenian hotel hit for six'. These were mild compared with what followed. A tabloid reporter with a sister in Ljubljana was fed the hint that women had been involved in whatever had happened. 'Naughty Brits may face sex charges' was a headline guaranteed to make the story run bigger and longer. Adria Airways had never carried so many journalists to its national capital.

The Slovenian police, who had started by thinking that they had no more than a severe case of drunk and disorderliness on their hands, were prodded by these headlines and spurred by the intervention of the Minister for Homeland Justice. He was an ambitious man who wished to gain a reputation for zero tolerance. He demanded a reassessment of the situation. It was fatally escalated by a decision not to discharge the detainees with a caution but to hold them in the cells whilst further enquiries were made. An official from the British Embassy, who had had to be summoned back from a villa on the Adriatic (not his own) where he had been spending a delightful break with a wife (equally not his own), was eventually allowed to meet the imprisoned men. He may have had a libido which needed to be kept in check, but he had a shrewd professional eye and a love of cricket.

He left his fellow nationals with a promise of all possible help with legal representation, but his first action was to seek out one of the journalists who were clogging the streets outside the Grand Hotel looking for more facts or fantasies. He thought he knew his man, but reckoned without the reporter's xenophobic sub-editor in London.

The headlines in the British press suddenly altered. 'Fun-loving cricketers kept in cells', 'Let them go', 'Play the game, Slovenia' and (the one which did most damage) 'Police brutality not cricket' were amongst the reports to which people in Britain awoke. They had the predictable effect of stiffening the attitude of the police in Ljubljana in charge of the investigation. Within twenty-four hours an Urgent Question tabled in Parliament brought a Foreign and Commonwealth Office minister to the despatch box in the House of Commons. The tale she could tell was based on incomplete information, and her failure to convince Members of Parliament that the Government was on top of the situation fuelled their anger and the following day's headlines. National pride was now intensely involved – on both sides. In Britain the loutish monsters of the early part of the week had been transformed into no more than over-exuberant sporting heroes. In Slovenia the reassessment had gone very much in the opposite direction. Crowds were out in the streets demanding summary and violent punishment of the detainees.

This unhappy sequence of events explained why the cricket team calling itself the Soul of Discretion found itself unable to fulfil its commitment to take part in a charity match at Helmerstead Hall in Hertfordshire on the approaching Saturday. Nor did team members have any easy means of communicating this information to the match organiser. The inflamed atmosphere had led to restrictions on diplomatic access. They need not have worried. Caroline Bingley-Adams, discounting what she had first read, had suddenly got the message. The horror of the situation rushed into focus. Her initial thought was to contact her Member of Parliament, but a recorded message told her that his office was closed until the following Monday. The message did not offer any alternative course of action if the matter was urgent. Her MP had no intention of his fact-finding mission in Hollywood being disturbed by complaining constituents.

This setback caused Caroline Bingley-Adams to abandon very quickly any concern she may have felt for the men incarcerated in Slovenia. Another line of action had occurred to her. She remembered a seminar where she had met someone who was connected with an amateur cricket team. She rang the organisation which had run the seminar and wheedled out of them (no mean feat in an era when data protection is king, but Caroline could be extremely persuasive) the names of those who had attended. She recognised Amanda Sutton's name as soon as she heard it. With an outrageous lie she pretended a closeness of relationship which helped her to extract a contact number. Caroline then rallied all her resources of charm and persuasiveness to tackle Amanda about the Outlaws or whatever they called themselves. It was a long shot, a desperate long shot. It would have to be desperate to risk inserting the Outcasts into the carefully arranged scenario planned for Helmerstead Hall. Not even Caroline Bingley-Adams knew everything being planned.

After Amanda had somewhat doubtfully conveyed the message it was left to Stewart Thorogood to sound out the rest of the squad both as to willingness to step into the breach and availability. He doubted whether at such short notice it would be possible to raise an eleven. On what had looked like being a weekend off and with Amanda working, he and three others had planned a West Country weekend to investigate five new real ales. It would be a heavy sacrifice. Charlie Colson was the first to ask what the ale situation at Helmerstead Hall was likely to be. Stewart cursed himself for not thinking of that when talking with Caroline Bingley-Adams. He was more confident in his approaches to his colleagues after being told by her that the main bar at the match was being organised by Riddingtons, out of whose brewery nothing remotely gaseous emerged. Their famous 'Ripper' bitter was worth travelling some distance to consume. That information was sufficient to put Charlie Colson (a by now uncomfortably pregnant Liz was weekending with her mother) and David Pelham on board. And as his calls progressed Stewart Thorogood was surprised by the responses he received.

Having known for some while that the Outcasts had no cricket arranged for the weekend in question, Rashid Ali had resolved that he would at last tidy his office. He had been nagged by his secretary for months about the mounting piles of paper which adorned the room. She had threatened to tackle the job herself, but Rash had warned her off by emphasising that only he could tell what needed to be filed and what might be shredded. The piles themselves were quite neat, but even Rash recognised that they were becoming obtrusive. He had shrunk from the task knowing that several hours would be involved. He would have to re-read some of the case files just to be able to decide their fate. So he had had to make a real mental effort to screw himself up to do the job in one fell swoop. He would have it all done in a weekend and his secretary would get a real surprise on the following Monday. But in fact she wouldn't. Stewart's phone call melted Rash's resolve in seconds. It would after all be cricket as usual.

Jon Palmer had told himself that he would be a modern father. The duties would be shared with Adrienne. They had an alternate night duty rota. Jon had negotiated himself some paternity leave, but he had a big stake in the business. Car sales were not exactly buoyant, especially in the big car sector in which his firm specialised. Baby Andrew Simon (after Simon Crossley) was proving to be an astonishingly good baby who cried little and slept a lot. Beyond bonding with his tiny son by his presence Jon felt that his contribution was limited. He reckoned that more fatherly activities would come along later when Andrew reached the toddler stage. His sitting at home all day did not appear to be helping even Adrienne, who had taken motherhood in her stride. She found herself having to fuss more over her relatively idle husband than over her infant. What Jon had not taken in his stride was nappy-changing. So gradually he had found excuses to go into work and then eventually to resume cricket. Adrienne could read him like a book and made no protest. When Stewart's enquiry came, Jon was ready to answer the call.

Dean Faulds had made a decision. It had been put off for too long. His flat had not been decorated (some would say cleaned) since he acquired it following his divorce. Returning to single status he had reverted to a lifestyle which closely resembled his student existence. Untidy was a flattering description of his accommodation. Dean barely seemed to notice the conditions in which he lived. His visitors did. Yet it was not until one night in the pub when he made a comment about the inadequacy of his love life to Winston Jenkins that he received a wake-up call. 'What self-respecting girl is going to spend five minutes in that tip of a flat of yours?', Winston (tongue loosened after six pints) had daringly said. The point had not sunk in until the next day. Dean rushed out then to buy several litres of vinyl emulsion. The cans had stood for several weeks in a corner of the bedroom until they had been joined by a brush and a roller. More weeks passed whilst Dean slowly and painstakingly sifted through ankle-deep debris on the floor to separate rubbish from worthwhile possessions. The exercise was slowed by the discovery of long-forgotten CDs which had to be played. Gradually Dean forced himself to the point where the decks had been sufficiently cleared for painting to begin. The next weekend was the deadline. When he answered Stewart's call the deadline was breached.

Before he tackled the next name on the list, Stewart took an incoming call. It was Harry Northwood. This was in itself unusual. So at first was the nature of the call. Harry was full of polite conversation, showing more interest in Stewart's health, fitness and general perspective on life than he had ever previously demonstrated. Stewart felt that there was a point which would eventually be reached. He interrupted what was turning into a lengthy discourse on the situation in the Middle East with a minatory warning, 'Harry'. 'Oh yes,' spluttered the student at the other end of the line, 'I'd heard that there might be some cricket on this weekend and . . . and I'm desperate to play.' 'OK, you're on', said Stewart without hesitation (this call had to end). With details quickly imparted he hung up, not needing to know at that moment the cause of Harry's desperation.

Stewart Thorogood would not have wanted to know the precise nature of the reasons which had prompted Harry Northwood's call. Harry's urgent desire to be playing cricket under the umbrella of the Outcasts had its roots in a light-hearted agreement to take part in a rugby match. He had become friendly at university with a group of fellow students who were rugger fanatics, but played only at a cheery 3rd XV level. Short of a man with little time to spare before the match was due to start, they had leaned on Harry to make up numbers. In borrowed kit he was told that he should be out of harm's way on the wing. That was not how the members of the opposing team had seen it. Whether more damage was suffered by the bor-rowed kit or the man wearing it was debatable. Harry's only satisfaction was to have scored his team's only try. Running blindly and without any sense of strategy he had accidentally intercepted a pass and managed to collapse under the posts with the ball as he was tackled. That had added a touch of respectability to a final score-line of 97-5.

In the bar afterwards, however, all were equal. Soon Harry discovered that these rugby players were sprinters when it came to putting back the beer. He thought of himself (under the tutelage of the Outcasts) as more a distance man (he didn't stay long enough to get to know the staying power of particular team-mates). He had had seven pints and refused an eighth when after an hour he remembered that he was due at a party back at his hall of residence. What he only just remembered was that he was supposed to bring a bottle (preferably spirits). Passing a downmarket bottle store he had managed to get some variety of Balkan Vodka for £4.99. At the party it was poured without ceremony into a large steel bowl on a table in the centre of the main room. Quite what he was actually drinking was unclear, but it came in small glasses and repetitively. It couldn't possibly be doing him any harm. He felt fine.

Harry was unsure when the dancing began. A large girl had suddenly plucked him into an embrace and whirled him into an adjoining room where some un-live music was playing. Harry felt his head spin, but the dancing was of the close encounter variety and punctuated by clinches which seemed to increase in length. At the third clinch Harry realised that his partner had changed colour. (The same could have been said of him, but in a different sense.) He was with perhaps partner number three when there was a brisk change of tempo. Someone had proposed a conga. Out the column went into the night air. The cold was the first thing Harry noticed. The next thing he noticed was that for the second time that day his clothing had suffered a severe reduction. He had lost his T-shirt and his chinos had not been cut-off when he had arrived at the party. The line of conga dancers eventually dissolved and, changing partners, couples danced around the Hall's central quadrangle. The last person Harry danced with was the Principal's sister. He was to deny strongly that he had made any improper advances before passing out.

Someone had put Harry to bed. When he finally regained consciousness the following day his head ached as it had never ached before. His whole body ached as it had never ached before. He stank. Slowly and shockingly he discovered why. Truly it had been the night of the great puke. The evidence was liberally spread. The room had become unfit for human habitation. Harry was still feeling like death when he was hauled before the Principal later in the day, by which time a full list of charges had been compiled. Suspension was ordered and Harry was dispatched with the chilling reminder that he had been extremely lucky not to have choked on his own vomit. Any momentary relief over that thought was dispelled by the realisation of the awkwardness of his new situation. A parental visit was scheduled for the weekend.

Harry had been forced to think fast – not easy with a blocked brain. He could not entertain his parents on the campus and there was absolutely no question in any case of his mother seeing his room (one of the musts of any maternal visit). He could not go home without dangerously complicated explanations and he could not just take off and disappear for a while. A call on his mobile from Charlie Colson asking if he had heard that the Outcasts had acquired an unexpected fixture set his thoughts in motion. Charlie's breezy farewell remark 'Look forward to having a few beers with you' unfortunately set Harry's guts in motion as well. On recovery Harry reckoned that he could just about sell his parents the story that he was urgently needed by the Outcasts, an outfit to which by now they had become reconciled. Perhaps, he told himself, one of his team-mates could give him a bed until the suspension was lifted. And so that was how he came to be on parade at Helmerstead Hall.

After numbers either unanswered or busy, Stewart Thorogood's next contact was Kevin Newton. He had expected to be at Gatwick on Sunday to welcome (eagerly it had to be said) the woman who now dominated his thoughts. However, he had just had a text message to say that she would be arriving a day late. So he enlisted and in a quick conversation across the office was able to establish Toby Lederwood's willingness to participate as well.

John Furness rang. 'You were trying to get me.' Stewart explained and put down on his list another recruit. He then had ten names, which seemed at first sight to be excellent progress. At second sight he realised that so far he had acquired only three bowlers. Tom Redman's leg-spin would not have headed his priorities for eleventh place, but he was the next Outcast he was able to reach. Very unusually Tom was able to declare both himself and brother Nigel available. Their ever-ailing mother was not an obstacle on this occasion. She had been tempted into taking a cure at Flemingtons in Devon. The temptation had been very carefully contrived. The recommendation of one of her (few) trusted friends, the supply of a beautifully prepared brochure, the willingness of a long-harassed doctor to attest to the benefits which might accrue and the promise of her sons to pay for the whole course combined to attract Muriel Redman's interest. A reminder that a highly rated West End chef was in temporary charge of the kitchens finally tipped the scales. Muriel Redman declared that she probably could manage the journey if she could be escorted on to the train and met at the other end. This exercise was essayed not just to give Tom and Nigel a free weekend, but as part of a long-term plan on their part to prepare their mother for the idea of another (longer, if not permanent) stay in Australia with their sister. By such happy coincidence Tom and Nigel were free to respond positively to the idea of cricket on Sunday. It was a much better prospect than the stock-taking which had otherwise beckoned.

With twelve players on board, but not yet an ideal team, Stewart had to suspend operations as he had agreed to meet Amanda for a post-work drink and snack. Before going out he left messages on answering machines or texts on mobiles. The drink and snack turned out to be something more substantial after Amanda met him with friends in tow. When finally they got home the light on their own answering machine glowed brightly. The harvest was rich. Colin Banks, Greg Roberts, Phil Cole, Winston Jenkins and Basil Smith were all ready volunteers. To have Basil Smith available at short notice was the biggest surprise because his wife, Jane, was not the greatest enthusiast for her husband's recreational activity. However, as Basil's call had explained, Helmerstead Hall was something of a draw and so Jane would look forward to accompanying him.

As he listened to the content and tone of these responses, Stewart realised that in his haste to convey his original message he had perhaps pitched it wrong. What should have come across as a query about availability for selection had been interpreted as a request to play. This left him with seventeen enlisted players and two other calls as yet unanswered. He could hardly not chase Ray Burrill and Richard Furness just because he now had a team and a half at his disposal. Yet his further efforts in their direction still failed to achieve contact. John Furness did not know where his brother was, and when finally it occurred to Stewart to try the veterinary surgery where Ray Burrill worked, the message he got was that Mr Burrill was away in the country tending a sick animal. In a way this was true.

Up to this point Stewart Thorogood had been thinking exclusively about players. With a sudden jolt he remembered transport. Arthur and his coach would be a key part of the operation, but Arthur had been told that no matches were in the schedule until the following week. Stewart went through some worrying hours before hearing from Arthur. To his great relief he was assured that all would be well.

There were other details to be sorted. The Outcasts would need to take a scorer. Since becoming a father for the second time Simon Crossley's availability at short notice could not always be guaranteed. Sophie had given birth to Michael Ricky (Rahul had narrowly missed out in the name stakes) some two months earlier, a brother for Brian Sachin. Simon, who had edged ever nearer to cool since coming under Sophie's influence, was a fully participative dad, and Sophie under Simon's influence had become a willing Outcasts' groupie. Whilst Brian Sachin had also been a regular if only vaguely conscious supporter of his father's cricket club, Michael Ricky was thought as yet too young to make his debut. When Simon's services were sought for the unexpected charity match, Sophie consented to his leave of absence. So Simon, sporting a second earring (it was not to be revealed that this marked the arrival of his second child lest unkind remarks were made about where a third might go) and an embryo goatee beard with which he was experimenting at Sophie's prompting, declared himself available.

An umpire, however, was not required. The game at Helmerstead Hall being a semi-showbiz production would have two 'personality' umpires. Stewart Thorogood could hardly fail to inform Syd Breakwell what they were doing, but was nevertheless embarrassed to have to explain that there was not the usual slot for him. To Stewart's relief Syd was not in the least put out. Any suppressed disappointment in his voice vanished with the question 'Can I still come along for the ride?' Stewart's 'of course' led to Syd quickly adding that there wouldn't be any harm in having a relief umpire available, and then more mysteriously 'the wife needn't know'. Like Arthur, Syd Breakwell had been another looking for an excuse to avoid an unwanted activity. They had agreed to attend their neighbour's barbecue – or rather Syd's wife had accepted the invitation. Syd had been looking forward to it with as much enthusiasm as to an appointment with the dentist. In fact Syd had thought to himself on more than one occasion that even his dentist's mouthwash tasted better than the home-produced wines his next-door neighbour insisted on inflicting on his guests. 'But we've got to go,' said Syd's wife, 'it's his sixtieth.' Now at the eleventh hour had come a reprieve. 'You must go,' said Syd to his wife, 'after all it is his sixtieth, but I simply can't let the Outcasts down when they're playing somewhere as prestigious as Helmerstead Hall.' Syd never actually told a lie. There was no reason why his wife would learn that he was not officially on duty. He would be picked up by Arthur in the usual way and it would all look perfectly normal – even to the next-door neighbour if he happened to be watching.

Not having to settle down to regular work until September, Richard

Furness was determined to make the most of his last summer of freedom. He had returned from New Zealand fairly flush with funds and only needed to do some casual work here and there (mostly in bars) to keep himself in spending money. By word-of-mouth recommendation from a chum he had landed a three-week assignment (weekdays only) at a smart, recently opened bar-café in the West End of London. It was called Bert's Bar (more for alliteration than for any association with its owner) and it was there that he had met her. She had arrived with a group of female friends all of whom could have passed for eighteen even if some of them were not. She was. Waving a proof-of-age card whilst Richard, mindful of the strict rules of the establishment, was still wondering whether he should ask for one and risk starting their relationship (on which he had already set his mind) on the wrong footing, she briskly ordered a round of alcopops. As it and others were consumed Richard felt that he was under scrutiny from several pairs of eyes. He should not have worried. In the smart yellow tunic which was the house uniform he had scrubbed up very well.

Richard had disappeared temporarily to obtain a replacement bottle of a top-of-the-range gin. On his return the table previously occupied by the girl and her friends was deserted. Richard was disappointed. Constrained as he felt by the formalities of the establishment for which he was working, he still scolded himself for a failure of technique in not acquiring a name or contact number. No one else on the bar staff knew her or remembered seeing her on any other occasion. Richard was despondent. Yes, there were plenty of other fish in the sea. With his record he did not need reminding, but he did not like the supreme varieties escaping his net. He should not have worried. The next day she was back. This time she had just one friend with her. Richard recognised that as insurance policy; arriving alone would have been too obvious. They chose a table in the small area set aside for eating, and after an initial drink ordered two house salads, which were a cross-breed between some of the more usual marques. Taking the salad bowls to them provided Richard with an opportunity for a little social interchange which had within scarcely more than a day transformed into a rather grander, more intense social interchange.

Something of a similar nature was taking place in Cambridge. Ray Burrill's first encounter with Andrea Firbrook, and more particularly her father, had not been propitious. The meeting, more particularly with her father, had taken place in compromising and embarrassing circumstances in the family home adjacent to the Outcasts' match against the northerly Essex village of Doredell.* A true friendship, more particularly with Andrea, had been established. Her father's suspicion had waned, but remained a difficulty; her mother when she finally met Ray was at best neutral, believing her daughter to be too young for any serious relationship, especially with an unproven veterinarian. So Andrea had done what girls faced with such a situation usually did; she had moved out. Fortunately she had been able to move in with two girlfriends, who had a rented house on the western outskirts of the city and a vacancy. This had allowed her relationship with Ray to prosper – within limits, but the limits were a lot less restrictive than had she continued to live at home.

When she had fallen ill the news came to Ray Burrill in a cryptic text message from one of her housemates. Andrea herself could not be reached. Leaping to wildly pessimistic conclusions, Ray had dropped everything and made speed to Cambridge. The virus (a near-universal medical diagnosis for the unknown but non-life-threatening ailment) had certainly laid Andrea low and Ray's heart went out to her, much as it had done those months ago when he had first met her carrying an injured pet. Dramatically (and well over the top) he had decided that he must stay by her side. To emphasise his total therapeutic commitment he symbolically switched off his mobile. She would have his undivided attention. Whether ultimately it was the half-heartedness of the virus or the whole-heartedness of Ray's attention, Andrea's condition rapidly improved. After an evening during which each was able to reassure the other of their growing affection, Ray decided that he could safely reconnect with the outside world. After listening to Stewart Thorogood's message, he too reckoned that he had been picked to play. There was little time to lose.

Richard Furness had played away from home many times in his young life, but never in quite the luxury he found on being led by new acquaintance, Suzy Waterbeach, through the door of what she casually described as her parents' town pad. Wealth shouted at him from every corner, not that he was in a mood to take in any detail. Far more important business was at hand. Before he asked, Suzy had said that her parents were in the country, the housekeeper was off-duty and her brother was staying with friends. So the coast seemed clear for what both Suzy and her guest appeared to have

* *Incidentally Cricket* (2003).

– urgently – in mind. Suzy delayed for no longer than it took to collect a magnum of champagne and two crystal glasses before showing Richard that the luxury of downstairs was replicated on the upper floors. The night beckoned.

It would not have been accurate to say that the earth moved, but it was certainly true that the house shook. The music began at a high decibel level at around 11.45 pm according to the bedside clock. Richard and Suzy were no more than half way through the bottle of champagne when they were frozen in shock. Suzy recovered first. She recognised the music. 'It's Carl', she said. 'That's got to be his group, but what the hell are they doing here? My brother', she added as she saw the blank look on Richard's face. It was obvious that she was in no rush to make introductions. The music suited neither sleep nor romance. The fact that the former triumphed over the latter was down to the alcohol. At the critical moment when they were drifting into slumber the music must have ceased. The peace which returned to the house enabled sleep to continue until its natural conclusion at eight o'clock the following morning.

Ever the gentleman but with an imperfect memory of the previous evening, Richard Furness, waking first, stole downstairs to the kitchen to make coffee for himself and Suzy. The person seated at the table wore what even at that angle was a breathtakingly short terry towelling robe. Whoever

else, reasoned Richard, she could not possibly be the cleaning lady. 'I'm Pip', she said, unabashed in the presence of a strange male wearing only a pair of boxers torn in one place (in the rush). 'I didn't know Carl had a kid brother.' The events of the night clicked into place in Richard's mind. Explanations and introductions were made. Upstairs, introductions were not necessary, but explanations were. Suzy and Carl stared at each other across the landing as voices below made it clear that concealment was not an option.

For all that it was surprisingly convened it was quite a jolly breakfast party. The practice session at their friends' place had been knocked out by a power cut in that part of London. So they had de-camped to the handiest alternative. The lads had gone about two o'clock, but Pip had been feeling tired. Carl's voice trailed away at this point, but he knew he was not convincing his sister. They both needed to take a vow of silence. Then suddenly Carl leapt up: 'My God, I'd better go. I'm meant to be playing cricket. It's a big charity match at the Hall.' This announcement had a mixed reaction. Pip looked crestfallen; Richard had an expression on his face which seemed to be saying 'Oh, really'; and Suzy radiated enthusiasm. 'Oh, let's go too, Richard,' she said, 'I want to show you our place in the country. We could have fun there.' This was followed by Carl asking Richard whether he played cricket. On getting a nod, he went on, 'Well, you might even get a game. You never know with these celeb. sides. They often show up one or two men light.' Whether it was the fun suggested by Suzy or the cricket by her brother, Richard found himself going along with the idea. Carl decided that he must leave at once. Suzy and Richard followed in her Mini. After a detour to drop off a disconsolate Pip and to pick up Richard's kit (his brother had already left the flat) they set off for the country.

No one liked to let Arthur down. After final arrangements had been made, an early departure had been agreed. All bar one of the eighteen available players (Basil Smith was required to drive his wife to the event) plus scorer and redundant umpire were where they should be at the appointed hour. It had been reasoned that as this was after all a charity match, a fun match indeed, there would be no harm in stopping off on the way for some pre-match refreshment, provided, of course that a suitable watering-hole could be identified. In light of previous experience there was some scepticism when Toby Lederwood said that he knew of an excellent ale-house in the village of Calton-by-the-Water. Before taking him at his word three Outcasts undertook independent verification. This confirmed that in Calton in deepest Hertfordshire where the water had long ago dried up, beer in its finest form flowed copiously at the inappropriately named Bucket and Spade. No harm it was felt could be done by programming this hostelry into the itinerary. It would put everyone in the right mood fully to enter into the spirit of the afternoon's festivities.

Between intention and fulfilment a gap occurred. The Outcasts had set off sufficiently early from south-west London that they had avoided any heavy traffic such as might have been engendered by a major social, sporting and charitable event at Helmerstead Hall. Arthur's coach slid into the deserted car park of the Bucket and Spade at what could have been only shortly after opening time. Nevertheless they were not the first customers. A table in the corner of the bar was occupied by an elderly gentleman who was addressing a bottle of champagne. The Outcasts almost felt that they were intruding on his privacy. However, there was more important business at hand. Arrayed before them was an unexpectedly wide selection of real ales. This became a serious distraction for at least some of the players. Debate was naturally provoked. Which to choose? How to compare? Stewart Thorogood as captain for the day had to assert himself to dissuade some of his team-mates from going through the card.

As the wonderful ales slipped down the various throats much of the talk was about the forthcoming match about which they knew so little. Their substitution for the previously ordered team had been accomplished at such short notice that they did not know exactly whom they would be playing. Expectations were not high and they lowered with each round. 'The usual wankers', was one thought. 'Arty-farty showbiz types', was another. Trying to steer things on to an even keel, Stewart Thorogood observed 'There could be one or two serious players amongst them.' And so it went on. All this unmistakeable talk about cricket eventually seemed to stir the other occupant of the bar.

'Tell me,' he said to Arthur, who was hovering on the fringe of the group ready to encourage them back on to the coach, 'are you guys on your way to watch a cricket game? Is it the big one up the road?' Some explanation was necessary. C. Ramsgate Fishburn was very impressed to find himself in the presence of one of the teams participating in the match he aimed to attend, but Arthur forbore from furnishing too precise a description of the true nature of 'the big one up the road'. A favour was requested. The elderly American was having difficulty obtaining a taxi to take him to Helmerstead

Hall. Arthur was too polite to observe that, if he as a visitor had wanted to get to Helmerstead Hall, he would not have been starting from the Bucket and Spade. He could scarcely imagine that the American would have chosen the Bucket and Spade for the same reason as the Outcasts. But no problem. There was room on the coach for a passenger. Arthur considered it a contribution towards the special relationship.

No member of the party had drunk to excess during the stopover, but those who had been determined to sample the full range of guest beers on offer at the Bucket and Spade (and sample in Outcasts' custom and practice did not mean a mere taste) were arguably below the peak of their game by the time the journey recommenced. C. Ramsgate Fishburn was full of champagne, his landlord's late breakfast and curiosity. Addressing Syd Breakwell, he enquired whether cricketers always prepared for a game as the Outcasts had visibly done on this occasion. Examined literally it was a difficult question to which to give a wholly accurate answer. Syd was thinking what to say when Charlie Colson across the aisle chipped in with 'Always – it's virtually a club rule.' This comment appeared to be taken seriously by the American, despite it having dissolved into a cackle of wild laughter. After a moment's pause Charlie had something to add. He leant over confidentially towards the American and, adopting a solemn manner, advised him that real ale was the key to both playing and watching the English game of cricket. C. Ramsgate Fishburn looked impressed and made a note on a pad.

His other questions about the afternoon's activities could not be answered by either Syd Breakwell or by Charlie Colson, who had in any case fallen asleep. The Outcasts were short of hard facts about what lay ahead. Even after arrival at Helmerstead Hall their confusion was not immediately dispelled. Fortunately they had got there with time to spare. Directed to an entrance marked 'Players, Exhibitors and Tradesmen', they had become aware of two things as they drove down the long, sweeping drive: the grandeur of the Hall and its setting and, secondly, indications aplenty that the event itself was conceived on a lavish scale. Coming to rest by the side of what could be nothing other than a cricket pavilion the Outcasts sensed a convivial but hopefully none-too demanding day. At this point Arthur coughed apologetically and asked to be excused. He had received a message that morning about an old coach in which he might be interested. It was to be found no great distance from Helmerstead and he would dearly like the opportunity to examine it. Stewart Thorogood felt he could hardly demur. In any case they all had his mobile number and he theirs. He promised that he could be back for the climax – and he truly was.

The Outcasts were greeted effusively by Caroline Bingley-Adams. It was absolutely super of them to come and wasn't it absolutely awful about those cricketers being locked up in Slovenia. It was going to be an absolutely super day and everyone was going to have a super time. It was marvellous that they were able to do so much for charity and it would be heaps of fun. So, concluded the Outcasts, they seemed to be welcome. Yet despite the warmth of this welcome Caroline Bingley-Adams kept looking about her with an anxious air. When asked by Stewart Thorogood if he could be introduced to the captain of the opposing team, a pained expression passed across Caroline Bingley-Adams' exquisitely made-up face. Somewhat falteringly she had to admit that the celebs were not as yet all present and correct. She was able to hand Stewart a souvenir programme and scorecard which had been printed in anticipation of the Soul of Discretion cricketers being on parade. However, it provided the first evidence of the likely opposing line-up, evidence which was soon shown to be unreliable.

On the left-hand page of the centre spread of the programme were listed twelve names, none of whom would be appearing – they were the men who seemingly when it came to the test had failed to be the soul of discretion. Opposite were twelve names under the heading 'All-star Showbiz XI'. Wisely between the heading and the first name were the words in minute italics: 'is expected to include'. Even had expectations been fulfilled the team as listed would not have convinced everyone that it was either all-star or the cream of showbiz. Stewart read through the names:

Darren Hawk
Darren Fox
Ronnie Eagle

These were all first-class cricketers and Stewart recognised that they would be a formidable batting trio. He could not at first imagine that any member of the Outcasts would be capable of containing them let alone dismissing them. On second thoughts he reckoned that they might be in it for a laugh and so it might not be so bad after all.

Rob Steelback

Here was a recently retired first-class cricketer. Stewart gulped. Would all four of them play it for a laugh? If not, it could be mayhem.

Crispin Foot

He was a ballet dancer. Stewart had heard the name, but could not picture the man. Of his cricketing skills he knew nothing.

Jeremy Large

Stewart learned later that the name was pronounced Lager. Its owner had attained national fame doing a rather unusual form of Godspot on national radio. Although not an ordained minister he filled churches wherever he went, gaining and exploiting a reputation for good works. His style irked real clergymen, but they knew that when he was the visiting preacher the collection plates would be full to overflowing.

Wayne Gaine

This man was an aspiring but occasional impresario who had registered a few successes mainly in provincial theatres and entirely with shows of a highly suggestive nature.

Don Hennelly

Never a chart topper, he had specialised in songs from the shows for which there was always a steady demand, even if it had increasingly come in Don Hennelly's case from Women's Institute concerts, residential homes for the elderly (where a degree of deafness ensured his most enthusiastic receptions) and holiday camps.

Simon Short

It was stretching a point to describe Simon Short as a well-known broadcaster, because as of that date his role as a newscaster with a twenty-four hour news channel had been confined to weekends and Bank Holidays when his colleagues preferred not to work.

George Others

He was described simply as a publicist. Two Outcasts, who were not particularly keen to be identified as readers of glossy gossip magazines, muttered that they thought they had heard of him.

Gianfranco Retezzi

The renowned Italian opera singer, who had actually begun life as Stan Lovecroft in Muswell Hill, could reasonably lay claim to a star name, but whether he could hold a bat was another matter.

Guy Harper

This all-star personality was simply but immodestly labelled as a financial entrepreneur. Again there was no hint of how entrepreneurial as a cricketer he might turn out to be.

Stewart Thorogood thought that it was a very mixed bag, but the presence of four players with county experience made it extremely unlikely that any combination of Outcasts would be able to give them much of a game unless it was indeed played completely for laughs. Once installed in a spacious changing facility in what must rank as one of the smartest cricket pavilions in the northern hemisphere, Stewart re-examined the eleven names he had jotted down on the back of an envelope during the pre-lunch part of the coach journey. His choice had been:

> Jon Palmer
> Stewart Thorogood
> Kevin Newton
> Rashid Ali
> Dean Faulds
> Harry Northwood
> Ray Burrill

89

Charlie Colson
Tom Redman
Basil Smith
Colin Banks

It was quickly evident that some reassessment would be necessary. His numbers had already reduced. It was with no real sense of loss that Stewart greeted the news that Charlie Colson and David Pelham had moved with speed towards the large and prominent beer tent to instruct the American hitch-hiker in the complexities (and delights) of cask-conditioned English ales. The disappearance of Colin Banks reported by his long-suffering friend and flatmate, Greg Roberts, was more of a blow. On song Colin was a more than useful quick bowler. Pretty women, however, were a distraction. For Colin, arrival at Helmerstead had been akin to a small child being let loose in a sweetshop. There were beautiful girls to be seen at every turn. At the last sighting Colin had already acquired a companion. His looks and chat-up technique rarely failed – at least not in the short term.

Kevin Newton was apologetic. He wanted to play, but he had a problem. He was getting a series of contradictory and confusing messages about Gloria Lockwood's travel arrangements and whereabouts. Three text messages presumably from family and friends gave him three different flights of three different airlines on which Gloria could be embarked. He had assumed they referred to Sunday, but a further (corrupted) message hinted otherwise. It raised the doubt in Kevin's mind that Gloria just might after all be arriving on that very day and he was supposed to be playing a match. With an abundance of players at Stewart's disposal he begged to be excused. He said that his mind was a jumble and he would not be able to concentrate. Stewart believed him. None of the Outcasts had been left in any doubt by Toby Lederwood's tales from the Caribbean that Kevin was completely in thrall to the reportedly stunning Gloria.

It then became apparent to Stewart Thorogood that he had seen no sign of Basil Smith, who had opted at his wife's insistence for separate travel arrangements. This too was a disappointment. Basil was a steady off-spinner, who could (just about) more often than not be counted on to play a containing role. At that moment Stewart could not know how much Basil Smith wanted to be present in the team, whether playing a containing role or not. Instead he was stuck on the Yarfield by-pass in a car which obstinately refused to move. An air of tension prevailed. Jane Smith, who was more intent than her husband on reaching Helmerstead Hall, had fuelled the atmosphere by saying, 'I thought I told you to get this car serviced.' There had followed an argument which had lasted as long as it had taken Basil to notice a sign ahead which looked as though it might indicate a garage. Leaving a protesting Jane behind him, Basil set out in hope. It was soon dashed.

The site now occupied by Martin More Motors had once been used as a filling station and repair shop. Perhaps that is why at a distance it had that appearance. In its present manifestation it offered no comfort to Basil Smith. A pale-faced youth in a grimy green overall informed him with due modesty for his own trainee status (and capability) that there was no mechanic on duty on a Saturday, and then gratuitously added with a flicker of a triumphal smile that, even if there had been, they did not do casual repairs. Basil Smith tramped back to his car resigning himself to reliance on the Road Services Association to come to their rescue. Retrieving his mobile phone he dialled the necessary number. He had no illusions about how long it might take the RSA to get someone out to them. What he had not bargained for was how long it took to get through to the RSA to register their plight. His next call was intended to be to Stewart Thorogood to notify him of the delay. Unfortunately the twenty-five minutes of airtime he had used in communicating with the RSA had exhausted the battery of his phone. This information produced another caustic comment from his wife.

Basil Smith made his second visit to Martin More Motors to request the use of their telephone. He was met by the same pale-faced youth whose green overall seemed to have increased in its griminess since he had first seen it. Could he use the phone to make an urgent call? No, he could not. The pale-faced youth was emphatic on the point. It was not management's policy to allow use of their business line. After all, the youth had added with a smirk, someone might have an urgent reason to contact them. Before Basil Smith could raise an arm to deliver what would have been a highly satisfying physical response to this intransigence the youth offered an eleventh-hour concession, pointing to a pay phone at the edge of the forecourt. From outward appearance it did not seem that it had been vandalised, but after five minutes of jiggling with it to an assortment of buzzes and clicks, Basil realised that something had been done to render it inoperable. Turning back towards the main building he could see that the pale-faced youth was ostentatiously using the company telephone with a malicious grin on his face. Basil admitted defeat and trudged back to his car (in which his wife simmered) to await the favours of the Road Services Association.

Caroline Bingley-Adams' smile was wearing thin. She had thought that her worries were over when she had so quickly overcome the loss of one of the teams due to play in the match. It had never occurred to her that there might be trouble in delivering the team of celebs so lavishly detailed in the souvenir programme. She had been utterly convinced by her father that he could deliver. However, a series of phone calls he had taken the previous day began to undermine the original team selection. The biggest blow was the loss of the county players. Atrocious weather on the previous day meant that the knock-out match in which their teams were involved would have to be postponed to the reserve day, Saturday. Crispin Foot, it was learned, had broken a toe. Gianfranco Retezzi, the opera singer, had ostensibly a sore throat, but in reality an unexpected assignation with a member of the chorus. Without revealing all the details Caroline's father had assured her that adequate (he deliberately put it no higher) substitutes would be found.

It was therefore an uneasy Caroline who had met the charity organiser in

Helmerstead the previous evening. Like her he was all smiles and assurance, but both had things to hide. He had brought with him all the publicity material connected with the fund-raising. He explained to Caroline that although TRANSECT was the umbrella charity involved he had decided that it would fit this particular occasion better if there was a focus on a specific idea: Wickets for Waifs. Sport, he hurriedly explained, could do so much to brighten the lives of children in deprived parts of the world. Cricket, he gushed with an enthusiasm which was one hundred per cent bogus, had a special appeal in some of the countries in which TRANSECT had a presence. At a cricket match here in the heart of England he was convinced, he said, that there would be great empathy with a long line of orphans and the dispossessed aspiring to try their hand at this most noble and inspiring of games. When Caroline reached for her hankie he was sure that he had her well and truly hooked.

Caroline's brandishing of her hankie was not in fact related to the culmination of the sob story she had just heard. The move was in preparation for the sob story on which she had decided to embark. She allowed a deceptive tear to trickle down her cheek. The charity organiser was led to believe that he had not lost his touch. In reality Caroline had been unmoved by the plight of destitute kids in Africa or indeed wherever. She had one concern and one alone, and that was to be seen as pulling off a major charity event. This she believed would fortify her social position. How she did it was of secondary interest. Success was what mattered – a huge great smasheroo of a success. Suddenly this had been put at risk by the withdrawal of half of the expected personalities. She did not reveal to her companion the full extent of the team's depletion, merely saying that there were one or two enforced changes and so it was absolutely vital that he should fulfil his promise to play. The charity organiser inwardly groaned. His attachment to the whole venture might have loosened, but he forced himself to remember the rich pickings which would come his way. What he had seen of all the other preparations (sideshows, stalls, exhibitions and refreshments) told him that Caroline Bingley-Adams, whatever else he thought of her, had brought together the elements of a major success. In that context what were one or two celebs to matter? He steeled himself and gave Caroline's knee a comforting pat.

Nevertheless the charity organiser's expedition to Helmerstead had begun badly. One minute it had been there, the next minute it had gone. He used an inconspicuous van when attending charity money-raising occasions to avoid any appearance of opulence. Neither his Bentley nor his 4x4 would have been right. Already running late for his appointment with Caroline Bingley-Adams he had retrieved the inconspicuous van from its inconspicuous lock-up, parked it outside his flat entrance and gone inside to start loading leaflets and other paraphernalia. Delayed by a few moments whilst he took a message off his answering machine he came outside to an empty space. To someone apparently the van had not been completely inconspicuous. Whilst he seethed he decided that he could afford neither time nor effort to report the theft to the police. Even if he had been robbed of his Bentley he would have expected no more than a world-weary response from the police. At least, he admitted to himself, he would have wanted a crime number. In the case of the van, the provenance of which he doubted, it might be a mixed blessing. There was no convenient alternative to the 4x4, which was under lock and key in the flat's garage.

Use of this powerful, opulent-looking gas guzzler had the advantage of making up time on his journey, but it still weighed on the charity organiser's mind that it was a wholly inappropriate vehicle in which he, as the supposed advocate of the needy of the Third World, should be seen. He was doing 90 mph along the Yarfield by-pass when he saw a sign ahead of him which might have meant a petrol station. It might be sensible to top up the tank of his thirsty vehicle in case garages open at weekends in this rural area were hard to find. He slowed sufficiently to note two things. The establishment he had spotted did not after all possess any visible fuel pumps. What it did offer, however, was what looked like a very conveniently-sized white van. Plastic stickers on its windscreen announced that it was for sale (a real bargain) for £2999. It was worth further investigation, the charity organiser concluded.

He pulled on to the forecourt, got out of the 4x4, stretched his legs and circumnavigated the white Transit van. He found that the rear doors were unlocked and so he was able to look inside. He saw then that it had once held seats and been used as a bus. He also realised that the former side windows had been painted over together with some lettering on the sides of the vehicle. All this he discovered without interruption from any human agency. The place was strangely quiet for a commercial centre. The charity organiser leant inside and gave a long blast on the horn (two-tone naturally) of the 4x4. That had an effect. Within moments a man appeared hitching his trousers and stuffing his shirt back into them. 'I'm Ted More', he said, 'Can I help?' There was a brief pause before the charity organiser replied, as his attention had briefly strayed to the figure of a pale-faced youth in the doorway whose soiled green overalls were open to the waist revealing an equally pale chest. Putting aside any unworthy thought, the charity organiser sought to do business. He succeeded. Shortly afterwards with his own vehicle in store he proceeded to his destination in the white van he had hired for forty-eight hours at a price which after initial reluctance Ted More could not finally bring himself to refuse.

Re-modelling his team, Stewart Thorogood was weighing the respective merits of Winston Jenkins and Phil Cole (how much each had drunk at the lunch-time stopover) when Richard Furness strolled into the pavilion. Each was surprised to see the other. With explanations (in Richard's case sanitised) out of the way Stewart made a swift decision. Apart from his all-round abilities Richard had one priceless, if only temporary, asset. He was sober. Stewart's revised team list was complete. It read:

> Jon Palmer
> Stewart Thorogood
> Dean Faulds
> Rashid Ali
> Toby Lederwood
> Harry Northwood
> Ray Burrill
> Richard Furness
> John Furness
> Tom Redman
> Nigel Redman

It was agreed that the duties of twelfth man would be shared. His job done, he then awaited word that the opposing team was fully gathered. Such faces as he had so far seen in and about the pavilion were unfamiliar.

Familiarity or lack of it was the thought passing through the mind of Caroline Bingley-Adams as she typed up a team sheet which a few moments earlier had been dictated to her over the phone by her father. 'Best I can do I'm afraid,' he told her, 'but, don't worry, they'll all be there.' These soothing words offered only the mildest relief to his daughter. When she had finished typing she noticed that there were only eleven names on the paper. She hoped it did not matter, but she congratulated herself on making sure that the charity organiser was on board. She looked at the list again before printing off copies. It was certainly not as celeb as she had originally intended. Even as she spoke the names to herself she felt less than convinced. The team, in no sort of order, now was:

Jeremy Large
Wayne Gaine
Rob Steelback
Don Hennelly
Simon Short
Guy Harper
George Others

These were the survivors of the team set out in the souvenir programme. The late recruits were:

Beaufort Strange
Fred Fortune
Carl Waterbeach
Hugo Crabscote

It took a combined effort on the part of the Outcasts gathered in the pavilion to establish just exactly who these substitutes were when the new list was handed to them. Beaufort Strange was an actor. Several Outcasts could attest to that, but not one of them could actually remember any part he had played. Had a national survey been undertaken such a reaction would very likely have been confirmed. Fred ('Have you heard this one?') Fortune was a stand-up comedian. The name rang a bell with Toby Lederwood and earned a grimace from Jon Palmer and Dean Faulds. It was established that Carl Waterbeach, described as an up-and-coming musician with a band called Natural Turnip, must have been drafted in because he was the son of the owner of Helmerstead Hall. Some Outcasts remembered seeing Hugo Crabscote on television where he was wheeled in from time to time as a financial analyst (mainly because he was cheap).

The cricketing pretensions of this second-choice eleven were largely unknown, although John Furness volunteered the supposition that Hugo Crabscote was (he had heard) a regular club cricketer. Beyond that nothing, apart from the realisation that this unquantifiable opposition numbered only eleven. By comparison the Outcasts were over-endowed, even though these resources were scattered in places suspected and unknown. Stewart could see where this might lead. It was time, he decided, to get down to business. He marched off towards the opposition changing-room and encountered his first shock of the afternoon.

On becoming the new owner of Helmerstead Hall, Edward Waterbeach CBE (the knighthood lay achingly in prospect), writer, theatre owner and record producer, had made an early move towards acquiring local respectability by going to great lengths to do business with traders and craftsmen in the area. The first essentials of becoming a property-owner in a new part of the country are a good plumber and a good electrician. Edward Waterbeach had studied the list of recommendations supplied by the agent for the estate of Sir Blain Rough and decided to put it to the test. At the outset he wanted the plumbing checked and the wiring replaced.

What you could say about David Needham was that he was willing, honest and hard-working; what you could not say was that he was a thoroughly competent plumber. He had learned the basics of his trade from his father, but had not progressed very far beyond them. His father's name (he was also called David) and reputation had opened many doors for his son. Although he was by then retired, many clients probably thought that it was the father rather than the son who would be ministering to their needs. Some came to recognise the distinction the hard way. Edward Waterbeach was one of these. The tap which continued to drip and the not quite cured leaking pipe were minor irritations over which the householders might shrug their shoulders and seek a second call-out. What hit Edward Waterbeach was not a minor irritation, more a minor disaster.

Before carrying out certain tests David Needham had turned the water off at the mains. Of that there was no doubt. His action was witnessed. What possessed him to single out the ensuite bathroom of the master bedroom for special attention by turning the taps full on was not known. This action was not witnessed. Had there been a witness it is more likely that the position of the plug in the bath would have been noticed. David Needham went cheerfully about his work tracing and testing the pipework and occasionally replacing sections. When he was satisfied that all was done, he turned on the water at the mains and left for the day. He was not destined to return. Structural damage was avoided, but a major clean-up and redecoration exercise was necessitated. Electrical repair work was also called for, and in consequence of Edward Waterbeach's first taste of local craftsmen, Charles Brett could consider himself very fortunate to be summoned.

He, however, gave a very good account of himself. He completed the electrical repairs efficiently and cleanly within a few hours and went away from Helmerstead Hall with a contract to update the whole wiring system and a modest but elegant string of pearls which had nestled at the bottom of a very full jewel box. The completed contract yielded a handsome sum of money, a small gold bracelet and an on-going relationship with the household of Helmerstead Hall. This relationship had led quite recently to Charles Brett being called to install a sophisticated digital sound system which could be accessed in every room used by members of the family and their guests. It was another lucrative deal for the electrician. It was also timely.

By then Charles Brett had made his life-changing decision. He lacked only opportunity. This he felt was supplied when he heard about the spectacular charity event which was shortly to be held at Helmerstead Hall. It struck him that this could be a significant diversion which might provide him with his own opportunity for a spectacular heist. The sound system job gave him free access to all parts of Helmerstead Hall. When he left with the work completed he had ample knowledge of what was where, portability and value being the main criteria. Was it people who became rich quickly, he mused, who liked to keep large amounts of cash around them in vulnerable places? Having gone over the building with a fine toothcomb, he felt that he knew all its secrets. He left behind one of his own.

Stewart Thorogood entered the opposition's changing-room and took an involuntary step back. No one visiting Jurassic Park could have been more surprised than Stewart at the scene he encountered. Its occupants were dressed – at least those who already were – in a strange variety of costumes. A lady detached herself from the crowd and introduced herself as Don Hennelly. 'I'm captaining this lot, you must be the Outlaws' skipper.' On closer inspection his opposite number was a man, but the flowery top over a pink pleated skirt and a mass of blonde curls had led to a few moments of doubt. 'Nobody told us it was fancy dress', faltered Stewart. (Caroline

Bingley-Adams had quite deliberately withheld this information in the shrewd belief that it might have weighed against the Outcasts agreeing to take part.) 'Costume dress', insisted Don Hennelly, although Stewart Thorogood forbore from asking what his female attire was supposed to represent. On looking round he could now see that some other team members were in period cricket clothes. Yet there was no consistent theme. There was a clown, a chef brandishing a frying pan (Stewart idly wondered whether he would use it as a bat), a pirate and a clergyman. It was clear that some of the late recruits were still debating which of the pre-arranged sets of clothes would best fit them.

Whilst Stewart Thorogood was still trying to absorb this ghastly scene Caroline Bingley-Adams appeared with two men in white coats. 'Oh good!' she said, addressing the team captains in a belief which was wildly premature, 'I'm glad you two chaps have got to know one another. I want you to meet the umpires. It's time to toss.' This last statement was made only after her eyes had anxiously scanned the changing-room and established that the minimum essential complement was present. Stewart thought that there was something vaguely familiar about the umpires. Don Hennelly needed no introduction, giving a stage hug to both men. 'Billy, Tommy, great to see you.' Stewart's introduction was more circumspect. 'I'm Billy Figg and this is Tommy Fagge.' At first sight the distinction was not easy to make. Both men were short, rotund and red-faced. Confusion was further served by the fact that beyond their white coats and caps they were identically dressed. It was when the one called Billy Figg uttered the words 'Shall we go for a walk?' that for Stewart the penny dropped.

Figg and Fagge were a comedy duo whose act had padded out many a variety show on television in an age when the variety show was a staple part of the schedules. The type of act which Figg and Fagge purveyed was close to being out of fashion when it first hit the screens and it had little chance of longevity once a new kind of comedy came into being and variety shows declined in popularity. For a while the two comedians had enjoyed what for them was a high standard of living. The fees from their television appearances and occasional stage shows had been boosted by appearance money for opening supermarkets, country fairs and the like. Their disappearance from the small screen had been accelerated by behavioural problems. They had adopted a lifestyle hitherto foreign to them. It was unsustainable. There began a trail of affairs, broken marriages, night club punch-ups and driving offences. A taste for drink did not help. Their professional appearances became more and more irregular. They wallowed in booze, self-pity and penury. The turning point came when Tommy Fagge met first God and then Joan Malcrow. In both cases it was love at first sight. Christianity did for Tommy Fagge what no other influence, parental or educational, up to that point in his life had done. He cleaned up his act in every sense and his revival – soon to influence his partner – was then engineered by the woman he had met at prayer.

Joan Malcrow was a shrewd theatrical agent with an innovative flair which had both boosted and revived careers. After Tommy Fagge had wept on her shoulder she could easily have dismissed him as a lost cause. But she was a Christian and she had felt some affection for this elderly man who seemed desperate to re-discover pride and respectability. She had many connections in the business. One was in her estimation a young and brilliant script-writer. The result of the marriage between the aspiring script-writer and the two fading comedians led to a pilot programme which was designed as a parody of the type of act they had previously done. Broadcast on an obscure digital channel it led to a series which had a cult following. However, it was the dog food advertisement which had really catapulted Figg and Fagge back to public notice. In their case the warning to actors never to appear with animals was disproved. The sight of one or other of these two portly gentlemen being knocked over by large friendly dogs in pursuit of their meal tickled the nation's funny bone. In their late sixties Figg and Fagge had at last made it, better than at any previous time in their lives.

Whether they felt they owed it to their new-found reputation or to the light-hearted nature of the general festivities that afternoon it was clear that the two umpires were intending to have fun at anyone's expense. A large section of the visiting public having taken for the moment their fill of games, sideshows and refreshments had turned its attention to the much heralded cricket match. A roar of laughter met Stewart Thorogood and Don Hennelly as they walked out to the pitch to toss the coin which was carried by the chef in his frying pan. Stewart did not think that Don Hennelly's costume was deserving of so much merriment. It was not until they reached the middle that on turning Stewart realised that they had been followed by the two umpires, who were themselves followed by a large Old English Sheepdog. Both Figg and Fagge, by now well practised, had

managed two tumbles each on their way to the wicket. 'Just to get everyone in the right mood', explained Billy Figg.

One person far from being in the right mood was Phil Cole. He had opted for first spell of duty as twelfth man for the Celebs XI before realising that the team he was aiding was turning out in costume. He was designated as an elf. A tense scene took place between him and Caroline Bingley-Adams. She said that it was essential Phil should not be odd man out. She said that it would confuse the spectators. When she sensed Phil's resistance she tried to appeal to his better nature by stressing the charitable purpose of the occasion and how it was important to enter into the spirit. As far as Phil was concerned it was not the spirit but the elf costume he was unwilling to enter. He knew that his fellow Outcasts would never let him forget it. He maintained his resistance and said that in any case the team would be unlikely to need a twelfth man. That was a tactical error, because Caroline said that it would not then matter very much if Phil put on the outfit because he would not have to stray from the pavilion. That was not to Phil's liking at all as he had designs on the refreshment tent with its promised array of beers. He was about to renege on the whole idea when Caroline resorted to one last ploy: tears. Phil was accused of spoiling her day, the day she had toiled over many months to organise. Phil felt awkward. He was uncomfortable with crying women. He began to feel a wretch. Despite feeling desperate he succumbed. Caroline rallied very quickly. She too had been desperate, because she had promised the charity organiser he would not have to field throughout the Outcasts' innings.

Stewart Thorogood came back into the pavilion at speed pursued by a playful Old English Sheepdog, which had transferred its attentions from Figg and Fagge once Stewart on leaving the pitch had begun to jog. The dog clearly thought that this had the makings of a new game and gave chase. Stewart accelerated. So did the dog, doubtless reckoning that Stewart with his more athletic figure would be an easier pushover than either Figg or Fagge. This further canine episode delighted the crowd at first, but there was disappointment when Stewart reached the pavilion steps without taking a fall. 'We're fielding', he gasped without additional comment. The waiting Outcasts merely shrugged. There was more enthusiasm from Phil Cole, who recognised that he could put off for an hour or two longer the donning of the dreaded elf costume.

Figg and Fagge remained out on the pitch providing impromptu entertainment. Some in the crowd thought it was a poor substitute when the Old English Sheepdog departed (under escort) to be replaced by the Outcasts led by Stewart Thorogood. The captain had obviously displeased spectators by failing to be the dog's victim, because he was greeted by booing which was perpetuated when he took the ball in preparation to bowl the first over. The Outcasts had made themselves unpopular in one or two places over the years, but it was rare, Stewart reflected, for hostility to set in so early in proceedings. He was forced to wonder how on earth the day might develop. How it did develop would have been beyond his imagining. Fortunately the crowd settled as Tommy Fagge waved to the scorers to indicate that play was about to start.

Simon Crossley was an immaculate scorer in an immaculate scorebox. The detached building stood at what would be deep extra cover when the bowling was from what was known as the Hall end. Outwardly it followed a conventional design, but did not rely on rollers to show the batsmen's and the total score. This was done by electronic means with a pad which lay between the two desks at which the scorers sat in front of a panoramic window. On such a warm day the glass panels were folded back to the sides. Simon glanced towards his opposite number. The gentleman scoring for the not quite all-star eleven was very much the opposite of Simon. He had been a member of the staff at Helmerstead Hall for many years. On reaching retirement age he had been retained on a part-time basis to carry out odd assignments. To Henry Moulden keeping the score at a cricket match was as odd as it could get, but he was confident that it was a simple enough task.

Henry Moulden's confidence waned on seeing Simon Crossley's array of scoring equipment. He greeted the younger man stiffly and sat at the vacant desk. He was dressed in a three-piece tweed suit, no part of which he felt inclined to discard in deference to the temperature. This was not the only factor in what promised to be a thoroughly uncomfortable afternoon. He was not at ease with the cheerful informality of his companion. Suspicious alike of male jewellery (which indicated one thing) and tattoos (which indicated another), Henry Moulden's affinity towards his fellow scorer was further impeded by the sight of Simon's pink cut-away vest over cut-off worn denim jeans. Another barrier was the goatee beard. In Henry Moulden's book beards were a bad thing as well. The strained atmosphere in the scorebox was in total contrast to the hilarity outside.

In signalling for play to start Tommy Fagge had forgotten one of the essential elements required for a good game of cricket: batsmen. By delaying it was clear that they wanted to make an entrance. Showbiz rather than cricketing instinct was to the fore. Beaufort Strange and Fred Fortune craved dramatic effect, and appearing as they were doing in a cricket match in rural England they certainly achieved it. Beaufort Strange's pink tutu was in complete contrast to Fred Fortune, who looked as though he had walked straight out of the *Lion King*. The crowd roared in delight. Fred

Fortune was provoked into roaring back and Beaufort Strange gave a twirl. It was all great fun, but the joke was lost on two of the spectators who had arrived just in time for the start. This had nothing of the appearance of cricket matches previously seen by Geraldine Rogers and Margaret Hamersteen. They had come to Helmerstead by arrangement to rendezvous once again with their friends who were the Soul of Discretion. They wondered whether Disney had beaten them to it.

Outcasts CC versus A Celebrity XI

The teams (in batting order)

Celebrity XI	*Outcasts CC*
Beaufort Strange	Jon Palmer
Fred Fortune	Stewart Thorogood
Rob Steelback	Dean Faulds
Don Hennelly	Rashid Ali
Carl Waterbeach	Toby Lederwood
Hugo Crabscote	Harry Northwood
Simon Short	Ray Burrill
Wayne Gaine	Richard Furness
George Others	John Furness
Guy Harper	Tom Redman
Jeremy Large	Nigel Redman

| 12th man: Phil Cole (borrowed) | 12th man: various |

The Celebs XI innings

'ABOVE ALL, HAVE FUN', Caroline Bingley-Adams had called out when Stewart Thorogood descended the pavilion steps. As he now looked around him, whilst Beaufort Strange was making a great performance out of taking guard, Stewart wondered about the borderline between fun and outright farce. Fred Fortune at the non-striker's end was frisking around on all fours. The very demeanour of Tommy Fagge and Billy Figg raised doubt about how the game would be conducted. Stewart's expectations were not high as he ran in to bowl the first ball. They sank immediately afterwards. He had produced a loosener which went down the leg side. Beaufort Strange made an exaggerated waft at the ball without any intention of hitting it and Stewart awaited the inevitable call from the umpire of 'wide ball'. He suffered a double disappointment. Tommy Fagge's response was a delayed shout of 'no-ball' quickly followed by 'free hit'. He had evidently watched a lot of limited overs cricket on television, although this theory was partly contradicted by the way he chose to signal it. Rather than rotate his hand above his head he rotated his whole body with a distinct theatrical flourish. The crowd loved it.

Stewart Thorogood most certainly did not love it. Into the type of cricket played by the Outcasts the concept of the free hit had not so far penetrated. Putting aside any thought as to whether his foot had crossed the line to justify the call of no-ball, Stewart realised that he must contain the damage. He had to set a field to try to guard against Beaufort Strange actually hitting the bonus ball, without there being evidence thus far of Beaufort Strange's ability to hit any ball. Stewart nevertheless decided to play safe and despatched his fielders to boundary positions. It was not safe enough. The delivery he unleashed was straight and orthodox. To his amazement Beaufort Strange executed a dance down the wicket and struck the ball far and high. The fielders at long-on and long-off could only watch it sail over their heads. Tommy Fagge made a great show of signalling six runs. The crowd loved it.

There was plenty of time for Stewart Thorogood to reflect whilst a search party set out to retrieve the ball from a distant part of the grounds of Helmerstead Hall. Its approximate location proved easier to identify than Toby Lederwood in the advance guard would have thought possible in light of the throng of visitors and array of amenities. An agitated knot of people was already forming around an object on the ground. A protruding leg indicated that the object was of human form. It was not difficult to deduce from the body language of the assembled group what might have happened. Toby Lederwood anticipated that this was not going to be an entirely straightforward case of asking for the ball back. Indeed, if humanitarian instincts had not prevailed, the wiser course of action might have been immediate retreat. As it was, the arrival on the scene of a cricketer with another in his wake provided a palpable target for criticism. Toby Lederwood was greeted with the understandably angry but personally preposterous question: 'What did you want to do that for?' His inquisitor stepped aside and Toby looked down, first noticing the cricket ball which had come to rest in a mound of supermarket chicken liver paté, but then forcing himself to focus on the prone figure of a middle-aged man with a shaven head stretched out in the remains of a picnic. The shaven head bore, apart from large gold earrings, an ugly red weal which made it clear that the ball had not taken an uninterrupted flight into the container of supermarket chicken liver paté.

The day had begun badly in the Randall household. Maurice Randall had woken with two things in mind. In the first he was repulsed. His wife, Babs, said that even though it was the weekend she didn't feel like it and anyway there was the lounge to paint. Maurice Randall had no intention of painting the lounge that day, or if he could help it, any other day whilst the cricket season lasted. Essex were playing a league fixture against Middlesex at Southgate and he had told Charlie and the boys that he would be there for a few bevvies. His escape from domesticity rested, he reckoned, on a charm offensive. Unfortunately the charm offensive had encountered an early setback. Ploy two was a cup of tea in bed, but when he came back upstairs the bed was empty, although only for a moment. Tripping over Babs' slippers (hefty objects the size of Pekinese dogs) Maurice deposited the tea and toast with thick-cut marmalade on the sheets and pillow on his wife's side of the bed. 'I bet you done that deliberate', Babs charged him as she emerged from the bathroom. The tension between them rose. It was destined to get worse.

The next portent of the day's downward spiral came with raised voices from the children's bedroom. What began as an argument between Craig aged eleven and Danny aged ten quickly became a fight. Maurice was sent in to separate the combatants and took two sharp punches and a kick himself before achieving his objective. He banished the older boy to the bathroom and took the other to his mother, leaving behind a badly buckled DVD which had been the cause of the row. However, by then the master bedroom was empty. Babs' whereabouts were soon declared as a shrill message curled upstairs. 'You stupid bastard.' In the kitchen the pan in which Maurice had been in the process of boiling an egg for his breakfast had boiled dry and now had a hole in its bottom. Maurice knew what was coming. 'My mother gave us that set of pans.' But there was more. The two slices of bread he had put in the toaster for his soldiers had somehow ignited. Smoke which filled the room was quickly doused, but from an unexpected and unwelcome direction. A vengeful Craig in the bathroom above had developed a new form of entertainment. Babs screamed. Danny laughed. Maurice slapped him across the legs. Danny screamed. Maurice cursed and shot upstairs.

Craig, now fearing the wrath which was to come, was reluctant to respond to his father's entreaties to open the door. His one compromising gesture before deftly climbing out of the window was to turn off the taps. Maurice did not think in terms of window and ladder. He thought only door. It was the second shoulder heave (the first being painfully fruitless) which gained him entry. Looking through the open window he was in time to see Craig and Danny reunited in fraternal friendship rubbing a stone along the side of his neighbour's new car.

When peace – at a price – had been restored Babs insisted that the boys had been cooped up inside too long. They needed to be taken out and given something fresh to do. Maurice agreed until he realised that she meant that very day. Unfortunately for his plans he got not further than an initial 'But'. Carried along with the force of her idea Babs remembered an advert she had seen in the local paper about a grand family day out at a big place not far away. Where was the paper? Regrettably from Maurice's point of view it was under their feet. Newspapers had been laid on the kitchen floor to soak up the water. Blurred but unmistakeable was a picture of Helmerstead Hall. There was no deterring Babs, who pressed on with putting together the components of a picnic. Cricket at Southgate was off. Maurice's only consolation lay in noticing that there would be a cricket match and a beer tent at his substitute destination. Sadly, he was to experience little of either.

Hard on the heels of Toby Lederwood came Ray Burrill. On taking in the prostrate figure of Maurice Randall, Ray greeted the anxious spectators with the urgent plea 'Let me through, I'm a vet.' Afterwards one person claimed that on the uttering of these words a grimace had passed across Maurice Randall's face and another that he thought he had heard the poor man mutter 'Not a bloody vet.' Neither suggestion was corroborated. Whether the ministrations of Ray Burrill could have materially aided the victim was not a matter put to the test, because help of a more relevant medical nature presented itself in the shape of Paul Wyatt, an officer of St Joan Ambulance. The uniform, if not the extreme youth of the person wearing it, inspired greater confidence than Ray Burrill in his whites. Appearance was largely deceptive.

Paul Wyatt had not long been a member of St Joan Ambulance. He had done the basic training. Field experience was still lacking. The outing to Helmerstead Hall had been intended by his superiors to be a contribution to the learning process. Since becoming enamoured of his co-recruit, Laurel Rouse, Paul had seen the opportunity differently. The development of his friendship with Laurel had been proceeding splendidly before they were disturbed by banging on the door of their vehicle by someone who had had the presence of mind on seeing the accident to recall the presence of St Joan Ambulance. Adjusting his dress and retrieving his cap, Paul Wyatt had rushed to the scene and made an instant and luckily for him correct judgement. 'This man needs urgent hospital attention.' He proceeded to act on this assessment and phoned for the paramedics. Thereafter he and Laurel did what they could to sustain Maurice Randall until specialist assistance arrived. It was a while before they could resume the sustenance of their own relationship.

Ahead of the paramedics came Caroline Bingley-Adams. Alerted to the fact that there had been an incident, she was quick out of the blocks. Nothing could be allowed to interfere with the smooth running of the event. She took in the recumbent form of Maurice Randall, noted the presence of St Joan Ambulance and urged resumption of play. Plucking the cricket ball from the supermarket chicken liver paté, she flung it with surprising vigour back into the playing arena. Caroline then took herself off to the caravan which was her office to prepare a press release extolling the excellence of the response to the incident which had laid low one of the visitors. She would come to regret her haste in despatching it by email to the local press.

The appetite of the spectators of the cricket match had been whetted by the antics associated with the delivery of no more than two balls. The unexplained delay in the resumption of play gave rise to a degree of restiveness. It took the form of relatively good-natured barracking which was food and drink to Tommy Fagge and Billy Figg. With support from Beaufort Strange and Fred Fortune they reacted by playing the crowd as if it was an audience at the Todmorden Empire. They were so successful that it was almost an anti-climax when the ball re-appeared.

Much of the humour of the occasion had by-passed Stewart Thorogood. No-balled (dubiously he thought) and struck for six, he was not in carnival mood. This was evidenced by the third ball he bowled. It was woefully short and even a lesser performer than Beaufort Strange could have taken advantage of it. The boundary might have been saved had Stewart (and the umpires) waited for the return to the field of play of Toby Lederwood and Ray Burrill. The same excuse was not available for what happened next. Three further deliveries of mixed quality were struck with power and sometimes with luck to different corners of the field, in every case eluding a fielder. The crowd's enthusiasm rose apace. Stewart's did not. It was in the most extreme denial of charitable spirit that he ran in to bowl the last ball of the opening over. It was full and it swung. The stumps were spread-eagled, but not (Stewart saw with murderous satisfaction) before the ball had hit Beaufort Strange full toss on the toe cap of his boot on the way to its destination. He too was spread-eagled.

What had been a sharp and incisive piece of cricket did not appear to please the crowd. It was greeted in stony silence. Whether the people watching feared an end to the fun or whether they were more concerned for the welfare of Beaufort Strange was not immediately clear. On either count Stewart Thorogood sensed resentment. His own irritation with the batsman faded as quickly as it had flared. He had not seriously wished

Beaufort Strange harm. He hurried to his aid and was relieved to find the actor wiggling his big toe speculatively and announcing 'I don't think it's broken.' Within a short time he was able to hobble off the field. It seemed that the public of Grange-over-Sands would not be denied the lead performer in the following week's presentation of *An Inspector Calls*. What looked more probable was that the Celebs XI would after all require the services of their elf when it was their turn to field. Phil Cole was temporarily spared this realisation as he had taken residence in the refreshment tent.

Apart from a wicket the first over had yielded 23 runs. This was decided after a debate had taken place in the scorebox, not between the scorers, but exclusively in the head of Simon Crossley. He had been as surprised as anyone on the field by Tommy Fagge's decision to signal a free hit. This had raised the question in Simon's mind as to how to score the no-ball itself. Was it in these circumstances worth two runs or one? Simon saw that there was no point in entering into discussion about this intricate matter with his opposite number. Henry Moulden showed every sign of needing help with the fundamentals of scoring before coming even within a mile of such niceties as the value of a no-ball in certain conditions of play. Simon reached the conclusion that some creativity might be needed on his part if the laws of the game and the rules relating to the match were at the mercy of Messrs Figg and Fagge. He settled for the conservative option.

The power failure at Helmerstead Hall was timed at 2.45 pm precisely, just as Charles Brett had planned. Soon, as he had expected, his mobile phone chirruped into life. 'I'll be there directly,' he told the anxious caller, 'I can't think what's gone wrong.' Charles Brett was keen to implant the idea that this could be an exercise of great complexity requiring several hours' work. His swift arrival on the scene could be relied on to engender such a mass of goodwill that his time on the job would not be questioned. He moved forward.

The charity organiser was considering the possibilities which the day offered. The crowd attending the event was gratifying in size. What was less clear was its potential. He had negotiated a deal by which all gate money would go to the good cause. This would be supplemented by a levy on all stall-holders. Yet there had to be more. He had a number of tricks up his sleeve. The necessary material was stowed in his van. He looked out for

Caroline Bingley-Adams. A raffle was the first thing which seemed appropriate, not to say profitable. She would surely have no difficulty with that, especially as he had all the necessary components to hand. Yet all the while he found himself looking across to the mansion and thinking that it must house a yet more handsome long-term yield.

There was not a lot of choice open to Stewart Thorogood in deciding which of his fellow players was to bowl the second over of the innings. The only other Outcast in the team with pretensions to pace bowling was Nigel Redman. As he turned out irregularly he was very much an unproven force. He made up for long absences with huge enthusiasm. This was commendable in itself, but did not always guarantee consistency of performance. This was shown to be the case not just from game to game, but also from ball to ball. For once the quality of Nigel Redman's first over was of secondary importance, because it was delivered to someone whose pretensions to opening the batting were every bit as uncertain. On another day Nigel's feat in bowling a maiden would have won hearty plaudits, but on this day the credit had to go to the batsman. Fred Fortune, the lion, seemed as keen to swish his tail as swish his bat. He pranced around in the crease so energetically that not even Nigel's wildest delivery could be signalled as a wide (Billy Figg was in any case quite hazy about such matters). The only ball Nigel managed to direct in line with the stumps was somehow obstructed. By this time the bowler himself was so confused that he did not bother to appeal (Billy Figg was in any case quite hazy about the LBW law as well). Although lacking the big hitting of its predecessor the over was well received by the crowd and Fred Fortune took an extravagant bow.

Not everyone had been poised to savour these early exchanges. The view of the match from the refreshment marquee could best be described as imperfect. By standing at its open front, patrons were able to get some view of the play, but this meant standing some distance from the bar. This was not an option which had been selected by Charlie Colson and David Pelham. The marquee was crowded and it had seemed to them foolhardy to lose valuable drinking time by having to queue afresh for each round. Their newly acquired American friend seemed grateful for their thoughtfulness in this respect. His initiation in fine English ales was being given the fast-track treatment. As he received a further pint, accompanied by Charlie Colson's loving description, C. Ramsgate Fishburn experienced some difficulty in recalling the precise reason why he had made the journey to Helmerstead.

The batsman who had succeeded Beaufort Strange had so far had little to do apart from patting the lion on the head at the completion of the second over. This too had raised a laugh, but Rob Steelback intended to leave the broad comedy to others. He regarded himself as a serious cricketer. Someone, he reckoned, had to play a long innings if the Celebs XI were to score enough runs to make a full match. Such time as he had spent in the changing-room had not persuaded him that much could be expected from the other members of the team. He privately resented having to appear in costume, but under sufferance had settled for the guise of an eighteenth-century cricketer, albeit with twenty-first-century protection. The Outcasts were an outfit of which he had never heard. On the strength of the two overs so far bowled, even allowing for them being looseners, he did not imagine that the opposition was such as to prevent him putting on a display to please the crowd whilst actually playing some proper cricket. In the space of the next five minutes he was forced to re-assess.

Two contrasting reasons gave Rob Steelback cause to think again. Stiffened by his experience during the first over, and encouraged by its climax, Stewart Thorogood bowled altogether better in his second. There were no easy runs for the seasoned professional batsman and he was relieved when from the fourth ball he was able to nudge a single just wide of an optimistically positioned second slip. Stewart's second ball had risen sharply and it had looped tantalisingly off the shoulder of the bat to where second slip might have been. Captains are sometimes criticised for what is called following the ball in their field placings, but when the captain is the bowler it can often seem quite sensible. Stewart achieved nothing remotely threatening with the remaining two balls of the over which were directed to Fred Fortune. It was the latter's clowning which dispirited his partner. Fred Fortune gave no indication that he knew what the bat was for, preferring to step well away from the line of the ball if he reckoned it was not going to hit the stumps and wave a paw at the crowd. It took Rob Steelback an over or two more to realise that Fred Fortune was playing another kind of joke as well.

Much as Stewart Thorogood before him, Nigel Redman strove hard to bowl an improved line and length. For all his efforts Rob Steelback could see that Nigel was not as accomplished a bowler as Stewart. He was content with a single off the first ball. It had needed no effort. He then watched Fred Fortune go through his routine again in facing the next four balls, none of which Nigel was able to direct straight at the stumps. The sixth ball would comfortably have missed the stumps too, but almost surprisingly Fred Fortune swished his bat rather than his tail and roared at Rob Steelback to run. Had it not been for a fumble in the field by Harry Northwood, Rob Steelback might not have made his ground. What might with no loss of accuracy have been called a paw-bye was recorded.

For the first time Fred Fortune found himself facing Stewart Thorogood, to whom a degree of geniality had returned. He had discovered a reasonable line on or outside the off stump. His first ball was probably six inches wide. Fred Fortune made no attempt to play it, but, shading his eyes, pretended to peer at it as it went past into the hands of Rashid Ali. The crowd had another excuse to laugh. Fred tried the trick again to a ball which passed much closer to his off stump. There was for the first time a hint that Fred might not be quite the fool he was pretending to be. When Stewart's third ball was evidently zeroing in on the off stump the batsman produced for the first time a proper cricket stroke and blocked the ball with a flourish. The spectators, however, thought that this was another piece of play-acting and reacted with delight. Another miss and another block followed in such a manner that people still thought that this was joking rather than batting. The final ball of Stewart's over strayed down the leg side, and as much to the surprise of Rob Steelback as anyone else Fred Fortune glanced it towards fine leg effortlessly and quite elegantly for a single.

This pleasing English country scene – a combination of a game of cricket and a country fair with a boisterous refreshment tent embellished already with the resting figure of C. Ramsgate Fishburn laid across three chairs (on which he had been carefully placed by David Pelham and Charlie Colson, who were still very much upright) – was suddenly rudely disturbed by the wailing siren of an ambulance arriving at high speed with two top-qualified paramedics on board. Help for the stricken Maurice Randall had arrived, but not within a response time which would have satisfied the management of the Bodywell NHS Ambulance Trust. It might have been worse if the qualifications of the driver of the vehicle, Gregory Braine, had not also extended to stock car racing. For Gregory and his partner, Lloyd Hart, it had been a trying day.

Despite reorganisation, retraining and ingenuity, ambulance trusts across the land have not managed to filter out every frivolous call. The attitude of mind of a section of the British public has not fully adjusted from the old image of the ambulance service to the new highly technical paramedic team. For some people, when there is a crisis at home it is a case of any port in a storm. Some abusers of the emergency services had cannily begun to find ways of penetrating the defensive screen. One such was Miss Jane Bushville. Her techniques might well have been harnessed profitably by the country's security services. She had easily fooled the Bodywell NHS Ambulance Trust with her cries of pain, use of the words 'blood' and 'knife' and an extremely well judged but deeply veiled hint of third party involvement. Not only had she got Gregory Braine and Lloyd Hart on her doorstep, but also an armed police response.

Any impression of danger had been quickly dispelled by the appearance at the door of a beaming Miss Bushville. 'Thank you for coming so quickly. I was quite worried.' She held up a plastered wrist. 'But the kettle's boiled and I'm sure you'd like a nice cup of tea.' Then on noticing the police presence, 'I'll have to put out more cups. Oh dear! I hope I've got enough biscuits.' The commander of the police unit declined the invitation as politely as he could through gritted teeth and stood his men down, although some of them would not have minded a cuppa. Their swift disappearance denied them knowledge of the enormity of Miss Bushville's ruse. The two paramedics naturally did their duty and examined the patient. Her wrist was cut, but it was only a nick. They checked her blood pressure and pronounced her fit and well. 'Just be careful with that knife in future', warned Gregory Braine as they prepared to depart. And, of course, she had been, not wanting to do herself any serious harm. All this had taken place in the kitchen. 'Oh, just before you go,' she said, 'could you do me a very small favour.' She signalled to the door of the living-room.

Wasting the time of the emergency services is a serious matter. Trained professionals can easily be diverted from other activities of a life-and-death nature. Such in the eyes of Gregory Braine and Lloyd Hart had been the poker game to which they had then returned after restoring Miss Bushville's budgerigar to its cage. Both men had been several pounds down at the moment of the call-out and there was much making-up to be done. Perhaps their concentration had been disturbed by attending to the unscrupulous spinster, but things went from bad to worse. When they were assigned to the emergency at Helmerstead Hall Gregory Braine had to throw in a hand of four nines which might have recovered his losses, but only when his partner practically dragged him from the room. Hence the drive to Helmerstead had been somewhat frantic and undertaken in a mood of scepticism. A cricket match, for heaven's sake.

Caroline Bingley-Adams was half way between her caravan and the mansion when the blaring noise of the approaching ambulance arrested her. Instead of being greeted with gratitude Gregory Braine and Lloyd Hart were scolded for the noise they had created. Caroline Bingley-Adams did not want the even tenor of the day to be disturbed. Everyone was enjoying themselves (excepting Maurice Randall), but she refused to countenance a major emergency being made of a trivial incident. Having delivered herself of a suitable rebuke and urged the paramedics to get the unfortunate Maurice 'out of the way', she resumed her march towards the house to deal with whatever footling problem Edward Waterbeach had now claimed to have on his hands. 'Men!'

Two groups of people had been largely unaffected by the screeching arrival of the paramedics. Those who were engrossed in a serious analysis of English ales refused to let their concentration be disturbed. Their researches continued without any noticeable break. Outside in the open the cricketers with no more than a momentary turn of the head got on with their game. At the start of the sixth over it was Fred Fortune in the lion costume who was due to get on with his little game. Nigel Redman once again had the ball and was warming to his task. The better he bowled the more glimpses there were of Fred Fortune's ability to hold a bat. When the chips were down he used the bat in orthodox fashion. If the ball bowled by Nigel Redman was harmless, Fred Fortune chose to fool around in search of a laugh rather than a run – except when it came to the final ball of the over. Then with almost a nonchalant flick of the wrist he steered the ball past point for another single. The crowd sensed that he was teasing the bowler; at the other end Rob Steelback wondered whether he was the one being teased. Once again he had been denied the strike. The team score was stagnating.

Charity match or no charity match Rob Steelback felt compelled to have a word with his partner, who had then positively frisked his way to their meeting place in the middle of the pitch. 'Don't you think we should be pushing on a bit?' said the eighteenth-century cricketer to the lion. 'Not to worry,' said Fred the lionheart, 'I'm just having a bit of fun. If these are the best bowlers they've got, we're going to have a lot more fun later on.' Rob Steelback contented himself with a gruff 'hhmm' and stalked back to the non-striker's end without being able to banish the thought that the fun was very much at his own expense. When the same pattern was repeated for two more overs he decided that he would have to draw on the wiles he had absorbed during all those years on the county circuit.

Fred Fortune should have recognised that he was pushing the joke too far. The crowd had been amused at first, but was becoming restless. Action was needed – the violent laying of bat on ball. Fred had maintained his little caper when he realised how it had riled Rob Steelback. He had failed to realise that he was the only person left who was enjoying the joke, a situation which in his professional life as a stand-up comedian he had experienced in theatres and clubs across the land, but from which he had never learned. The Outcasts' captain, Stewart Thorogood, had equally failed to pick up all the nuances. He had decided on a change of bowling, but thought that this period of apparently becalmed batting might be a good time to risk his leg-spinner, Tom Redman. If the batsmen were in defensive mode, Tom might spring a few surprises. In a way he was right.

Outside the cricket arena the ambulance carrying Maurice Randall and his wife slid silently away with a final but distant glare from Caroline Bingley-Adams. Having consigned the patient into the expert care of the paramedics, Paul Wyatt and Laurel Rouse had looked forward to resuming the application of expert care to each other. They faced an unforeseen handicap. It took the form of Craig and Danny Randall. In her understandable anxiety for the welfare of her husband Babs had clambered aboard the ambulance in the wake of the stretcher without giving more thought to the boys other than to shout 'Clear up those picnic things.' What they were supposed to do after that was left unexplained. It was not until Maurice Randall's second brief interval of consciousness shortly after arrival at hospital when he whispered the question 'Where are the lads?' that Babs gave them a second thought. 'They're . . .' she said, and the words died away. After a few moments' pause she said 'Oh, Jesus', and she was not a religious woman. But by this time her husband's eyes had closed again. Paul Wyatt's exclamation back at Helmerstead was no less profane.

Two people in particular shared the restlessness of the crowd. The concern of Geraldine Rogers and Margaret Hamersteen did not stem from the state of the game, but from their inability to recognise any of their friends on the field of play. They were all listed in the programme of proceedings, which had cost them three pounds (all for charity), but the fielding side bore no relation to them. In her pre-match announcement Caroline Bingley-Adams had made reference to an amended list of celebrities, but, calculating that very few people present would know the difference between the Soul of Discretion and Adam, she had stayed silent on the other wholesale team change. Geraldine Rogers and Margaret Hamersteen decided that they would have to make some enquiries.

Whilst setting a field in conjunction with his captain, Tom Redman weighed the ball in his hand. It was very rare in Outcasts' cricket for him to be given an early bowl with a relatively hard new ball. So on this occasion Tom felt quite excited about the prospect. The pitch looked hard. The ball might bounce. It was a good opportunity for him. He loosened his shoulders and turned his arm over once or twice. He wrapped his fingers round the ball, marked his short run, took another glance at the field placings and prepared to bowl.

The batsman was unable to hit any of Tom Redman's first three deliveries and Rashid Ali behind the stumps was unable to intercept two of them. The total advanced by courtesy of nine wides. This inauspicious beginning, apart from giving spectators something else to chuckle over, probably had the effect of leading Fred Fortune into a false sense of security. Tom Redman's next delivery had the virtue of being straight, but the defect of being short. Fred Fortune took two steps down the wicket; three would have been better. The ball actually spun and bounced. It took a leading edge and went vertical. 'Mine', said the bowler advancing, anxious to atone for the three wide balls. 'No', said the batsman with a kind of roar as he appeared to confront Tom Redman. In a serious game with serious umpires he would have rendered himself certain to be dismissed for obstructing the field. However, this was unlikely to happen at the hands of Messrs Figg and Fagge. Fortunately for the bowler the batsman in his antics had overshot the line of the ball's descent. Rashid Ali had kept his eye firmly on it, moved swiftly behind Fred Fortune and taken the catch with aplomb. Fred Fortune departed to a generous round of applause in which Rob Steelback just managed to stop himself joining.

Edward Waterbeach appreciated the organisational skills of Caroline Bingley-Adams and was fully supportive of her efforts to make a huge success of the event to which he had lent his facilities. He was therefore reluctant to pass bad news on to her. What he was nevertheless obliged to say was that tours of the Hall would have to be cancelled or at the very least postponed as there had been a complete power failure in the building. He was very sorry, but he was sure that Caroline would understand. There could be insurance implications. They had to play it safe. 'Bollocks', replied Caroline Bingley-Adams, determined that nothing was going to detract from her plans. 'They'll be taken round in the half-light if necessary; it'll add to the atmosphere. Now get that electrician of yours to pull his finger out.' Charles Brett, who had arrived to an effusive welcome a short while ago, had no intention of doing that. He was driven by a determination of which neither Edward Waterbeach nor Caroline Bingley-Adams could be aware. Not intending to brook any opposition from the former, Caroline went to where a respectful queue had formed and directed one of the guides to take the first group into the house.

The next batsman to appear was not the next name on the list which Caroline Bingley-Adams had typed on an amendment sheet. She had been in a hurry and had had no instructions as to batting order. Spectators in most charity matches would have no difficulty in recognising most of the celebrities paraded before them. They would not have needed to place reliance on a score-sheet. At Helmerstead it was different. The so-called celebrities were not front-line faces, and the recognition factor was further upset by the use of fancy dress. The fact that the captain of the Celebs XI at this moment chose to alter the batting order was a complication which passed over the heads of many of the onlookers. In the scorebox Simon Crossley hurriedly reached for his crib sheet as to a burst of music and song a cross between a pantomime dame and a *Coronation Street* barmaid tripped out to the crease.

Don Hennelly had told all the members of his team to be padded up and ready to bat as he might want to vary the order according to circumstances. For circumstances he meant mood (Don Hennelly was nothing if not theatrical) as he thought that a certain character at a particular time might be needed for the purpose of stimulating the crowd. By promoting himself to go in at the fall of the second wicket he was forced to recognise that he would lose control of this critical aspect of the game by being out in the middle and not in the pavilion. He left instructions as to who should be the next man in whatever the situation. In his own case he hoped that recognition would be assisted if he was accompanied to the wicket by the sound of one of his own recordings. It was unclear what impression he thought he was making by the combination of his flouncing feminine appearance and a rich baritone rendering of 'Roses of Picardy'. The incongruity produced mixed emotions in the crowd, not all of which were flattering.

In the meantime a discussion had taken place between captain and bowler. Two sharply contrasting assessments could be made of the four balls so far delivered. The charitable view was that they were looseners from a very occasional bowler who was a bit rusty; the more censorious opinion was that they were absolute dross. Stewart Thorogood privately espoused the latter alternative, but strove hard not to discourage Tom Redman. He took an indirect approach. 'How's that shoulder of yours?' Tom's face acquired a puzzled expression. 'There's nothing bloody well wrong with my shoulder. What are you getting at?' Stewart realised that his approach after all had not been as indirect as he had intended. 'Nothing,' he said hastily, 'I just thought you might be a bit stiff.' He added jocularly to ease the situation 'Perhaps you haven't been lifting enough pints lately.' However, Tom seemed particularly sensitive and was prepared to prolong the argument. Stewart wished he had never started the exchange, but he knew he needed eight overs out of Tom and had been looking to encourage him into a less ruinous performance.

Lifting an insufficient number of pints was not a problem affecting some other members of the Outcasts squad. David Pelham and Charlie Colson had led the way by being the first to have sampled all five varieties on offer. There was now a lively discussion as to respective merits. This was being noisily conducted as Winston Jenkins, Phil Cole (with scant regard for such duties as might later befall him) and Greg Roberts (with even less regard for his current role as twelfth man) played catch-up. The pints continued to come. If there was any concern felt by any member of this elite drinking group, it was not about the match, only about whether the barrels would run dry.

Tom Redman might soon have wished that he was part of the elite drinking group. The increasingly aerated conversation between himself and Stewart Thorogood had only been ended through intervention by Tommy Fagge urging resumption of play. The bowler feeling peeved nevertheless obeyed. He knew he had started badly and had therefore taken amiss the enquiries of his captain. But he had just taken a wicket. To bowl accurately he needed to be relaxed not anxious. Unfortunately he had not settled, and the next ball he bowled was wildly off line, by-passing both batsman and wicket-keeper by a wide margin. Had Stewart Thorogood not motioned the fielder at fine leg to be even finer another four wides would have been conceded. There was laughter in the crowd as some people thought that Tom was spraying it around deliberately. The next attempt was no better, but matters were made worse when Don Hennelly put his bat to his eye in mock imitation of a telescope following the direction of the ball, which was again rescued by fine leg. Peevishness gave way to downright anger, but whether it was this which restored normality or a fraternal word from brother Nigel was uncertain. Line became much more adjacent and length better with the result that four balls were bowled legitimately at a cost of no more than two runs. The final delivery was a perfectly pitched leg-break which took the edge of Don Hennelly's bat and would have been caught by first slip if Stewart Thorogood had had the courage to put Toby Lederwood there and not at fine leg. Instead a single was scored.

The charity organiser took advantage of the flexible batting order and the captain's absence to go about his business. He discarded his appointed costume and sincerely hoped that he would not have to re-adopt it. There was a good chance that he could avoid having to bat and he had no intention of fielding (a plan of which the pressed twelfth man, Phil Cole, had not the slightest intimation). For general anonymity he put on his whites. First, he had to find Caroline Bingley-Adams to set in motion the raffle and then he wanted an opportunity to talk to Edward Waterbeach, for whom he had one or two propositions in mind. He also wanted to look around the mansion. He enjoyed the feel of refinement and luxury. If Edward Waterbeach could achieve so much by honest means, the charity organiser was sure that he could find a fraudulent short cut to emulating him.

There were three spinners in the side and only two pacemen – if, Stewart Thorogood thought, that was not too flattering a term to attach to himself and Nigel Redman (particularly Nigel). Conventional wisdom suggested that he should hold back some overs of quicker stuff until the last part of the innings. On the other hand, without his bowling particularly well Nigel Redman had got through four overs at a cost of only three runs. There seemed to be some sense in keeping him going as he had shown every sign of improving accuracy. So he tossed the ball to Nigel, saying 'Do another couple and we'll see.' What he saw after the next six balls made him doubt his judgement, but he felt committed. For all his bizarre appearance and readiness to have fun it was quickly apparent that Don Hennelly knew one end of the bat from another. Nigel Redman's awareness of this was the most painful. The first two deliveries of his next over were cover driven to the boundary without either being obvious candidates for such treatment. Nigel reacted with a much shorter ball which deserved punishment, but in spinning round to try to pull it square Don Hennelly seemed to be impeded by his costume. His stroke was stifled, but still earned one run. Rob Steelback played and missed at his first delivery in the over from Nigel, loudly and somewhat rudely chastised himself and played the next ball with elaborate defence. Perhaps buoyed by this superiority Nigel overpitched and was driven straight and hard. He had less than a second to decide whether he should try and stop the ball or save his fingers, foot or shin. He timed his dive to perfection, probably around half a second after the ball had passed out of harm's way.

The great American reunion took place between the skittle alley and the face-painting stall. It was at first a one-sided encounter. 'Why it's Mr Fishburn', exclaimed Margaret Hamersteen. The only affirmatory response came from Geraldine Rogers, the object of their attention being unconscious at the time. It was the consumption of a pint of Larchwood's inaptly named Nationwide bitter (it was available usually in only two counties but had been an inspired choice for this occasion) which had finally caused C. Ramsgate Fishburn to detach himself, as he seemed to recall, from his friends in search of some English fresh air. This same English fresh air had proved a little too much for him, and he had sat down for a rest which had quickly become a resumption of the nap to which he had previously succumbed. Other visitors had considerately stepped round him. Not so Geraldine Rogers and Margaret Hamersteen. With that charming up-front directness which characterises so many Americans, Margaret Hamersteen took her stick, leant on it and with her free foot delivered a sharp kick into the ribs of her prone fellow countryman. 'What the hell are you doing here?' were the words which accompanied the blow. As he slowly and unsteadily clambered back into an upright position the American researcher declared 'That's exactly the question I've been asking myself.' 'You could use some coffee', he was told by Geraldine Rogers. The three of them found a dispensing point for tea and coffee in a paved enclosure adjacent to the pavilion. It was there that the answer was revealed.

Richard Furness was restless. He had been happy enough to find himself unexpectedly reunited with fellow Outcasts, but the overpowering reason for his wanting to be in Helmerstead had not been cricket. Suzy Waterbeach lay beyond the boundary and Richard had no desire to keep the lady waiting, but every other possible desire. Equally he recognised that he was an integral part of the Outcasts' bowling complement in this match. Without wanting to give away too much Richard asked his captain when he was likely to be called up to bowl, adding, as if to imply a professional input, that he would prefer the Park End. Richard's thought was to rattle off his eight overs and then get the twelfth man on the field in his place. Happily for Richard this thought was unmarred by awareness of the current location and condition of his side's twelfth man.

Greg Roberts was as much a stranger as C. Ramsgate Fishburn to Larchwood's Nationwide bitter. He had consumed a second pint of it before sharing the reaction of the American. In Greg's case he had not forgotten why he was there. Although a weak performer at the game his attachment to cricket and to the Outcasts was strong. Had he been a member of the team he would have limited his beer consumption. But as twelfth man at what was after all a charity match he felt altogether more relaxed. Nevertheless he knew that he had a responsibility and realised that he had been missing for a quarter of the innings. He swayed back to the pavilion, the fresh English air having much the same effect on him as on C. Ramsgate Fishburn. However, as an Englishman and as a cricketer Greg waited until reaching the changing-room before falling asleep.

Stewart Thorogood, knowing that there had to be eight overs from Tom Redman, decided that he could not replace him at the Hall End after only one. He bolstered his decision by reminding himself that Tom's previous over had ended better than it had begun. So he gave him the ball, a pat on the back and a word of encouragement. He hoped that this might dispel the earlier tension which had developed between them. This must have had the right effect, because Tom conceded only four wides at the start of his second over. Avoiding a glare from Stewart Thorogood, who had immediately begun to fear the worst, Tom gripped the ball tightly and sent down two fizzing leg-breaks, both of which evaded Don Hennelly's lungeing bat. Then, as if that effort had been too much, Tom could not manage anything better than a long-hop which Don Hennelly cut hard through point. It should not have been a boundary, but, straining for a glance of Suzy, Richard Furness had not been paying full attention. Too late he reacted to a shout from the bowler and too rashly to a derisory comment from a juvenile spectator. The altercation took a while to dissipate. Nevertheless the effect on the bowler was salutary. His concentration returned and he produced a couple of decent length balls which cost nothing. Noting the length and remembering the two big leg-breaks, Don Hennelly played them with excessive caution. Remembering with satisfaction the two big leg-breaks, Tom Redman made a supreme effort. He produced a beauty which ripped across Don Hennelly's defensive bat, this time taking its edge. Stewart Thorogood's defensive field had not stretched to having a slip and so two runs rather than a wicket resulted.

The charity organiser's search for Caroline Bingley-Adams had proved fruitless. She was not in her caravan/office and nor was anyone else. No one in its immediate precincts could throw any light on the subject and the charity organiser was left fuming. He was not the only person to be in a thoroughly poor mood. A few minutes earlier Caroline Bingley-Adams had received an urgent call for assistance from St Joan Ambulance. Their vehicle had been sabotaged. Starting with the belief that St Joan Ambulance's presence was meant to be a help and not a hindrance, Caroline was displeased by having to be diverted from what she regarded as her main duties. Leaving her caravan with such speed that there was no time (or thought) to post a 'be back soon' notice, Caroline had run across to the ambulance to get this latest nonsense sorted. As she approached she could see nothing wrong. The fact that all four tyres had been slashed meant that the ambulance still maintained an even keel. The damage had to be pointed out to her, and even then she did not appear fazed, her first thought being that the officers were not obstructed from carrying out their duties. 'It's those bloody kids', complained Paul Wyatt. Caroline noticed that the pristine state of his new uniform was now compromised by grass stains. These had been acquired, Laurel Rouse recounted, when Paul had sprawled across the ground tripped by Danny whilst chasing Craig, the perpetrator of the outrage. Too late had the St Joan Ambulance officers thought to put their duty of care to their vehicle above the duty of care to the Randall brothers who had been so unexpectedly thrust upon them. They now naturally thought that responsibility for these temporary orphans should pass to the organiser of the whole event. Caroline Bingley-Adams did not see things the same way. The boys were nowhere to be seen. To extract herself from the situation with minimal fuss Caroline muttered something about seeing what she could do and took her leave. She would later come to regret her indifference. Left once more to themselves Laurel said to Paul, 'We'd better get you out of that uniform and I'll see if I can clean it up a bit.' Giggling, she led her partner back into the ambulance.

By the time Caroline Bingley-Adams had tramped back to her office, a journey punctuated by several interchanges with the general public who saw her clipboard as evidence of a person in authority, the charity organiser had moved off in pursuit of another prey. As he was carrying one or two items in his van which he wanted to use in his efforts to woo Edward Waterbeach, he thought he would drive over to the mansion. Then he remembered that in the transfer from his 4x4 into the leased van the boxes containing the key items had been the first across. They now had in front of them the cartons containing amongst other things prizes for his instant raffle. As he approached the van he bumped into one of the opposition's cricketers. It was a somewhat moody-looking Kevin Newton. There had been no word from Gloria. This had left Kevin feeling detached from the day's events. Wandering back to the pavilion, he had found an unconscious twelfth man. He had therefore changed into his whites so that, if need be, there would be a ready substitute available. Asked by the charity organiser on the spur of the moment if he would lend a hand with shifting some cartons into the pavilion, Kevin readily agreed. Whether the charity organiser had intended to share the task was unknown, because just as Kevin staggered off with the first load Caroline Bingley-Adams rounded the corner. The charity organiser immediately seized the box containing the raffle tickets. It needed an unexpectedly lengthy application of unctuous charm to win her approval for the surprise raffle. When finally the charity organiser was allowed to turn back to his van he was greeted by a smiling Kevin Newton and the words 'Job done'. At least, Kevin Newton told himself, the stand-in twelfth man had done something useful. More than useful, as events would prove.

Nigel Redman's sixth over had made one thing clear to his captain. There would not be a seventh, at least not for a while. Rob Steelback had been in for seven overs and scored only six runs. At last given the strike at the start of an over he was determined to exploit the opportunity. In fairness to Nigel Redman he had not bowled badly, but the scorebook would give a different impression. Rob Steelback had become impatient with the lack of opportunity and his impatience bubbled over to Nigel's cost. Three imperious drives scored twelve. Rob Steelback had it in mind to take a single off the last ball, but when it was dragged woefully short by a tiring and frustrated Nigel the batsman, adrenalin flowing, could not resist the temptation to swing it over square leg for six.

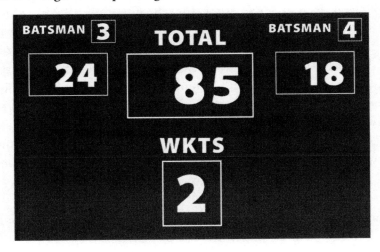

The tours of Helmerstead Hall were a complication. Charles Brett had not anticipated that so many people would be milling through the building. There was distinct separation between the domestic quarters regularly used by the family and the public rooms which carried some historic interest (however much exaggerated). King Charles II's licentious rampages had covered many parts of the country, but evidence that any of his couplings had taken place at Helmerstead Hall was not incontrovertible. Nevertheless a loose approach to history had been adopted many years ago and somehow the story had stuck. Even more dubiously other tales had been appended to a point at which it was boasted on behalf of the mansion that half of the crowned heads of Europe had passed through its doors. It should be said that the story limited itself to fairly obscure crowned heads, but what they may have lacked in fame was compensated by notoriety. No one in distant days, it would seem, had stopped at Helmerstead Hall simply for a haunch of venison and three veg. Such was the embellishment achieved with the passage of time that it was easy to believe that most of the young women from surrounding villages had come harshly to terms with the facts of life within its walls.

This historical uncertainty, so useful in persuading people to part with their entrance money, had the disadvantage of encouraging visitors to stray from the official tour in search of the lilac bedroom or the summer boudoir in which some particular liaison may have taken place between minor royals representing eastern and western European countries. This lack of discipline on the part of the visitors (not the minor royals) was a nuisance to Charles Brett. His ambitions were concentrated on the private quarters of the Waterbeach family. There were one or two items in the public rooms which he had coveted, but whose capture was now frustrated. Portability was another key consideration. Accumulation of his hoard was facilitated by what he could move in his tool bag. It was not until he was almost ready to leave that he was prepared to gamble on some larger pieces. Visitors to the Hall popping up here and there were a most unwelcome inconvenience causing him to stretch his stay. He knew there was a limit to how long he could string out his supposed repair operation.

Stewart Thorogood was wondering how long he could string out Tom Redman's bowling spell. Two overs had cost 20 runs, but that was only off the bat. He reminded himself that leg-spinners were always a risk, that Tom needed time to get into any sort of rhythm and that he had taken a wicket. Furthermore he realised that there was little alternative to Tom bowling a full ration of eight overs. Yet Stewart still harboured a bad feeling about it. What finally tilted him to keeping Tom on at the Hall End was that Don Hennelly and not Rob Steelback was on strike. Tom Redman was spared any insight to the thoughts running through his captain's head as he confidently marched to the end of his run and waited for the ball to be thrown to him. He was lucky that his first ball was not called a wide as it passed some distance from off stump. It was followed by a well-pitched leg-break which the batsman was late to recognise. Thereafter the over deteriorated. Two full tosses followed by a ball which was too short and too wide were all struck for boundaries, two clearing the rope. Both Stewart Thorogood and Tom Redman in their own ways were conducting reassessments as the final delivery of the over was due. It was well flighted – there could be no argument about that – but it was never going to pitch. Don Hennelly advanced greedily towards it, but he underestimated the extent to which it was overpitched. The ball sailed past his swinging bat and landed full toss in the hands of the wicket-keeper. Rashid Ali had time to spare in removing the bails before the batsman could recover his ground. Tom Redman had his second wicket before applause for the Celebs' hundred had scarcely died down.

'Well,' said Geraldine Rogers finally as she returned her empty cup to its saucer, 'I wouldn't have known that they played cricket in Scotland.' 'Don't be silly, dear,' her friend had replied, 'if the Slovenians play cricket I don't see why the Scots shouldn't.' C. Ramsgate Fishburn had at last explained to his compatriots the reason behind his travels. He had given an outline of the scope of his project. His aim was to examine the growth of cricket and the differences between its impact on European society and American society. Mentioning that his work had been commissioned by the United States Educational League for Environmental and Sporting Studies, C. Ramsgate Fishburn expressed the opinion that there was a market 'out there' for a book on this subject. Geraldine Rogers and Margaret Hamersteen were in no position to comment.

But Margaret Hamersteen did have a question she thought was pertinent. 'Why exactly are you here in Helmerstead?' C. Ramsgate Fishburn seemed slow to answer. He took another swig of coffee. He then muttered something about seeing cricket being played in an absolutely classic English setting. Acknowledging that this might not be a wholly convincing explanation as to why Helmerstead, as opposed to two hundred other places, the American researcher seemed to screw himself up to making a specific revelation.

At the hospital meanwhile, Maurice Randall's health remained a matter of uncertainty. He alternated between consciousness and unconsciousness. In fact unconsciousness was prolonged and consciousness no more than brief punctuations of it. These were distinguished mainly by the words 'Give us a pint', and it was not thought by those attending him that he was referring to blood. Nevertheless it was seen on the whole as a positive indicator and his wife was sufficiently buoyed by this assessment that she actually found a moment to think of her sons who had been left behind at Helmerstead Hall. Babs suddenly remembered something. Rummaging in her handbag she found the flyer which had originally persuaded her what the family outing should be. It included a telephone number, and Babs decided that it was time to make a call.

When Marion Booth had agreed to run the bagatelle stall she had thought that it would be a fairly low-key, even genteel activity, catering mainly for those children who spurned more vigorous tests of skill. She could not have anticipated clients like Craig and Danny Randall. The stall had been sited in a secluded corner and had not attracted much custom. The bagatelle unit belying its age was a superb piece in first-class condition and possessing a strong spring mechanism. After the episode at St Joan Ambulance the Randall boys were in need of a secluded corner away from the heat of the possible chase. Top score on the game at the moment of their arrival was 3,520. A ten-year-old girl called Lindsey Carter was in the process of trying to better it. She had started well, but her skill and her luck began to ebb when Danny positioned himself at the opposite end of the board and made faces at her. Craig behind her embarked on a series of disparaging comments. Lindsey's nerve broke at about the 2,500 mark and she finally ran off in tears. Craig handed over 20p to Mrs Booth and took command of the board. It proved to be a long occupation.

No music had accompanied Don Hennelly on his return march to the pavilion. He was surprised to pass en route the figure of Elvis Presley, a.k.a. Carl Waterbeach. This did not conform to the instructions he had given. As Carl Waterbeach was already half way towards the wicket this apparent act of defiance could hardly be countermanded. Don Hennelly resolved to restore some order to the situation. He was disappointed to find on arrival that the team had suffered attrition. There was the immediately comforting

sight of a batsman padded up in apparent readiness for the fall of the next wicket. Beyond this the distinguishing feature of the changing-room and its hinterland was the absence of anyone who looked like a cricketer. Don Hennelly corrected himself. In truth, in view of the costume requirement none of his side particularly looked like a cricketer. The man in his sight was nearest to what might be recognised as a player. Hugo Crabscote was decked out in nineteenth-century garb. His presence begged a question. Don Hennelly had left an instruction that Hugo Crabscote should have entered the arena at the fall of the third wicket. The reason for his failure to comply with his captain's command was not one which Hugo was keen to reveal. He answered Don Hennelly's query with a mumbled excuse about a sudden bout of stomach pain which had caused his retreat to the lavatory. In truth, like Outcast Colin Banks, Hugo Crabscote had a healthy appetite for female glamour and had become seriously diverted by a chance meeting with a stunning redhead called Annabelle Crouch.

Don Hennelly demanded to know the whereabouts of the rest of his team. He was told by Hugo Crabscote not to panic. 'They were around', he was told. To be fully accurate the interpretation of 'around' needed to be somewhat loose. Some were close at hand whilst one or two were further afield. The dismissed batsmen had wasted no time in seeking the solace of the refreshment tent. With slightly less excuse this had also been the destination of two players who had regarded themselves as sufficiently lower order that they had not wished to hang around for any off-the-cuff reclassification by their captain. Two others had entered into the spirit of the occasion by stepping outside and signing autographs for anyone who recognised them. A few did, but recognition had more to do with the costume than the face of the person wearing it. The charity organiser was bent on (for him) more serious matters. Though this was meant to be a fun event Don Hennelly smarted from the act of defiance of his team members. Moodily he began a search. As events would prove he had no need to be too worried.

Stewart Thorogood was trying to work out how to use his unbalanced set of bowlers to best effect. Nigel Redman had to be rested, that was for sure. His cover story, for Nigel's benefit, was that he needed to keep his two remaining overs for 'the death'. That tale, if it was to carry conviction, meant that it was probably impolitic for himself to replace Nigel at the Park End. In that case he was left with his two other spinners, so far unused. Ray Burrill was frequently Mister Reliable and so Stewart was banking on him to put in a steady spell. Richard Furness, only recently back in the Outcasts' fold, was more mercurial. He could be very effective, but Stewart was not sure about his match fitness. Had he known much about what had happened in the last twenty-four hours, he would not have been unsure at all. As things were, he decided to take a chance. Richard Furness was delighted. His plan for an early substitution was revived. He realised that he had to turn in a good performance so that he might be allowed to bowl his eight overs off the reel and then escape for a spot of passion before it was the Outcasts' turn to bat.

The first over bowled by Richard Furness did nothing to upset the scheme. Two balls were over-pitched and milked for a couple of elegant runs in each case by a confident Rob Steelback. Then Richard settled and completed the over without further cost, earning a nod of approval from the former professional and a sigh of relief from his captain. There had been little time for Stewart Thorogood to wrestle with the dilemma over his use of Tom Redman. His realisation that a ration of eight overs had to be bowled by his leg-spinner was tempered by the thought of the damage which could be done in the process. The capture of another wicket with the final ball of his last over together with the arrival at the crease of a new batsman tilted Stewart towards giving Tom a fourth over. Mindful that Tom's first three overs had cost 36 runs Stewart knew that he was indulging his gambling spirit.

Even allowing for the fact that he was dressed in an Elvis Presley costume Carl Waterbeach looked the part. Unfortunately he did not altogether feel the part. A night of little sleep had caught up with him. A longer wait in the pavilion before having to bat would have suited him. He had taken some pills to quell the ache in his head and some more pills to quell the uneasiness in his stomach, but they had not yet kicked in to sufficient effect. But at the critical moment when the third wicket fell he had found himself alone. Rather than face cross-examination by his captain about this state of affairs, Carl had quickly decided that batting was the better option. Now as he prepared to take strike he was less sure. Tom Redman was fortunate that Carl Waterbeach's recovery was still a work in progress as the fifteenth over of the innings took its course.

The recovery of C. Ramsgate Fishburn was more advanced. Several cups of coffee had had a salutary effect. He had also seemed to draw strength from the company of Margaret Hamersteen and Geraldine Rogers. Under questioning he began to unbend. Why indeed had he come to Helmerstead? The ladies were there, as they thought, by appointment, but so far they had had no sight of the cricketers they had expected to meet. C. Ramsgate Fishburn then admitted that he too thought that he had an appointment. He revealed more detail about the nature of the academic exercise he was undertaking under the auspices of the United States Educational League for Environmental and Sporting Studies. He had been planning an important section on the extent to which Scotland had exported cricket to the world. In that connection he had been in touch with a Scottish academic who had promised him valuable insights. It was the Scot who had proposed that their rendezvous should be Helmerstead as his daughter and grandchildren lived nearby. Contact was to have been by mobile phone, but when he had tried to call the Scot a disembodied voice had informed him that the phone was not responding. C. Ramsgate Fishburn had to admit that there had been a period that afternoon when he himself had not been responding. 'But', he said, brightening up, 'at least I have the good company of you two ladies.' 'You won't get much about cricket out of us', Margaret Hamersteen dryly responded. 'Let's take a walk.'

So far had Caroline Bingley-Adams dismissed the Randall boys from her mind that she could not at first make much sense of what the woman at the other end of the phone was saying. As soon as the penny had dropped she sought to disengage herself from any duty of care. The possibility that Babs Randall might be distraught at what had happened to her husband and now belatedly concerned for her sons did not for a moment register with Caroline Bingley-Adams. She quelled any suggestion that a duty of care lay with her by demanding that the parents should instead get back to Helmerstead as quickly as possible and take responsibility for their kids. This aggressive strike produced only tears from Babs and finally a sobbing question 'Do you know where they are?' Caroline did not, although she soon would. Any thought for the welfare of the children or for that matter their stricken father was below her threshold of recognition. She ended the telephone conversation on a peremptory note, suggesting that Mrs Randall should make some arrangements of her own to recover her children. Now, about the raffle, thought Caroline to herself.

Tom Redman was very satisfied with his fourth over. One or two balls were off line but Carl Waterbeach treated them with caution. There was scope for a single off the final delivery had Carl been alert, but, in case he had been thinking about it, there was a stentorian cry of 'No' from the other end. Rob Steelback had no intention of losing the strike. He strolled down the pitch for another exchange with Carl Waterbeach. The first somewhat one-sided conversation had taken place on Carl's first appearance in the middle. It had largely been devoted to an assessment of how the wicket was playing and an appraisal of the bowling. Now, thought Rob Steelback, I had better ask what I should have asked before. 'How are you? Are you all right?' Carl replied that he was fine without quite looking fine, but, as if to add emphasis, he gave a twirl of his bat. And then he rashly added 'Let's rock 'em.' For his part Rob Steelback had something like that in mind, but he wondered if Elvis was capable of a duet.

If ambient conditions had been right, Richard Furness would have taken Rob Steelback's wicket in the over which followed. The first ball was just the right length and turned in orthodox fashion away from the bat. Rob Steelback gave a faint nod of approval. The second ball emulated the first and was just the right length except that it did not turn in orthodox or any other fashion. It was pushed through just slightly quicker and went straight on. Rob Steelback played for the turn and was struck firmly on the pad. An objective observer even without the benefit of electronic gadgetry would have said that the batsman had been caught plumb in front of his stumps. Rob Steelback gave an almost imperceptible nod of approval, but Billy Figg gave no nod of any kind. He greeted Richard Furness' impassioned appeal without even so much as a second's consideration. 'Not out', he roared and Rob Steelback, who knew his cricket better than Billy Figg and had been about to depart, froze. That was the first unfavourable condition.

There was nothing disgracefully bad about Richard Furness' next two deliveries, but, as so often happens when a batsman has a lucky escape, he rubs salt in the wound by seizing the initiative. Twice Rob Steelback found the extra cover boundary. Then the pendulum swung again. Dean Faulds had tried on two successive occasions to interrupt the ball on its way to the boundary. His impressive sprints had failed. No change in the field setting had been made by the bowler or captain and so Dean had trudged back to his appointed position square of the wicket. Richard Furness reacted to Rob Steelback's aggression with a variation in flight and spin. The batsman riding his luck struck another blow towards extra cover, but it was a false shot and the ball though hit hard was in the air. A fully fit fielder would probably have gained the speed to get underneath it. Dean Faulds, however, was still recovering from his previous exertions. Even so he might have made it had it not been for a bizarre incident. A mobile phone rang close by with a distinctive call sign familiar to Dean. He could not stop his left hand moving towards his pocket and so sadly it was not where it should have been when he arrived in the ball's dropping zone. Richard Furness glared at Dean Faulds whilst the batsmen ran three. Dean Faulds glared at the spectator whose phone had triggered his mistake. The last ball of the over was an anti-climax, a straightforward delivery met by Carl Waterbeach with a straightforward defensive prod.

By now bagatelle corner had become less secluded. Its population had grown for two reasons. First, other children had sought out the stall. They had not been made welcome by the players in residence. A stream of coarse expressions had greeted them. Modern children have become used to this and, to the alarm of Marion Booth, retaliated in kind. The increased level of noise gave rise to attention further afield. People wondered whether there was some new attraction which they had been missing. If nothing more it was a colourful language exhibition. But it was something more. The brothers Randall, who had been recycling the original 20p piece with which Craig had played his first game without a distracted Marion Booth noticing, decided on an exit strategy based on a bigger prize. Lungeing for the receptacle in which the stall-holder thought she had been accumulating money, Danny pushed her to one side causing her to fall and strike her head against the side of the bagatelle board.

The reaction of an angry parent, Douglas Carter, the father of the girl who had earlier been displaced at the bagatelle board, was not to leap to Marion Booth's aid but to apprehend Danny Randall. This lack of chivalry was further compounded by his accidentally treading on the outstretched foot of the stricken lady. Being already unconscious, she was fortunate to feel no pain. Danny Randall was fleeter of foot than Douglas Carter and accelerated out of reach of retribution. His brother departed in another direction after tipping over in a final act of spite the bagatelle board. Of sturdy construction it toppled heavily on to the recumbent form of Marion Booth. Again she was unable to feel the pain as it crushed her lower abdomen. At this point someone did put the poor woman's welfare to the forefront, shouting out 'I think I've seen St Joan Ambulance on the ground.' She had, but unbeknown to her, the mere presence of the vehicle was not the whole story.

Paul Wyatt and Laurel Rouse were in no position to make a rapid response. Such in fact was their position that their first instinct was to freeze when they absorbed the shock of someone knocking frantically on the door. Sufficiently comprehensive had been their training that they had remembered to wedge a chair under the door-handle so that a member of the public could not intrude. Their duty necessitated them making a response to the somewhat coincidental shouted message: 'There's a woman on her back out here.' In the circumstances the answer from Paul that he would be there 'in a jiffy when he'd finished dealing with an intimate case' showed good presence of mind. Presence of body took a few minutes longer, and it was a rather bedraggled officer who presented himself to enquire where the latest victim lay. Paul's trousers looked cleaner than they had been, but they had lacked an iron. He hoped that it was the man, not the uniform, which mattered – a view with which Laurel Rouse had fervently agreed.

On arrival in bagatelle corner Paul Wyatt brought all his skills to bear in his examination of the still recumbent Marion Booth. 'She's poorly', he revealed to the circle of onlookers. This prognosis was insufficient to satisfy everyone. 'Shouldn't you try giving her the kiss of life?' asked one. This presented the officer with a difficulty. Paul Wyatt had progressed quite well in his young life with kissing the living, but he had had trouble during training in mastering the technique of reviving the near-dead with the kiss of life. Anxiously he crouched over Marion Booth and then straightened up with a relieved smile to announce his pleasure that the lady was breathing unaided. 'But she's still poorly', he admitted. Fortunately at this point he was joined by a fully uniformed Laurel Rouse, who had wasted no time in calling in the paramedics. Until their arrival, she told spectators, she and her partner could be left to comfort the unfortunate lady. Not perhaps totally convinced the crowd drifted away.

The paramedics Gregory Braine and Lloyd Hart were undecided. Their losses had continued. Should they quit or was their luck about to turn? This tantalising question had to be left unanswered as another shout came in. 'Not the bloody cricket match again' Lloyd exclaimed as they raced towards the ambulance. 'What are they doing there, acting out computer games? It had better not be another hoax.' Much the same thought crossed the mind of Caroline Bingley-Adams when she heard the sound of the ambulance cutting across the high spirits of the festive occasion. She reluctantly wended her way through the throng of visitors to the corner of the grounds into which the ambulance, directed by Paul Wyatt, had disappeared. When she arrived on the scene the first thing to catch her eye and cause her concern was the toppled bagatelle. The toppled Marion Booth came a distant second. The bagatelle was an antique rashly lent by Edward Waterbeach. Caroline Bingley-Adams was horrified to see it overturned and on the ground. The unfortunate Marion Booth had by now been extracted from beneath it and was being wheeled away from the accident scene to leave Caroline to concentrate wholly on checking for damage to the bagatelle. She found it warped and scratched. With difficulty she restrained herself from shouting 'You careless, stupid woman' as the former guardian of bagatelle corner was lifted into the ambulance.

The charity organiser had not yet made his move on Edward Waterbeach. He had allowed himself to be distracted. He had glanced in the direction of the cricket and had been amused by the contrast between ancient and modern which greeted him. Elvis in conversation with an eighteenth-century cricketer had to be a rare sight. As the action resumed the next delivery was struck hard, high and out of the arena. Had the charity organiser turned away to leave the scene the ball would have bounced and very possibly struck the back of his head. As it was he caught it in front of his face with great aplomb and took some vain satisfaction from the admiring looks around him. He flung it back to Richard Furness and then hesitated. Even those with the least interest in cricket can still enjoy the sight of big hitting. Perhaps there would be more of the same. The charity organiser dallied expectantly.

Hopes elsewhere were quite the opposite. Stewart Thorogood had gambled. Seduced by Tom Redman's previous over Stewart dared himself to get another of the leg-spinners' quota out of the way. He rationalised his decision on the grounds that a leg-spinner needed time to loosen up and get into his stride. The difference as Tom began his fifth over was that the batsman on strike was Rob Steelback and not the curiously subdued Carl Waterbeach. Within minutes Stewart Thorogood knew that he had miscalculated. The blow for six which the charity organiser had fielded proved to be only the first instalment. The second ball of the over was struck straight and just as cleanly taking Rob Steelback past his fifty. Its successor sailed over deep extra cover. It was a minor miracle that no spectator was injured. Seemingly the first six had alerted the crowd to the possibility that mayhem could be about to happen. Danger evaporated with the next delivery, which was merely a peerless on-drive all along the ground. For the crowd it was almost an anti-climax. Strangely Tom Redman had not wilted under this onslaught. After conceding four boundaries he bowled a very respectable length ball, which did not turn, and the batsman patted it away just behind square for a single. So geared up had they been for violent action that some spectators actually booed.

Stewart Thorogood had watched the spectacle in numb dismay. He had not felt that any direct intervention on his part with the bowler was going to make any difference. Rob Steelback had brought his considerable professional skills into play against an amateur bowler whose skills were slight. Stewart was therefore as surprised as anyone when Tom Redman completed his over with a well-pitched delivery which did turn. In the process it took a thin edge from Carl Waterbeach's listless bat and was very well caught by the only fielder left close to the wicket, namely Rashid Ali crouching behind the stumps. Tom Redman celebrated his third wicket with some fervour. However, he could not convince the rest of the team that he had set out cunningly to buy the wicket, because he had ended up purchasing the wrong man.

At the fall of Carl Waterbeach's wicket the Celebs' captain, unlike previously, did have a choice. Don Hennelly had managed to cajole three of his team into readiness, but three were still out of his reach. Hugo Crabscote's 'tummy bug' had not recurred, Annabelle Crouch having taken herself off to inspect the mansion. This left Hugo with nothing to do for the moment but bat. This fitted with his captain's original plan and so, dressed as a nineteenth-century cricketer, he went out to join his eighteenth-century counterpart. The pair of them represented the best batting talent of their team. They were pretty sure of that themselves, and it was not long before Stewart Thorogood reached the same conclusion. Don Hennelly could not take any chances. It needed the fall of only two wickets before his existing resources were exhausted. The missing men had to be found. It was quickly apparent that a more thorough search would be required. It was a search he realised would be less than straightforward when he spotted two of the costumes which they should have been wearing hanging on pegs in the changing-room.

Such worries did not have to cloud the thoughts of Rob Steelback and Hugo Crabscote, who, after a short exchange, discovered that they were of one mind as to how to proceed. For his part Stewart Thorogood could think of nothing better than continuing to bowl Richard Furness at the Park End, especially as Richard was pestering him to be able to bowl his overs in one spell. Richard's third over did not dissuade Stewart from giving Richard his head. True, he conceded two boundaries, but the other four balls in the over were very steady. One of them was good enough to induce an error on the batsman's part, but there was no fielder close enough to take what might have been an easy catch.

As the fielders changed ends Tom Redman was at pains to point out that he had now taken three wickets. 'Yes, but three for plenty', Stewart had replied without any malice. He had not counted exactly how many runs had been scored off Tom's bowling, but plenty was a pretty fair label to put on a tally of 59 from five overs. Even in festival cricket this was quite a rate. Nevertheless Stewart gave Tom an encouraging slap on the back and told him to carry on. Two things prompted this generous decision. Stewart was still stuck with the belief that he had to get eight overs out of Tom. Secondly, he wondered if it was just possibly true that Tom's combination of (mainly) dross and (one or two) well-directed leg-breaks was buying wickets. Six balls later he knew it was false.

When their family saloon finally chugged (the operative word) into the grounds of Helmerstead Hall it was hard to judge which of Basil and Jane Smith was the angrier. It had been a nightmare journey, Jane Smith had said – more than once. It had completely spoilt her day. Basil had by now been charged not only with failure to service the car but with omitting to sell it long ago in exchange for another. She had never liked it. Basil had bitten his tongue after that remark had been flung in. He remembered, even if his wife did not, how she had insisted on its purchase, claiming that she liked its colour. Basil could also remember his suspicion that she had liked the salesman more. Blond, flash and sharp-suited, he was the eponymous car salesman. The special offers, discounts and star deals poured out of him. Basil's accountancy mind had been able to cut through the burble of figures. In essence what emerged was that just one model, which happened to be in the dealer's compound, was available at the given price – if you happened to like Empire Green teamed with burnt orange fabric trim, which Jane Smith said she did. Then it had been revealed that the car in question was fitted with certain extras which Basil Smith was far from having at the top of his wish list. He could manage without alloy wheels, headlamp washers, a rear spoiler and a leather-trimmed steering-wheel. So he had bartered. The salesman, who had winked once too often at Jane for Basil's liking, kept disappearing to see his manager and returning with minor concessions and inducements. Finally, with a modest shaving of the price and the gift of six wine glasses in Bulgarian crystal, a deal was struck in which Basil's heart was not firmly lodged. The long wait for assistance on the Yarfield by-pass following the special bargain's expiry had not been made more tolerable by Jane's insistent re-interpretation of history.

The relief engendered by the approach of the red van denoting the Road Services Association had been quickly extinguished. The earlier gloom became despair. Ron Hedges had been a motor mechanic for over thirty years, his skills having originally been learned in a correctional institution. At this advanced stage of his career there was nothing that he did not know and no opinion he had yet to form. 'Oh, it's one of those, is it?' was his greeting as he emerged from his van. 'That model's always been trouble. Of course you made a mistake buying Japanese.' It was swiftly apparent that this was no selective comment. Ron Hedges seemed to have no time for anything Japanese.

His instruction to Basil to open the bonnet was issued in the sort of tone adopted by a police officer when telling a motorist whom he suspects of being over the limit to get out of his car. There followed a series of 'Oh dears' punctuated by much shaking of the head. Having delicately prodded and jiggled some parts of the engine in latex gloves, he pronounced again: 'They had no idea when they designed this.' He turned to Basil to ask how many miles were on the clock. 'As many as that?' he said when Basil told him. 'Well, I suppose you can count yourself lucky. I've never seen one that's done half that.' By this time neither Basil nor even Jane were counting themselves the least bit lucky. It was Jane who asked icily 'Can you fix it?' The mechanic gave her a brooding stare. 'The best I can do with this is frig it up. That should do you for today, but once you've got it home I wouldn't hang on to it.' Basil felt that he wouldn't mind hanging one on Ron Hedges, but he did not want to make an already dire situation calamitous.

The RSA officer turned towards his van and bawled out the single word 'Trevor'. It became apparent why the uniform worn by Ron Hedges was in immaculate condition with no smear or grease besmirching it. From the rear of the van there emerged a much younger man in a set of overalls so covered in grime and grease that its underlying colour could scarcely be detected. The fact that Trevor had not been permitted to ride in the front passenger seat somewhat cruelly emphasised the relative stations of the two men – at least as seen by the senior of them. For all his dogsbody status Trevor wore a cheerful smile which refused to fade even while his superior was issuing his instructions. Then he got to work, watched closely by Ron Hedges and at a discreet distance by Basil and Jane Smith. They were not too far away to miss the fact that the constant stream of comment which flowed from Ron Hedges to his junior had nothing to do with the work in hand, but was instead a continuing lament against Japanese design, construction and place in the world.

When it looked as though the repair was nearing completion Ron Hedges broke off and marched towards the van. Reaching inside he returned armed with a clipboard. Calling across to the Smiths, he said, 'I'll just need to see your membership card.' A pained expression appeared on Basil's face. He looked at Jane. She looked at him. Ron Hedges stared fiercely in their direction. Basil's mouth opened and shut. No sound came out. The mouths of those who flanked him opened, but in their case plenty of sound emerged.

Hugo Crabscote had wasted no time in setting about the bowling. He did not imagine that his new acquaintance, Annabelle Crouch, would be spending the whole of the afternoon looking round Helmerstead Hall. He wanted to conjure up some time to further their relationship. Tom Redman was the first to bear the brunt of this desire. For someone new to the crease the footwork was terrific. Tom did not have the time to wonder about spin and direction as Hugo Crabscote advanced towards him and clipped the ball back over his head. Tom gambled against him being able to do the same again – and lost. At this point Stewart Thorogood intervened. Fielders were moved to long on and long off. This failed to have any effect on the duel between bowler and batsman, but a heroic feat of athleticism on the part of Richard Furness cut one off the potential run tally. This put Rob Steelback on strike. If Tom Redman was expecting to be driven, he was mistaken. He was pulled instead and this time conceded six runs. Then he was driven again, but the shot was worth only three runs, Harry Northwood sprinting from deep midwicket back towards long on to cut off another boundary. Tom's finest moment came with the last ball. He succeeded in deceiving Hugo Crabscote through the air, but the ball was driven back hard along the ground. Smarting from the punishment he had taken, Tom flung himself in its path and achieved a stop so brilliant that it earned a ripple of applause from a crowd which had gorged on big hitting.

Richard Furness raced to his bowling mark determined to cut the risk of his being replaced. He need not have feared. Stewart Thorogood was resigned to keeping him going. Richard had looked as good as anyone in what were plainly difficult circumstances. Stewart had the satisfying experience of not being let down by Richard Furness' fourth over. If in six overs Tom Redman had not managed to settle in to a steady rhythm, Richard appeared to have achieved it in three. Despite Rob Steelback's aggressive intent Richard restricted his scoring to one stroke for two runs. It was not his fault that the over as a whole cost six. Frustrated by playing four dot balls, the batsman took a wild swing at the final delivery, missed, and the ball deflected off his pad, beat Rashid Ali's outstretched arm and yielded four leg byes.

In her domain Caroline Bingley-Adams found two messages awaiting her. The first was from the hospital to say that Maurice Randall's condition was giving cause for concern. Although no more than a precaution at this stage it might be advisable if his sons could be conveyed to their father's bedside. Caroline frowned, inclining to regard what was said as melodramatic and in any case fending off any thought that she should be responsible for rounding up these abominable ruffians. The second message was more intriguing. Could she at her earliest convenience meet Professor Hamish McTartar outside the refreshment tent? He had a most important announcement to relay. Mysterious maybe, but to Caroline, who was as always thinking in money terms, it seemed worth investigating. Message number one was put aside. Maurice Randall's condition was not giving her any cause for concern.

In his domain Simon Crossley was enduring a lonely existence. Henry Moulden was proving no sort of scoring companion. The man looked to be out of his depth and was seemingly unwilling to seek guidance from his youthful opposite number. There was no conversation between them. Simon had tried several gambits with no success. Up to that point no non-playing Outcast had strolled up to exchange a cheery word or insult (his earnings, tattoo and goatee beard were still objects of amusement to his friends). There was nothing for Simon to do but concentrate on the game. Usually that would not have been a chore, for even within the bounds of the type of cricket with which the Outcasts were associated there was most times a competitive core. There was little evidence of this in what had unfolded so far in the beautiful setting of Helmerstead Hall. Simon had no real confidence that things would change. From his vantage point he had been able to see some of the Outcasts make their way to the refreshment tent. Only Greg Roberts had emerged, and even at a distance Simon could see that he was in no great shape. Simon sighed. Henry Moulden frowned. He had been uncomfortable from the start. Now he was experiencing physical discomfort. He needed to relieve himself, but was reluctant to reveal this weakness to his opposite number. He shifted uneasily in his chair. Simon sighed. This loneliness was oppressive. He needed relief of a different sort. How, he wondered, was the monotony to be broken? He would soon discover.

Charles Brett's modus operandi was to collect the items of interest to him and deposit them in a store room. Knowing the house as well as he did, there was no problem in selecting a suitable room. It was off the beaten track, but irritatingly close to it. The people milling around on tours were a complication, but, after he had thought about it for a while he could see a way of turning the situation to his advantage. In a cupboard in the store room was a Helmerstead Hall attendant's brown coat which proclaimed its wearer by virtue of having the words 'Helmerstead Hall' picked out on the back. Charles Brett had seen people wearing such coats. By swapping this garment for his own overalls he calculated that he could move amongst the visiting public without raising any questions even whilst carrying a valuable object. That settled, he concentrated on rounding up more of the smaller items which he could conveniently conceal in his work bag. Afterwards getting everything into the van, he recognised, would be the final hurdle. Although he did not know it, there would be one more.

The next five overs of the Celebs' innings had passed relatively without incident. No wicket had fallen and nor had there been a torrent of runs. Credit for this brake on the rate of scoring was owed to Ray Burrill, who had been introduced into the attack at the start of the twenty-first over. The passage of twenty overs had allowed the effect of lunch-time drinking to subside. Apart from an initial loosener which Hugo Crabscote had despatched smoothly to the fine leg boundary beyond the outstretched arm of a diving Toby Lederwood (the fielder won the plaudits of Ray Burrill for his efforts and a green stain from top to toe, which seemed to amuse some people in the crowd) scoring was reduced mainly to singles. Richard Furness seemed to take his cue from Ray Burrill, with his fifth and sixth overs being almost miserly. The attention of spectators drifted. Billy Figg tried hopping on one leg in a faint imitation of the celebrated former Test umpire, David Shepherd, but there appeared to be no particular reason for it and the performance went largely unnoticed. Someone shouted 'Fetch the dog', but the animal did not make an entrance. Sensing disenchantment with proceedings, Rob Steelback met Hugo Crabscote in the middle and after a quick discussion about the bowling Rob Steelback suggested that they had better make something happen. Shortly afterwards they did, but not quite in the way either of them had intended.

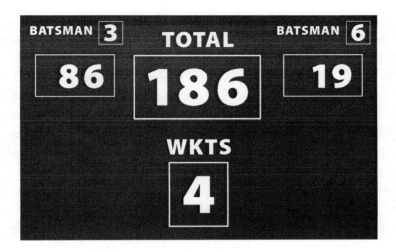

Although Caroline Bingley-Adams had never previously met Hamish McTartar nor seen a photograph, recognition was surprisingly easy. The professor's appearance was indicative although it might have been more circumspect for a supposed academic. At first Caroline Bingley-Adams hoped that she was wrong. The professional title did not sit well with a ragged kilt (in a tartan to which he could make no legitimate claim), a T-shirt stained to such an extent that its offensive slogan was almost but not completely obscured, and a partially bleached denim jacket. A tam o'shanter half-obscuring a shock of orange hair did nothing to recover the effect. He was seated on the grass outside the refreshment tent caressing a bottle of whisky, alas far from full. Caroline Bingley-Adams did not want this to be Professor Hamish McTartar, but she felt that she had to address this distinctive figure if only for the purpose of elimination. She felt her heart sinking when he responded to her enquiry with an affirmative grunt. He even rose unsteadily to bow in her direction.

The words which followed the bow were 'I am Professor Hamish Mc-Tartar and I have come here for a most important meeting.' A very thick Scottish accent made thicker by a degree of inebriation caused them to be difficult to distinguish. Caroline Bingley-Adams caught the first part, but it took a little longer to grasp the sense of the rest. 'Meeting', the professor repeated and then she got it. Confounding her earlier expectation, not with her she hoped. The next word did not entirely remove that possibility. 'Cricket', he said although it came out sounding a bit different from that. Professor McTartar then said something else. Caroline Bingley-Adams took a step nearer the better to hear, but quickly took a step back when his whisky-laden breath hit her. At that point Winston Jenkins emerged from the tent where he had been experiencing the hair of the dog. The black Welshman gallantly interpreted the words of his Celtic cousin. 'He's looking for an important American visitor.' Thus encouraged, the Professor explained himself further. Winston Jenkins was able to tell Caroline Bingley-Adams that Helmerstead was the chosen meeting-place for an academic colloquium on cricket which would lead to new insights into the history of the game. She was right to be unsure about this.

Hamish McTartar's connections with cricket went back a long way. There were few cricket clubs in Scotland which he had not visited. There were by now few which would still allow him to visit. His interest, at first welcome, was soon resisted. From club after club he was excluded. A combination of excessive drinking and over-enthusiastic partisanship is not unknown on cricket grounds, but Hamish McTartar had taken it to a level of abnormal and continuous nuisance. The ban spread to hostelries closely associated with cricket grounds. Gradually he was forced to sublimate his interest in cricket in his native Scotland to researching and writing about the game. Whilst he was effectively barred from watching cricket anywhere north of the border there was no restraint on his drinking and his partisanship. His scholarship lost whatever rigour it might have had. Facts became blurred by fantasy. None of this might have mattered before Hamish McTartar discovered the Internet. His website carried some of his intriguing claims beyond the geographical boundaries within which they could be rightly dismissed. No serious commentator would have believed that anyone anywhere was likely to devote more than a second's attention to the McTartar outpourings. But the serious commentator would probably not have heard of the United States Environmental League for Education and Sporting Studies.

Caroline Bingley-Adams had heard sufficient to strip herself of all interest in the unlikely professor. 'Well, I know of no American' was intended as her exit line. But Winston Jenkins did. 'Oh, yes, he's here looking for you', he chipped in helpfully. 'I've already met him.' And then, less helpfully, turning to the refreshment centre, 'He was here, but I don't know where he is now.' Caroline Bingley-Adams was on the move when he added brightly, 'I'm sure this lady could make an announcement over the PA system for him.' It was not a suggestion for which she had the slightest enthusiasm, trotting out three reasons why she found it impracticable. However, she could not stop Winston Jenkins warming to his theme and when Hamish McTartar himself began to advance towards her in supplication she hurriedly capitulated. 'It's Mr Fishgate', said Winston in imperfect recollection. Hamish McTartar was in no state to correct him. 'I need a drink', he said, unscrewing once more the cap of his prized whisky bottle.

After his experience Basil Smith would willingly have done something similar. Caught on the Yarfield by-pass without his RSA membership Basil had received a fusillade of barbs from Jane. Cash was the only answer to the problem which faced them. Fortunately Ron Hedges had his price, but it was a price which required a contribution from Jane's handbag as well as Basil's wallet. This had not helped the situation between them. Not even Basil pointing out how lucky it had been that the 'repair' had been completed before the membership card was demanded seemed to make any difference. Jane had been determined to prolong the argument about the car. It was a relief when they arrived at Helmerstead Hall. Jane had stalked off with the intent of inspecting the mansion and had become part of a group whose company she preferred for the rest of the afternoon. Basil set out to reconnect with the Outcasts and find out what was happening in the cricket match.

What was happening was arguably cricket at its best, a genuine contest between bat and ball. This was not necessarily what people were counting on watching at a charity match involving celebrities in fancy costume. The control which Ray Burrill and Richard Furness had managed to exert over the superior batting qualities of Rob Steelback and Hugo Crabscote would have delighted cricket's connoisseurs on an overcast day at Edgbaston, but it was starting to try the patience of a fun-loving bunch of day-trippers at Helmerstead Hall. It was trying the patience of the amorous Hugo as well. There had been the odd cry of 'Get on with it' and an occasional 'Wake up' call, but nothing which could authentically be called barracking began until the commencement of Richard Furness' final over. By this time two more tight overs had been bowled and the score had crawled rather than advanced to 189-4.

As Richard Furness, his brain now flicking to thoughts of a forthcoming off-pitch matinee performance, prepared to bowl to Hugo Crabscote, whose personal score had not increased in the space of three overs, crowd dissatisfaction impinged itself on the game. The batsman was slow handclapped. This took him so much by surprise that, if only to hold concentration, he blocked the first three balls delivered by Richard. Irritation then took over and he aimed an ugly swipe at the fourth, missed and, losing his balance, fell down. This gave spectators something to cheer. Rob Steelback strode down the pitch to check on his partner's wellbeing and to impart an advisory word. To steady himself Hugo played a safe defensive shot to the next ball. The slow handclap surged again. So did Hugo's rage. Richard Furness, relieved at job well done, was thinking now only of Suzy Waterbeach. His final delivery was close to being a long-hop. It was close enough to a long-hop for Hugo Crabscote, who was thinking longingly of Annabelle Crouch, to feel once again that he must answer his critics. With pent-up force he pulled the ball towards the square leg boundary. It never made it.

The quieter passage of play drove the charity organiser into thinking once again about his big game plan. He told himself that he must concentrate on getting on with it. The words 'Why, hello there' uttered in a soft, well-modulated voice were, when he identified their source, a further distraction. Greeted with a warm smile, he hesitated. There was something familiar about the face. 'Come on, don't say you don't remember', she said. The charity organiser knew that she was too beautiful to be lightly forgotten. He had met her before. He groped in his memory as she teased him. The circumstance of their acquaintance came back first. He daren't risk a name. 'Lovely to see you again. You're looking great.' (What the hell was she called?) 'What are you doing here?' While she answered he thought he'd got it: Cara with whom his passion had been interrupted by that intimidatory phone call from Caroline Bingley-Adams. Never happy when his investment failed to pay off, the charity organiser was not lightly going to pass up a second chance. 'Can I buy you a drink?' he asked. They moved in conversation towards the refreshment centre. 'It's Carla actually', she said as they went inside.

The American trio had conducted a comprehensive tour of the grounds of Helmerstead Hall taking in all the stalls and amusements. The former had occupied the greater part of their attention. Being Americans they found hints of 'Olde England' quite compelling in both crafts and comestibles.

There were knitted and crocheted items which smacked of local antiquity. Certainly they had been produced by people of antiquity. The sign over a stall reading Helmerstead Mothers' Circle should more honestly have reflected an older generation. Arthritic fingers had nevertheless done their best. A cruel observer might have said that the finished articles looked unfinished, but they possessed an air of charm which suckered some visitors into purchasing them. In some cases sales were aided by virtue of the items not being named. This allowed the purchaser's imagination some rein.

Old Mother Jigginshaw's jams caught the eye. The stall was well stocked with a multi-coloured array of jars offering preservatives of every fruit imaginable. Visitors were urged to try Old Mother Jigginshaw's unique recipe which, it was claimed, had been handed down through the generations. Aided by cleverly designed labels the jams had been selling well. 'Buy early to avoid disappointment', cried the ancient stall-holder as the Americans hovered. In truth, as locals knew only too well, the only way to avoid disappointment was to delay consumption. Old Mother Jigginshaw's recipe was indeed unique. Whatever the name on the label and whatever the colour of the product, the taste was identical. It was a remarkable formula and a remarkable process which together achieved such uniformity in the finished article. Nor was Old Mother Jigginshaw all she seemed. Skilful make-up and good acting added thirty years to the appearance of Florrie Jigginshaw, mother of thirteen, all of whom, it was thought, played some part in the council house industry she illegitimately ran.

No such chicanery played a part in the next-door stall which displayed sauces, pickles and relishes. Just incompetence. The lady purveying these items believed she could cook. All evidence was to the contrary. She could not get recipes right to save her life. In a well-meaning way she always erred on the side of adding a little extra and this usually had the effect of making the ultimate taste too hot, too sharp, too acidic or too rich. Yet from craft market to farmers' market to car boot sales she got away with it for any one of three reasons: the customer gave the product as a gift to someone else or put it on a shelf in the pantry and forgot about it or tasted it and blamed themselves for not liking it. Vera Naysmith always liked to sell her goods to visitors from overseas for this virtually guaranteed no come-back. If she could sell a large variety of items to one client, she could arrange shipment. She had that thought to the fore when she heard the accent of Margaret Hamersteen addressing Geraldine Rogers, 'Are you sure that's a tea cosy?'

In the seclusion of their mobile headquarters Paul Wyatt had once again removed his trousers. It had been Laurel Rouse's suggestion, much as on the previous occasion. The initiating thought had been purely utilitarian. Placed underneath the mattress with something heavy on top the trousers might lose some of their creases. With absence of trousers but no absence of desire the situation left undisturbed might have developed less purely, but this was not put to the test. A suggestive smile from Laurel was extinguished by frantic knocking on the door of their vehicle. Paul sheltered behind the door as his partner fielded the call. If he had been denied any part in proceedings on the field Basil Smith had acted decisively as a spectator. He had sprinted from his vantage point on the boundary to the St Joan Ambulance which had been in his sight line. 'There's been an accident,' he gasped, 'you're needed – quickly.' Coincidentally this same sentiment had been shared by Paul Wyatt a few seconds earlier. His reaction time to the new circumstance was extended by the need to retrieve his trousers which lay on the opposite side of the vehicle beyond the open door. In one move he thrust Laurel out of the way and with his other arm slammed the door shut in the face of Basil Smith. Basil's astonishment delayed his reaction time. This bought Paul Wyatt crucial seconds with which to restore himself to uniformed respectability before Basil burst through the door determined to reinforce the urgency of his message.

There could be no faulting the speed with which Paul Wyatt made up for this unfortunate delay. He sprinted ahead of Laurel and headed under Basil Smith's directions to the field of play. No actual play was in progress. Instead there was a huddle which it was revealed surrounded the prone figure of Tommy Fagge. Ever the comedian at heart Tommy Fagge had a feel for an audience. He had sensed that the quieter passage of play was not being appreciated by spectators and so had sought to keep them amused by one or two bits of play-acting. These had taken his eye off the ball. After executing a little piece of mime he had turned back to his duty a fraction of a second too late to escape the path of Hugo Crabscote's violent stroke. The ball struck him in the solar plexus and he fell heavily to earth, unconscious. Paul Wyatt's diagnosis was immediate. 'He's hurt', he announced with an air of authority. 'We must get him to hospital. I'll summon an ambulance.'

Having realised that he had removed his mobile phone from his trouser belt before the garment had been placed under the mattress, he raced off to retrieve it leaving Laurel Rouse to administer to the stricken victim. She established that Tommy Fagge had a pulse, but beyond that his condition was way beyond the cuts and bruises which most nearly fitted her experience to date. Faced with the question 'Can't you do something?' she could only smile (she had a sweet smile), loosen the victim's collar and smooth her hand over his brow. Besides that she prayed.

Her prayers were answered sooner than might have been expected. Having delivered Marion Booth to hospital, paramedics Gregory Braine and Lloyd Hart had lingered for a cup of tea before deciding whether or not to return to their poker game. Their indecision was once again resolved by outside forces. By now the route between the hospital and the hall was familiar and the paramedics made good time whilst marvelling at the apparent disaster area which the planned fun event had become. Hugo Crabscote was distraught. Rob Steelback was attempting comfort. Tommy Fagge was unfit and overweight. He had received a ferocious blow. Hugo Crabscote worried that it might be fatal. He was not the only one. However, the welfare of Tommy Fagge was not uppermost in the thoughts of Caroline Bingley-Adams when she arrived on the scene after discovering that the match had halted. She wanted the swiftest possible return to normality. 'Can't you move him?' she shrieked at Laurel Rouse. Fortunately Laurel's admittedly small reservoir of knowledge contained awareness that movement in such circumstances should be attempted only when the patient had been fitted with a neck brace and possibly other restraints.

The dreaded ambulance siren was shortly heard again and the expert paramedics were soon attending to the unfortunate Tommy Fagge. Caroline Bingley-Adams was left to fume while Gregory Braine and Lloyd Hart secured the patient and then gently lifted the stretcher to the ambulance at the boundary edge. 'Is he all right?' The question came not from Caroline Bingley-Adams but from an anxious Hugo Crabscote echoing Billy Figg. 'He'll live', replied Lloyd Hart, but his supposedly sotto voce comment to his partner 'probably' was overheard. Stewart Thorogood, who had been first on the spot when Tommy Fagge fell, now felt relieved that he had dismissed the idea that had first come to him, to prise the ball from Tommy Fagge's midriff, where it had been clasped by the unfortunate umpire, and claim a catch. He, like some in the crowd, thought that Tommy Fagge had been fooling before true realisation had sunk in. Now Stewart's mood had switched to the opposite extreme. Taking Caroline Bingley-Adams' arm he wondered whether the match should be called off. With a supreme piece of improvisation the look of horror on her face converted from what she thought the enormity of the suggestion to concern for the paying public and then more emotively to concern for 'those poor deprived children we're hoping to help'. The players prepared to resume, but, first, a replacement umpire was needed. By great good fortune there was someone on the ground tailor-made for the job.

Syd Breakwell was unaware of the events leading up to his summons for duty. He had not nursed hopes in that direction when he had seen the installation of Figg and Fagge. With most of his Outcast friends having deserted the pavilion Syd himself decided to take a walk and inspect facilities. After two unsatisfactory rounds of hoop-la at which he had rather fancied his chances he contented himself with the purchase of a jar of horseradish and senna relish for his wife; then, at a loose end, he thought that a glass of beer would not go amiss. And nor did it. The same could be said of the second (Syd had chosen Suggistons). There would not necessarily have been a third had Phil Cole not emerged from the throng and greeted him. Phil explained that their friends Charlie Colson and David Pelham were also in the bar area, but resting in a corner with their eyes closed. Syd would have bought a drink for Phil, but at that point he was supplanted by Basil Smith, who had reached the refreshment tent without any detour via the stalls and amusements. Basil, who had made the unilateral decision that Jane would drive back, ordered a pint for himself and for Phil, but Syd stuck to a half. This was probably as well, for two more followed. This was not entirely judicious for a man whose prostate had begun to exhibit signs of wear. He was half way through what he had decided was his last when he was finally located to be told that his services were needed. Uncharacteristically he drained the glass before rushing to get his coat and hat. Association with the Outcasts had obviously rubbed off on him.

Whilst Syd Breakwell prepared himself for duty Stewart Thorogood sought out his opposite number to discuss the matter of time lost to injury. To keep on schedule he suggested to Don Hennelly that they should restrict the match to thirty-six overs. The Celebs' captain was at first doubtful. He cited contractual commitment and giving the crowd its money's worth. Stewart countered with the need not to let the game overrun with effect on other activities and the fact that a loss of only four overs was probably not full compensation for the time which would have been lost by the time they resumed. Don Hennelly hesitated before finally suggesting a sacrifice of two overs. His willingness to compromise was brought on by Caroline Bingley-Adams' interruption of their conversation. Her imperious demand that nothing less than a game of forty overs would suffice swayed him. Stewart Thorogood promptly accepted Don Hennelly's offer to maintain a united front against the dominatrice. At the back of Stewart's mind had been the possibility of dispensing with the need to bowl the two remaining overs of Tom Redman's allocation, but even the loss of one was a gain.

The action resumed. Rob Steelback felt the need to get on with things. The innings had already become becalmed before it had been so unfortunately halted. Some spectators had drifted away in search of other diversions. This was after all a festival game. It needed enlivening. He had half thought of suggesting to Ray Burrill, whom he was about to face, that he should stop trying so hard in order to let the runs flow again. He desisted and in any case it was quickly shown that such advice would have been otiose. Whether affected by what had happened to Tommy Fagge, even though he, Ray, had not been the person bowling, or simply having had his concentration disturbed by the break, Ray Burrill's fifth over did not match what had gone before, and he provided three boundary opportunities which Rob Steelback did not fail to take. With the last of them he reached three figures and was given a generous round of applause. Coincidentally the Celebs' score passed the 200 mark.

It was only on looking round the field in search of Nigel Redman, whom he had selected to bowl his seventh and possibly final over at the Park End, that Stewart Thorogood noticed something else which had happened during the unwelcome break in play. Kevin Newton had joined them. Having bowled his allocation, Richard Furness had seized the opportunity of the distraction to get himself substituted. He had only limited time before he might be required to bat and he intended to make the most of it. Nigel Redman's last over had cost 18 runs, but he had not bowled to Hugo Crabscote. Stewart took the risk of bringing Hugo's batting back to life. In one sense the risk paid off. The accident had caused Hugo to slip into a mood of introspection. He prodded indeterminately at two ordinary balls from Nigel Redman and when the third took an involuntary edge and eluded the gully fielder Rob Steelback insisted on the single being run. As if to make a point Rob then proceeded to thump the remaining three balls of the over for four apiece.

The break in play had come as a great relief to Henry Moulden in the score-box. With a show of dignity he told Simon Crossley that he would stretch his legs, and the real reason for his exit might not have been apparent if he had remembered to re-zip his trousers. Simon debated with himself how he might tactfully draw Henry Moulden's attention to the matter. He mentally ran through all the expressions sometimes used to avoid making a direct observation. Too corny, he thought, and decided instead to say nothing. He justified this unkindness to himself a short while later when a call on his mobile from Sophie was greeted with a very severe look of disapproval from Henry Moulden. The ring-tone was certainly distinctive. It was shortly after the game had re-started that a second disturbance took place. A loud knocking noise came from outside the box. It was not the sound of a polite person knocking for admission. It was the sound of two very impolite people who had found something interesting to do with a length of metal. It was not a sound to be tolerated for long. Henry Moulden, his mood already soured by Simon's mobile, was the first to move.

Danny and Craig Randall had decided to give the stalls and other entertainments a wide berth for a while until the hue and cry had died down. So they had drawn nearer to the cricket. Passing an unattended garden tractor to which a trailer had been attached, Craig had seized a metal post. This was done as much for devilment as anything else, but moving behind the scorebox other thoughts came to the boys' minds. Craig thought that he could beat a rhythm on the back of the box (but failed). Danny thought that noise – loud noise – would do. Grabbing the metal post from his brother he launched a ferocious assault on the woodwork. He quickly achieved the satisfaction of bringing someone to the door. Set to run, they stalled on seeing Henry Moulden's appearance. They were not as reticent as Simon Crossley had been. The coarse terms which they used were way beyond Simon's list. At first shocked and embarrassed Henry Moulden was slow in his attempted retaliation. His sense of justice belonged to a bygone age. Had he possessed the agility he would have picked up the metal post (now abandoned by the boys), given chase and given them a firm whack on their anatomy. Instead he trod on the metal object, lost his footing and then his balance, crashing finally into the sharp corner of the box. The hullabaloo had eventually

brought some visitors to the scene. One lady fainted on seeing so much blood. Another had the good sense to seek out St Joan Ambulance, where another moment of tender intimacy was spoiled.

Having imposed her will on the shape of the cricket, Caroline Bingley-Adams returned to her office. Added to the two earlier messages was a third. Another bulletin had come from the hospital. Maurice Randall was 'holding on', but his children should be brought to the hospital. If she could have rounded them up, Caroline Bingley-Adams would have made prison the priority option. She was also advised that Marion Booth was 'comfortable', but she did not know what to do with that information. Then she saw again the name of Hamish McTartar, which was written on her pad. This triggered something in her memory about an announcement she had been urged to make. It had to do with an American, but she could not remember the name. Fish something, she thought. But she gave it no further thought when a knock on the door hailed the appearance of the charity organiser.

Their time together in the bar had reminded the charity organiser why he had picked up Carla in the first place. It had also reminded him that she possessed quite a taste for drink. If there was to be a finish to hitherto unfinished business, it had somehow to be arranged without wrecking his plans. 'Let's explore the house', he said to Carla in a meaningful way. However, there was one thing which had to be tied up before the tea interval in the cricket match. He wanted to check with Caroline Bingley-Adams that she had got raffle ticket sellers organised. So pouring another large glass of white wine for Carla and pecking her on the cheek, he said he would be back in two ticks before she had finished her drink. He was wrong.

Rob Steelback realised that an effort was needed to comfort his partner before Hugo Crabscote took strike again. He said all the right words. Hugo seemed to acknowledge them and recognise that he was there to please the crowd. Nevertheless when he faced up to Ray Burrill again the appetite for big hitting was not there. He produced some shots, but they were all along the ground and not always into gaps in the field. This time there was no single to put Rob Steelback on strike. Ray reckoned that he had re-established control and felt the better for it. Stewart Thorogood decided that Nigel Redman on the other hand had lost it. He thereupon planned to bowl the final four overs from the Park End himself. He told himself that it was the captain's responsibility.

Stewart began poorly but was lucky. Not just one loosener but three cost him four, two and one. With Rob Steelback then losing the strike the rest of Stewart's indifferent over was bowled to Hugo Crabscote, who was in a mood to examine this new (to him) bowler before trying anything aggressive. This was not what his partner had intended. What turned out to be a single had looked like two until it struck the despairing foot of Harry Northwood and was freakishly deflected to Ray Burrill. The latter then had to give some thought to how he could try to contain Rob Steelback, who clearly had the bit between his teeth. He conferred with his captain. Festival game or no festival game, the Celebs XI already had a total which would challenge the Outcasts. Six more overs could put the game completely beyond them. It was not so much a matter of winning or losing but making a match of it for the sake of the spectators. The resultant plan had two components: the first was to try to keep the dominant Rob Steelback off strike and the second was to bowl elusively without actually sending down wides.

At the outset the plan was perfectly implemented. With mid-off and mid-on placed well back Ray Burrill bowled a good length ball on an off-stump line. It invited the single, but Rob Steelback intended to decline. However, Hugo Crabscote was not party to his thinking. Although it was not his call he charged down the wicket at such a pace that Rob Steelback had no option but to move. Hugo Crabscote's bout of remorse was not over; it had just been replaced by another in which he felt he had been letting his partner down. Despite his renewed resolve he found himself up against Ray Burrill purveying a mixture of brisk off-cutters and widish balls. He managed no more than a single off the last ball and quickly found himself in discussion with Rob Steelback.

Caroline Bingley-Adams told the charity organiser that she had instructed the cricketers to act as a sales force for the raffle tickets. Even recognising that this meant employing the Outcasts the charity organiser readily fell in with the plan – too readily, for he had Carla on his mind. Had he pressed Caroline a little harder he might have found out that what she had said was not strictly accurate. In her own mind she had organised the cricketers, but the cricketers themselves were unaware that they had been so organised. To her there was no distinction. She had ordained it and therefore it would happen. They could not refuse to engage in such a charitable exercise. She really had no idea what she was taking on. Lulled into believing that all was well, the charity organiser made a swift return to his female acquisition in keen anticipation. A glass of white wine sat in front of her, but it was not the one he had last seen and nor its first replacement. 'Darling, I started a little tab', she greeted him. And indeed she had, saw the charity organiser, as one of the bar staff pushed a piece of paper towards him. 'Just one more, darling', she quickly said, her glass already drained. Instead the charity organiser gave her a squeeze, a most seductive smile and his arm. Firmly he guided her towards his van. 'Oh, darling,' she said with a giggle, 'have you got a mattress in the back?' Sadly, he thought, he had not. The hired vehicle had not had that feature as standard. However, Carla was not to know that. Suddenly she stopped, turned towards the charity organiser with a dreamy look in her eyes and vomited violently over him. She then doubled up and collapsed on the ground.

Whilst the normally shrewd Margaret Hamersteen and Geraldine Roberts were being unmercifully conned by Vera Naysmith, C. Ramsgate Fishburn had wandered on to the next stall which he could see was covered in books. On closer inspection he found that it was a treasure-house of cricket books. At a stroke he saw the boundaries of his study being expanded. What gems might he find here which could add depth and colour to the eventual treatise? Had C. Ramsgate Fishburn known anything at all about the stall-holder, Gervase Brigshaw, his expectations would not have been high. Gervase Brigshaw was a weedy little man, a description which was given added conviction by his choice of a brown cloth cap and a once-fawn raincoat. A cigarette drooping out of the corner of his mouth completed the image, with another in reserve behind his ear. Selling cricket books

at village or charity matches was not his main occupation. His principal source of earnings came from being a pickpocket, but the bookstall was a plausible cover. He operated on the assumption that anyone who dealt in cricket books must be a person of impeccable taste and standing, even though in his case he no longer looked it.

The gems found by C. Ramsgate Fishburn would certainly have had the effect of widening his canvas. For fifty pence he had a choice of *I Took Cricket to the Pygmies* by Major Delisle Bredwell, *Cricket in the Kitchen (100 easy cricket teas)* by Fanny Roux, *The Biomechanics of Over-arm Throwing* by Hubert von Stiff, *Run Amok* (an anthology of the worst run-outs in cricket history), *Up Yours – An Umpire's Perspective*, by Battersby Bird, *Pitch Doctoring for Beginners* by Damian Flood, *Scoring in the Dark* by Renshaw Tinnes, *Love on a Hard Wicket* by Timothy Lust, *Getting Stumped in Greece* by Heracles Hobson, *An Illustrated History of Cricket Administration in Mongolia* (vols 1 and 2) by Cyrus Reinhammer, *My Favourite Abdominal Protectors* by 'A Test Cricketer' in association with 'A Ghost Writer', *How to Stop the Runs* by Dr Carlton Gatting and *The Far Pavilions – A Guide to Lottery Grants* by Tessa Chancit. The more discerning customer, a category in which C. Ramsgate Fishburn was not to be found, might have stumbled across editions of Wisden from miscellaneous past years. However, inspection would have quickly doused interest as the volumes had been vandalised by someone who evidently nursed a grievance against Surrey.

As C. Ramsgate Fishburn contemplated what to him seemed desirable options St Joan Ambulance found itself under pressure. Paul Wyatt and Laurel Rouse had hastened, so far as their situation had allowed, to the scoreboard where at least some of their basic training had been put to use. As Laurel Rouse dabbed at the unfortunate Henry Moulden's face Paul Wyatt called for the paramedics. 'He's obviously in a bad way', he explained to an augmented group of onlookers. 'He'll be much better off in hospital.' Before the near-disbelieving paramedics could reach the scene someone ran up to report an unconscious girl near the pavilion. Not having previously been faced by quite so much blood, Laurel Rouse was relieved to get away from the shattered Henry Moulden. Her relief was short-lived when she found that she had swapped blood for vomit. The girl on the ground was unconscious and her breathing was uneven. Laurel did not like the look of her at all and was uncertain what to do for the best. She would probably have taken a leaf out of her partner's book and suggested immediate reference to the paramedics but she was forestalled by Caroline Bingley-Adams proclaiming 'She must be taken to hospital.' And she might in other circumstances have commanded the charity organiser, who had obviously been the companion of the young lady, to drive her there in his van if two things had not suppressed the order. The charity organiser turned towards her and in one look she saw the bespattered state of him in the foreground and in the distance an ambulance. 'Get that ambulance here at once', she barked at Laurel. 'Cheaper by the bloody dozen', muttered Gregory Braine to Lloyd Hart as they hoisted Carla into their vehicle alongside Henry Moulden. Caroline Bingley-Adams was once again relieved to get casualties off the scene. 'Please don't ring your bell till you're out of the park', she hissed to Gregory Braine. The fun had to be allowed to continue undisturbed.

The fun, albeit in subdued vein, had continued with Stewart Thorogood pitting his wits against Hugo Crabscote. He had been at the wicket during seventeen overs whilst scoring only 25 runs. Hardly a run feast, hardly festival cricket. Hugo was a troubled man. The accident to Tommy Fagge had taken some of the zest out of the proceedings. He knew that he should be pressing on but it was not in his character to give his wicket away. On the other hand, there was the thought of re-uniting with Annabelle Crouch. (Sadly the thought was no longer reciprocated by the lady in question, but Hugo would not discover that until later.) Hugo resolved to be positive. Stewart Thorogood was of the same mind. With both batsman and bowler striving to master their arts the result was a colourless stalemate. The score advanced by four, two of which were leg byes.

In the next over Ray Burrill was determined to be at his best to complete what had been overall an impressive spell. Rob Steelback was equally determined to accelerate. In this case the result was a score draw. The ball which Ray Burrill bowled to commence the over should not have received the treatment it did. The batsman took two steps towards it and with a crude slog sent it soaring towards deep midwicket. The crowd's expectation soared as well, but then dipped as the ball itself dipped short of the boundary and in the vicinity of a fielder hurtling round from his original long-on position. John Furness was proud of the fact that he got so close as to get a hand to it. The bowler saw it differently, but two runs was a better cost than four or six. Next he sent down his quicker ball which scudded into Rob Steelback's pads as once again he had given it the charge. John Furness was sent running again when Rob Steelback made another firm connection. This time he got both hands to the ball and dropped it. The cost was one run. Hugo Crabscote produced a delicate cut which earned another single. His partner again took the long handle to Ray Burrill and skied towards long-on. The unfortunate John Furness did not have so far to run, but he badly misjudged the distance. He came in too far and then suddenly had to back-pedal furiously. The crowd liked this bit and roared when the ball hit him in the chest amid a flurry of arms. Rob Steelback added another two to his score. It was with his last ball that Ray Burrill achieved his ambition. His perfect off-break comprehensively deceived the batsman even if it failed to take his wicket. With three overs left to be bowled the Celebs had 237 runs on the board and wickets in hand.

Richard Furness had not wasted time. After achieving a smooth substitution with Kevin Newton and ever mindful that the Outcasts' prime purpose in being at Helmerstead was to play cricket, he had kicked some life back into Greg Roberts so that his team was not without a substitute should a further one be needed. Cricket was then relegated from his thoughts as he linked up with Suzy Waterbeach and set out to explore the second of her family homes within twenty-four hours. The Waterbeaches, Richard discovered, lived mainly on the second floor above the public rooms. The full tour could wait until later he was told by Suzy, but there was one room he might be particularly interested in seeing. She was right.

The episode with Carla had acted as a wake-up call to the charity organiser. His interest in her ended with her removal in the ambulance. He quickly took a shower and 'borrowed' a shirt from one of his team-mates. His trousers had somehow avoided the torrent. There could be no more delays. He had to get alongside Edward Waterbeach. He drove the van across to the Hall, parked it outside the front door and made to enter in search of his quarry. He had reckoned without the official tours. Unlike Suzy Waterbeach, a family member, he was obstructed by officialdom. 'Did he wish to undertake a tour of the house?' No, he bloody well didn't. 'Then you can only come in with the express permission of Mr Waterbeach.' When the charity organiser blustered that he had been asked to call, his claim was doubted. 'I'm afraid that's unlikely, sir, because Mr Waterbeach presently is not here.' When asked where Mr Waterbeach might presently be the only information the uniformed official was prepared to vouchsafe was that he was somewhere in the grounds. The charity organiser stormed off in search, wishing he had with him the pair of rather fine binoculars he had left in his 4x4 at Martin More Motors on the Yarfield by-pass. There was no alternative but to mix with the crowd in an effort to find his quarry. Perhaps he would be lucky. In fact he would be extremely unlucky.

Geraldine Rogers had finally settled for a case of gooseberry pickle to send to a dear friend in Idaho. Not wishing to be left out, Margaret Hamersteen had selected some turnip chutney for her nephew in South Dakota. Had they been aware of these intended acts of kindness the dear friend in Idaho and the nephew in South Dakota would surely have prayed for icebergs to have drifted south into the shipping lanes. The promised despatch by Vera Naysmith left the two ladies unencumbered. C. Ramsgate Fishburn by contrast was armed with a carrier bag. He had felt that he could not leave without some souvenirs of the visit. His choice, influenced by the study which he was undertaking, comprised *A Simple History of Cricket*, the authenticity of which would be suspect to anyone who could not bring himself to believe that the County Cricket Championship was set up by Henry VIII; and, less influenced by the study which he was undertaking, *Cricket as an Aphrodisiac* (with full colour illustrations) by Herbert 'Bingo' Smith. The three Americans, shopping done, felt ready to tackle the mansion.

Stewart Thorogood braced himself to bowl the thirty-sixth over. Surely, he told himself, with only three overs left the batsmen would now cut loose. That is what Hugo Crabscote told himself as well after being encouraged along these lines in a mid-pitch chat with Rob Steelback. Stewart Thorogood had no wish to see the batsmen cut loose, partly out of self-esteem and partly because he nursed the inner belief that the Celebs already had attained a score which would be beyond the Outcasts' reach. In keeping with the spirit of the occasion he hoped that his team would make a fight of it. Thirty runs more and the total would be too daunting for his relaxed (a euphemism to cover drinking and other things which might be happening) side. So Stewart was bending his back and he was helped by the fact that it was Hugo Crabscote and not Rob Steelback on strike.

To give him credit Stewart bowled a good over for his side and yet one which contained a little bit of something for everyone. So wound up was Hugo Crabscote to hit the cover off the ball that he produced two enormous air shots, which despite their unproductive nature caused some amusement to the crowd. To the third ball of the over the shot was more restrained and better timed. It went like a bullet to the cover boundary. Heartened by this, Hugo tried again and was taken aback when another handsome stroke was brilliantly cut off by Harry Northwood. It took a moment or two for the pain to kick in, but Harry heroically cut off the flow of foul language which reactively came to his lips. Mistakenly Hugo upped his effort, swung furiously at the worst ball of the over, missed and fell over just clear of the stumps. The spectators thought that comedy was coming back into the game.

By the time Hugo Crabscote had recovered himself and his dignity Stewart Thorogood had retreated to the end of his run. When he turned he realised at once that something was wrong. The batsman seemed all right. He could see him crouched over his bat and waiting. And that was the trouble. He could see Hugo Crabscote all too clearly without the impeding bulk of Billy Figg. The umpires had disappeared. He of the dodgy prostate had decided that he could not last out the remaining thirteen balls. Relief had to be sought. Billy Figg had taken advantage of the break but was back fairly quickly. The dodgy prostate caused more than a trivial delay before full relief had been achieved. Syd Breakwell eventually reappeared embarrassed and apologetic. His absence was not without its effect. For the final delivery of the over Stewart Thorogood lost his line. The ball veered towards the leg side. Had his concentration not been broken Billy Figg might have branded it a no-ball, but he had overlooked the overstepping and Hugo Crabscote had executed a fine leg glance. This time it was Rashid Ali who tumbled to the ground, but it was to pull off a remarkable stop which denied the boundary which had seemed certain. Stewart Thorogood's over had cost no more than four runs.

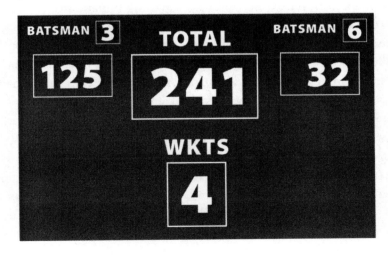

The penultimate over had to be bowled by Tom Redman unless Stewart Thorogood was to break new ground and employ a member of the side who was simply not a bowler. The idea did go through his head. He had mentally counted that Tom's six overs had cost over 70 runs (Simon Crossley would have told him 83). What was more, Rob Steelback would be facing. But, no, Stewart decided to stick with the Outcasts' approach to convention and beckoned Tom Redman. His decision was nevertheless to be accompanied by advice disguised as encouraging words. He need not have bothered. Tom, with three wickets under his belt, felt that he was the man of the hour. He marked out his run with determination. Without as much as a glance at his captain he waved his arms and motioned Dean Faulds to move from long-off to deep mid-off. After this impression of precision field-setting he gripped the ball, scythed his arm over a few times and then ran into bowl. His first ball was struck back over his head to the long-off boundary. Had Dean Faulds still been in his original position it would scarcely have mattered as the ball's trajectory carried it over the pavilion.

Stewart Thorogood underwent the momentary nightmare that the 30 or so runs he did not want to concede might all accrue before Tom Redman completed his over. It was too late to turn back. He was not thinking clearly when Tom asked him for a short leg and he weakly agreed. A somewhat nervous Ray Burrill settled into position, but not until extra protection had been called for and put in place. More crowd mirth accompanied this adjustment. Tom pursed his lips, gave a passing imitation of a man who knew exactly what he was doing and came in to bowl again. Without actual intention Tom dropped the ball a little shorter than its predecessor. Rob Steelback, bent on aggression, used his feet, but this time lifted the ball higher, putting Dean Faulds in a quandary. As soon as Tom had turned his back and set off on his run Dean Faulds back-stepped his way to his original position. When the ball was struck he thought at first that he was in the perfect spot. Then he thought again and rushed forward. As the ball began its downward flight he sensed that he might have overshot it. He back-pedalled again, this time in confusion as some raucous elements in the crowd shouted 'Left a bit', 'Right a bit', while Dean tried to steady himself.

Having made a tour of inspection, Edward Waterbeach returned to the house to be affronted by what he saw. 'Whose van is this?' he asked a member of the staff. The man was in a good position to provide his employer with full information on the subject. He now sensed how justified he had been in barring the charity organiser's way. 'I don't care who he is, move it', was Edward Waterbeach's rejoinder. The charity organiser, not believing that his vehicle was in any way at risk parked in such a prominent position, had obligingly left the keys in the ignition. So the van was moved round the corner of the building and into a yard. Satisfied that the front of the mansion was once more unsullied Edward Waterbeach retreated towards his ground-floor study deciding that a single malt would brighten his day. So too he thought would sight of his daughter. He gathered that she was somewhere around and wondered what she was doing. Better he did not know.

Suzy Waterbeach had just remarked to Richard Furness that they had now played two home fixtures and she would be looking forward to an away match. The very thought brought Richard rapidly down to earth. Since his return from the other side of the world he had been a man of no fixed abode. He had delayed finding a place of his own until he had started his full-time job. 'You can always come home, darling', his mother had said. That was nice for him to know, but with his very well developed social life home under the parental eye was the very last place he would choose to be. He had lasted a week in his brother's flat before John's patience cracked. If it had been just Richard's untidiness and wild timekeeping, the rupture might have been delayed, but most days John found that he had been getting two for the price of one. Whether Richard's friend had been male or female any normality in the flat had been wrecked. There had followed short stays in a series of dingy bedsits punctuated by a night or two guesting with friends, acquaintances and pick-ups. Never at any stage was he in a position to be the perfect host. Currently lodging with a retired couple who had both spent a lifetime working for London Transport and were now spending their leisure time inadequately looking after cats, Richard knew that 21 Doldrum Court was no place to bring a girl, and especially not one used to conspicuously luxurious standards.

There had not been much time in their relationship to date for Richard to be quizzed in depth about what he did and where he lived. Fearing that the unvarnished truth might have been too strong medicine for their nascent friendship to survive, Richard had rashly engaged in a degree of time-travelling by passing himself off as a banker. He had even been able to give the name of the bank, but as to where he lived he had so far got away with saying no more than 'south-west London', knowing it to be safe Outcasts territory. As he lay beside Suzy his mind raced through the possibilities. Which fellow team member might be ready to lend him their flat for the night? Before he had been able to settle on a list of the most promising possibilities Suzy sat bolt upright and announced that she had just had the most wicked idea. It was something she had always wanted to do. Richard listened and marvelled.

In the circumstances Dean Faulds did a remarkable job in clinging to the catch. Getting into the right spot to intercept the descending missile had been a remarkable feat in itself. This had proved to be only part one of the exercise. The ball struck him on the left shoulder and rebounded in front of him. He lunged at it and managed to parry it upwards, but over his head. Gyrating, he had dashed towards it and finally flung himself in a desperate drive to get his fingers beneath it before it completed its interrupted journey to earth. He was successful, the crowd was amused and the bowler overjoyed. Four wickets now, albeit at a cost of 89 runs. Rob Steelback was peeved by such a twist of fate, but had at least the satisfaction of generous applause from spectators, some of whom were loud in their cheers as he made his way back to the pavilion, where the pantomime dame was trying to marshal his resources.

The long and on the whole productive stand between Rob Steelback and Hugo Crabscote had lulled other members of the Celebs team still due to bat into a false sense of security. The player who should have been in next according to Don Hennelly's instructions had some while ago taken his pads and protection off for greater comfort and was now scrabbling to replace them. Unfortunately they were not quite where he thought he had left them. Don Hennelly snorted with impatience. Blackbeard the pirate was reportedly relieving himself. Amidst a flurry of sudden preparation the only person ready to bat, complete with red nose, full make-up and baggy trousers, was the clown, the role assigned to Simon Short. As he read the news for a television station far removed from where this charity match was being played he would have been unrecognisable without any costume. The fact that the clown's make-up ensured that he could have been anybody was therefore completely beside the point. The only snag in despatching him to the middle was that he was the least accomplished batsman on the list.

For the moment this did not matter. The batsmen had crossed – no fewer than three times – whilst the ball had been on its long and complicated journey. The sight of the clown instilled in the lacklustre Hugo Crabscote a final sense of determination. Had he remained in any confused state it would have been cleared by the friendly full toss coming towards him. He swung straight and he swung hard. Dean Faulds raced across, but entirely in vain. The ball soared over him and seven more runs were recorded. Syd Breakwell felt the need to assert himself after his previous difficulty. His cry of no-ball was late and erroneous. Apart from meaning that an extra ball had to be bowled the call had had little effect. Hugo Crabscote had already been committed to the stroke. It did not occur to Syd Breakwell (nor to anyone else) that, if only to follow Tommy Fagge's precedent, a free hit should have been decreed, but Syd had not seen that signal. The next delivery from Tom Redman was much more tentative, delivered from well behind the crease and presented itself as a half-volley. Considering his previous exertions Dean Faulds did very well to prevent it crossing the boundary. The batsmen ran three.

Much as Hugo Crabscote had screwed himself up for a final effort Tom Redman was thinking in the same vein – dare he? For many months he had been nursing his flipper, the prized weapon of any respectable leg-spin bowler. Tom Redman, not being a particularly respectable leg-spin bowler, started from a disadvantage. Yet he had practised assiduously, if in private. His friends would have been happier, had they known, if he had been devoting the time towards achieving some consistency with his leg-spin, even a topspinner; but the flipper required real art. In actual matches Tom had tried it on only a handful of occasions, and it would have needed the fingers of only a single hand to count the times it had pitched straight, let alone taken a wicket.

It was wasted on Simon Short. Any ball which was pitched in line would probably have sufficed. Yet when it was least necessary Tom Redman produced a beauty. It had the pace which Simon Short was not expecting first ball up and it was pitched dead straight. Much as he was reluctant to despatch the comic clown not even Syd Breakwell could fail to return a leg before wicket verdict. Tom Redman had stuck again. Astonishingly he now had a five-wicket haul. The rest of the team gathered round him in congratulations, putting aside the thought that he must have conceded a pile of runs in the process. Ninety-five in fact. Perhaps unwisely, Tom confided that it was the flipper which had done for the latest batsman. He waxed a degree too enthusiastically on this theme, because as the incoming batsman reached the crease Stewart Thorogood was provoked into saying 'Well, do it again then.' This was a mistake.

With the fall of the sixth wicket the chef was ready. His alter ego, Wayne Gaine, self-proclaimed impresario, had re-equipped himself with pads and box and answered the call of duty without giving his captain further cause for panic. Hugo Crabscote did not need many words to describe the nature of the bowling the new batsman would be facing. Nevertheless Wayne Gaine, totally immodest about his professional prowess, was decently reserved about his cricketing ability. He had decided that the right thing to do was to defer to the more obvious skills of his partner and farm the bowling. At least that was the plan until Tom Redman bowled. Tom should not have allowed himself to be goaded into trying again. His second attempt at a flipper left his hand all wrong and headed slantingly across the pitch, a high full toss leg-side bound. Wayne Gaine could not stop himself. There was no way he was going to tap it away for a single. Pivoting and with a full swing of the bat he helped the ball on its way. It flew over deep fine leg for six. For a while the ball was lost, which with only seven deliveries of the innings left was an inconvenience; at the same time it was a great convenience for Syd Breakwell, who experienced the urge for another toilet break. This at least had the benefit of offering Tom Redman some space to regroup. Stewart Thorogood, not actually lost for words, made a supreme effort to suppress them.

There was an unconscionable lapse of time before Tom Redman was able to bowl the ball which would complete his spell. First, it had to be retrieved, a task made more complicated by its concealment. The Randall boys had been lurking in the vicinity to which the ball was headed. 'Watch this', Craig said to Danny with a smirk. It was an accomplished trick for an eleven-year-old. He took the catch with aplomb and in a flash thrust it into the pocket of his baggy jeans before pretending that he had missed it and running in another direction in apparent pursuit. It took a minute before the search was supplemented by John Furness and twelfth man, Kevin Newton. Craig Randall would have been wise not to have hung around feigning assistance. He should either have surrendered the ball or scarpered, for one pair of eyes had spotted the deception.

The eyes belonged to Hamish McTartar. At this stage of the day they were linked to a brain which was toiling in bottom gear. The Scotsman was therefore slow in making his revelation. 'It's yon laddie.' This had to be repeated before anyone took notice of the eccentric figure. Fortunately Kevin Newton was in reaching distance of Craig Randall when he realised the meaning of Hamish McTartar's words. His hand clamped on the boy's upper arm and swivelled him round. The bulge in his jeans was immediately explicable. Having the presence of mind to avoid risking a child abuse charge by shoving his free hand into the jeans pocket, Kevin spoke in words he judged this boy would understand: 'Give me the f*****g ball this f*****g minute.' Craig recognised the underlying threat and parted with his trophy and a few choice words of his own. Wriggling free, he landed a kick on Kevin's shins before running away with Danny.

Once the full complement of fielders plus ball was back on the field the eyes of the Outcasts were on Tom Redman. One more delivery from him was unavoidable. There was no great expectation. If the chef had done it once, for all the Outcasts knew he could do it again. However, Wayne Gaine had no such intention. His plan was limited this time to keeping his wicket intact so that his more accomplished partner could club a few boundaries in the final over. How could he have known that Tom Redman would pitch the ball sufficiently on the leg side to find an area of bowlers' footmarks? How could he have known that Tom would manage to impart such a degree of spin on the ball that it would suddenly change direction? In one split second he was letting the ball go so that the umpire would surely signal a wide (Syd Breakwell had already started to loosen his limbs with that in mind); in another he was hastily jabbing at the ball and propelling it into the hands of Ray Burrill at short leg. If the fielder himself had had time to think about it, he might well have been flinching. Instead Ray was so much taken by surprise that he held the catch.

The meeting which the charity organiser had been so anxious to arrange took place in front of the pavilion, but not in auspicious circumstances. Fortified by his malt, Edward Waterbeach had not dallied indoors. He thought that he would watch the climax of the innings and cast an eye over the players' tea. He had no sooner left the mansion than Charles Brett parked his van outside the front door. Old habits died hard. He would normally use the front door and he wished to report to Edward Waterbeach that full power had now been restored. No official was inclined to dispute his entry knowing what the purpose of his presence was. As he was approaching the study the man he sought was being approached elsewhere by the charity organiser. The encounter was short-lived. The charity organiser had got no further than introducing himself when there was a violent tugging at his arm. He spun round to find the rouged face of his captain thrust towards him. 'For God's sake, get ready; you could be in at any minute.'

The charity organiser was reluctant to respond. Whilst he hesitated Edward Waterbeach had looked over his shoulder and seen something which displeased him. 'I don't believe it', he fumed. 'That bloody van. Who the hell's put it back there?' The charity organiser was unsure whether admission of responsibility was going to be a plus or a minus point in their relationship. On balance he thought that any possible mistake could quickly be rectified. He began an explanation, but his move in the direction of the mansion was restrained by Don Hennelly. 'You're needed here. Get someone else to shift it.' At that moment as if on cue the sleepy figure of Greg Roberts emerged from the pavilion. Don Hennelly and the charity organiser had the idea at the same time. Greg, puzzled, said, 'Oh, all right', and agreed to drive the van back to where it had originally been parked at the back of the pavilion. The charity organiser was given no chance to make good his situation with Edward Waterbeach because he was determinedly manhandled back into the pavilion by Don Hennelly. Meanwhile the figure of a vicar made its way uncertainly towards the wicket.

The unusually agitated, even aggressive, behaviour of the Celebs' captain towards his eleventh man had exceptional cause. The rapid fall of wickets had led Don Hennelly to make sure that his remaining batsmen were at the ready. Out of the corner of his eye he could see the clergyman, but there was no sign of Blackbeard and Spiderman. Then he remembered that the pirate had been seen in the lavatory and went in search. A sorry scene confronted him. Blackbeard had become Greybeard, almost Whitebeard. The artificial beard was speckled with white powder. The evidence of his eyes did not allow for any doubt. It was not cosmetic powder being used by the player to turn Blackbeard into a comic version of Saddam Hussein. Don Hennelly was in most ordinary circumstances a broad-minded man, but he was nevertheless taken aback. In his view this was neither the time nor the place. Limiting himself to a cutting 'Couldn't you have waited?' he went in search of his other remaining assets. The fall of Wayne Gaine's wicket prompted decisive action. The costumed vicar leaning nonchalantly on his bat by the pavilion steps received a hand in the small of his back and the valediction, 'In God's name we need your help now', words which revealed that Don Hennelly's good humour was returning.

Even so, with the best will in the world the Reverend Maxwell Clover was surprised to find himself propelled into action. Such an idea could not have been more remote from his mind when he set out for the grounds of Helmerstead Hall after the end of a Baptism Service. He had left the parish church of St Humphrey the Evangelist in a better spirit than on arrival. The original design of the day was for his nine-year-old son, Magnus, to accompany him on the promise of going afterwards to the pleasures on offer at Helmerstead Hall. When he realised the price to be paid for the later outing, Magnus, who was secretly in possession of the latest computer game circulating amongst his friends at the local Church of England aided primary school, faked a sore throat and a temperature and looked forward instead to an afternoon with 'Crash Slash Mash'. His father had been disappointed by this turn of events, but not nearly as upset as his wife. Her dismay did not relate to her son's health but to the thwarting of her own intentions. Believing that she would have the house to herself, she had made a phone call to ensure the very opposite.

So it was that through being himself mistaken for one of the celebrity players the Reverend Maxwell Clover was standing slightly bewildered at the non-striker's end as Stewart Thorogood prepared to bowl the thirty-eighth and final over.

Even at this moment Maxwell Clover was more the cleric than the cricketer. The disappointment of not having Magnus with him had been largely assuaged by the satisfaction he had felt with his sermon. Maxwell Clover always preached sermons whatever the nature of the service at which he was officiating. He thought that it had been rather clever to cast his biblical theme in cricketing terms. With an Ashes series upcoming he had delivered his words with more fervour than was his wont. His imagery had carried the implication that Australian batsmen should be cut down by the swords of righteousness and that their bowlers would be beset by scorpions. The devil would be defeated on the playing fields of this green and pleasant land. Stewart Thorogood was struck for four through the covers by Hugo Crabscote as the Reverend Clover wondered if he might have gone too far. Smite the foe, he had thundered, as the batsman hooked the ferocious fast bowler to the boundary. Stewart's second delivery was short and dealt with in that fashion. But be on your guard, he had counselled, to keep the devil's emissaries from your doors. Two good length balls were blocked by Hugo Crabscote. Look to take advantage in turning aside the temptations of Beelzebub. Stewart Thorogood conceded a single to a deft deflection to fine leg.

Whilst the sermon was re-lived in vivid terms by the Reverend Maxwell Clover, it would be hard to claim that it would be remembered elsewhere. The gathering that morning had consisted of no more than ten parishioners. His weak joke about the need for a substitute, as he developed his cricket analogy, had fallen on deaf ears. Sad to say, that had been true of most of what he had to say. His churchwarden, Mr Flitch, would probably have enjoyed it, but he had forgotten to wear his hearing aid. Most of the others present would not have admitted to a hearing problem, more to bewilderment. They would have been hard put to answer even the simplest question about what the vicar had said. It had not stopped them complimenting him as they shook his hand (thankfully) on departure. Oh yes, the Reverend Clover had concluded as he responded to Hugo Crabscote's call, there was no doubt that his sermon had been very well received, even though it was considered unusual to preach at a baptism.

So fierce had been Hugo Crabscote's concentration on getting a good finish to the innings that he had not noticed until the last minute that his latest batting partner was not wearing pads. In fact he did not seem all that familiar. However, Hugo had not spent a lot of time getting to know his team-mates. He had to admit that the new man looked the very essence of the country parson, complete with Panama hat and pipe. He jogged to the other end for a chat. 'Are you going to be OK like that, without pads and . . . things?' His voice tailed away. The vicar for all his serenity might still have been in his church. 'Have no fear, young man, God is my protection.' He then took up his position without bothering to take guard. None of this conversation was heard by Stewart Thorogood, who had stamped off to his bowling mark, anxious to be done with the innings and aware that the Celebs had reached a total which would be outside the range of the Outcasts. All his frustration was gathered in his final effort against what he saw as the latest in a mainly preposterous line-up, with in this case the arrogance to come out to bat as though on a country stroll. Well, he, Stewart, would show him. It was undoubtedly a very good delivery, which hurried off the pitch and would probably have taken middle stump if an extremely sensitive part of the batsman's anatomy had not been in the way.

'How was that?' came the appeal from the bowler. 'Jesus Christ', came the appeal from the batsman. An answer to Stewart Thorogood's question did not have to come from Billy Figg as the batsman collapsed on his stumps. It proved not to be our Lord who came to his rescue but St Joan.

Tea interval

THE PLAYERS GRADUALLY LEFT THE FIELD. Being men they were not indifferent to the vicar's plight. They had not felt able to march off until sure that he was all right or at least receiving attention. Their anatomical researches again interrupted, Paul Wyatt and Laurel Rouse had raced to the scene. The Reverend Maxwell Clover was sufficiently conscious to be capable of moaning and groaning. He was hurting front and back, for it transpired that when he fell a stump had penetrated his lightweight trousers – leg stump, it was later established. Paul Wyatt's diagnosis was swift: 'He's in pain', he pronounced with due solemnity. He was unclear whether or not he should remove the stump. His training to date had not extended to such a situation. He also hesitated to subject the other damaged area to close scrutiny. For a man who had little compunction in removing his own trousers he was curiously reticent in removing the vicar's. Fearing that she might be involved in an intimate examination for which she was not prepared, Laurel Rouse, to forestall it, was quickly on the phone to the paramedics. For their part Gregory Braine and Lloyd Hart with brilliant anticipation had decided to have their tea break in a lay-by close to Helmerstead Hall. It had been a cheaper option than poker and the Reverend Maxwell Clover, no gambler he, had cause to be grateful for it.

In his earlier tour of inspection Edward Waterbeach had done no more than glance into the tea tent. Paying no attention to detail he was persuaded by the presence of a group of ladies that preparations were in hand. Appearances can be deceptive. If he had had a concern over this matter, it was because the ladies, who usually looked after tea when matches were played at Helmerstead, had not been available on this occasion.

When first apprised of this matter Caroline Bingley-Adams had been dismissive. So far as the cricket was concerned she saw her role as delivering two teams. She could not see what more to it there was. After it had been explained to her that a cricket tea was an integral part of a cricket match she grudgingly said that she would take the point on board. She would have as easily jettisoned the point if, whilst researching local newspapers for publicity purposes, she had not come across a small, discreet advertisement. This informed the local public that the Hertfordshire Social Women's Saturday Club was available to cater for refined gatherings. It was the word 'refined' which caught the eye of Caroline Bingley-Adams. When she further noticed that the contact was Lady Angelina Foreshaw she was hooked. After speaking with the said Lady Foreshaw over the telephone she was convinced that this was another box ticked and that she could now get on with other more important items. She could, but not quite so easily as she had supposed. What Lady Foreshaw had loosely referred to as a proforma invoice proved to be an upfront demand for payment in advance.

'Dear Caroline (if I may be so bold)', she had written in an accompanying letter. 'We are thrilled that you have chosen our little Saturday Club to serve you on such a prestigious occasion. I could tell from speaking with you that you were a lady of taste and discrimination. I am sure that we will provide well for your famous cricketers and give them the treat to which they will no doubt be looking forward. How wise you were to choose our deluxe cream package' (Caroline could not remember any choice being mentioned). 'So right for a function at Helmerstead. Our little invoice is enclosed. As we are a self-financing organisation which provides a purpose in life for otherwise lonely widows, I would be most obliged if you could settle it by return to guarantee satisfaction.' The letter had ended 'Yours most sincerely, your grateful friend, Angelina.' In order to disentangle herself from any further responsibility for the provision of the players' tea-time refreshment, Caroline arranged for the speedy despatch of the cheque. Her only lingering thought was that it could have been cheaper. And she had never even considered seeking references.

The Hertfordshire Social Women were on site a full two hours before tea was due to be served. There were eight of them, led by Lady Foreshaw on her motorised invalid scooter. Four of the other ladies walked with sticks, one lady on two. Parking the smart red state-of-the-art scooter outside the tea tent, Lady Foreshaw resorted to her walking frame. 'Come, girls', she said and tottered inside. The provisions she had prearranged were already there. 'Right, girls,' she said, 'let's get going and give them a tea they'll never forget.' If this was a clarion call to action, the response could only be described as sluggish. Eventually half a dozen of them were lined up behind a trestle table which served as their preparation area. They should, of course, have ordered sliced bread for the sandwiches, but (for economy) the ladies had baked the bread themselves. Such had been their production rate in their small domestic ovens that some of the loaves had lost their initial freshness. The quality also varied with the baker. Similarly not all the ladies were good with a bread knife, and so the thickness and evenness of the slices were not consistent. The same unsteadiness extended to slicing tomatoes and cucumbers. Quartering the pork pies was an easier operation. The fault in this case lay with the pies themselves. Lady Foreshaw had an arrangement with nice Mr Dutton the local butcher whereby she took off his hands items which were past their sell-by date. She did not like to ask questions about the potted meat supplied by one of her most regular helpers, Mavis Pirbright, as it was always so plentiful.

The Saturday Club's cake makers were Mrs Tester, who provided sponges (which were not lighter than air), and Mrs Bright, who specialised in slab cakes (which were exceptionally solid). Flapjacks were provided by Miss Meadow to a standard which could only be described as granite. Finally there was the fruit. Again Lady Foreshaw's connections were helpful. There were always soft fruits which neighbouring farmers had been obliged to reject as sub-standard. These she was pleased to collect, making it appear almost an act of kindness to the donors. When doused in cream it was her experience that these strawberries, raspberries, gooseberries, whatever, were always consumed avidly and without complaint. Of course, she could not always guarantee the freshness of the cream.

There was suddenly a voice raised in panic. 'There are no tea bags.' It was Mrs Fingle at the urn. 'Don't worry, dear', came the quick response from Lady Foreshaw. 'I have them here.' From the large bag hanging from her walking frame she produced a plastic container. It was evident from the first glance that the tea bags were no longer virginal. Answering the questioning look on Mrs Fingle's face, Lady Foreshaw said 'They're still quite fresh. These people will never know the difference.' So into the teapots they went. 'Not more than three in each', came the stern warning. After this Mrs Fingle transferred herself to buttering bread, although 'buttering' was not the strictly accurate word. The substance being used came from large, unmarked tins. 'Much healthier for athletes', murmured Lady Foreshaw.

Assembling the sandwiches from the rough-hewn bread and fillings required two people. Those with the potted meat were easier, because the two surfaces seemed to adhere. Piling them on plates was also a fraught exercise. Anything beyond three layers threatened to topple off. One or two did, but they were quickly put together again when the components were collected from the table or the ground. There was a little contamination from grass, but it could easily be mistaken for chives. Eventually the work was done. At a signal from their leader the ladies removed their smocks to be revealed in skimpy black dresses with frilly white aprons. Little white caps were affixed to their heads. Lady Foreshaw herself was similarly attired. They formed a line in readiness. As Fred Fortune was later to mutter to Hugo Crabscote, it looked like the attack of the crones.

Tea at a cricket match is a special point of the day. Traditionally both teams gather for this re-grouping and refreshing interlude. Sometimes the players will integrate around the tables; at others they will keep separate whilst plotting tactics or, more likely in the Outcasts' case, deciding which ale house they will be patronising in the evening. It is generally accepted amongst cricketers at this level that attendance for the cricket tea is a courtesy which should be observed. Accordingly eighteen Outcasts closed in on the tea tent. Only Richard Furness was missing, having found something more greatly to his taste than tea. All eleven of the Celebs' team presented themselves including the charity organiser, who had yet to arrange to disengage himself from fielding duties. They were supplemented by the umpires and Simon Crossley. Players generally look forward to tea. There are plain teas and fancy teas. There are modest teas and extravagant teas. There are good teas and bad teas. And then there was in a category all its own the tea presented at Helmerstead that afternoon.

The umpires had arrived last and departed first. Syd Breakwell indicated to Billy Figg that he had a flask in his hip pocket, and the latter loudly said that before he could settle down comfortably for tea he must ring the hospital to get a bulletin on Tommy Fagge. Outside the tea tent they followed an aroma to a burger stall. Whilst waiting in the queue both the flask and the mobile phone were brought into operation. The first had better results than the second. It took three calls to reach the hospital, but, as the caller was not a relative, no information about Mr Fagge could be divulged.

Meanwhile Charlie Colson had tried a potted meat sandwich with complicated results. Nobly he proclaimed that as he was not actually playing in the team he should withdraw. This supplied a cue to one or two others. 'Not you, mate', said Stewart Thorogood as Harry Northwood scrambled to his feet. 'Some of us have got to stick this out.'

Such courage was wearing thin after twenty minutes. The Social Women saw it as their duty to ply the cricketers with one plate after another. Resistance was as hard to maintain as the food was to digest. In some cases a gulp of tea could wash away the taste only to replace it with something just as unsavoury. It was a cruel trial not helped by Mrs Pirbright, Mrs Bright and Mrs Meadows constantly presenting themselves with ingratiating smiles, soliciting praise for the items for which they had been personally responsible. A serious situation was developing with plates of food showing no marked signs of emptying. These included the plates in front of the individual players, especially where they had been suborned to try the various alternatives. The few cricketers who appeared to have cleared their plates had a pile of food at their feet. There was quite a slurry of fruit and cream on the ground as the taste of the cream had universally offended. A mass walk-out was prevented only by the arrival of Caroline Bingley-Adams, who had business to transact.

Caroline was carrying a pile of red plastic buckets and a quantity of raffle tickets. She had a purposeful look in her eye. She put the buckets down. One was immediately grabbed by Nigel Redman, who puked into it as unobtrusively as he could manage in the confined surroundings. There was a weak cry of 'Pass the bucket' from along the table and two others retched in sympathy. Caroline was not to be put off by this display. Nor were the Social Women, who descended on the sickly trio to enquire whether they now felt better and would like more to eat. At this the bucket went quickly back to Nigel Redman. 'The raffle', announced Caroline Bingley-Adams. She gave her instructions, about which there was no room for negotiation. She smiled sweetly at Stewart Thorogood. 'As you've got a few extra chaps here you should have no problem getting round this crowd.' The extra chaps naturally had other plans in mind.

After Caroline had left, Stewart Thorogood had to control what threatened to become a mutinous situation. He gave instructions for everyone to assemble in the dressing-room. Those like Charlie Colson, who had left the tea tent, should be rounded up. 'And find Richard as well, if you can',

Stewart added as an afterthought. The present thought was how to extricate everyone as gracefully as possible from the tea tent. He looked across and caught the eye of Don Hennelly, who was clearly having the same thought. However, their discomfiture was not yet over. The entertainment was about to begin.

Richard Furness was unlikely to be found in the immediate future. Clad only in a dressing-gown which Suzy Waterbeach had purloined from her brother's bedroom, he had been led by her – also lightly attired – down a narrow flight of stairs, along a short passage and through a panelled door, which did not look like a door. Nor did it look like a door on its other side, but more a mirrored alcove with shelves. They had entered what Helmerstead Hall was pleased to claim as its premier state room. It was dominated by a huge bed with royal blue and gold coverings. 'I've always wanted to try it', giggled Suzy, letting her robe fall to the floor. 'Are you sure?' asked Richard with for him uncharacteristic caution. 'What was good enough for Charles II is fine by me', she answered. With that she pulled the cover down slightly and scrambled into the bed. 'But', said Richard, noticing for the first time the roped-off corridor at the far end of the room, 'won't people be walking through here?' 'No,' said Suzy, gesturing to him, 'there's a sign up telling visitors that this room's off tour limits today. There are some repairs due. Now are you going to join me or what?' Richard tugged at the cord of the dressing-gown. He was.

Having gained entrance to the mansion, Charles Brett had been slow to emerge. The door of the study had been open, but of Edward Waterbeach there was no sign. What was in view was the bottle of single malt. Charles Brett recognised it for the rare product it was. He could not resist a small measure, discreetly using the same glass which Edward Waterbeach had left there. Just a sip at a time – it was so special to him. Nevertheless he remained alert for the slightest sound to indicate that the owner was returning. No sound came. Charles Brett looked at the bottle again. Just another finger perhaps. He would not be over the limit. The level left in the bottle would not appear much different. He poured the precious liquid into the glass. Once again he took his time. Still no Edward Waterbeach. He checked the time and then glanced at the bottle again. This time it did look as though the level had dropped. 'What the hell?' said Charles Brett seizing it and putting it in his bag which by habit and instinct he had with him. He could wait no longer.

Had it not been for the two good shots of malt whisky Charles Brett's blood would have run cold as he got to the front door. No van. Anyone losing a vehicle suffers a nasty feeling. When in this case the vehicle is stuffed with valuables (more valuable for not being his) its owner went berserk. Heads turned as he raged. Fortunately the outburst was short-lived, for at that moment the officious attendant, who had been on duty earlier, returned from his tea-break. The sight of his uniform attracted Charles Brett's fury, but the fury was quelled when he was told that the van had been moved on Mr Waterbeach's instructions and was quite safe. Charles Brett, rationality returning, had, of course, been thinking of more than the van, but it was still a great relief to be taken to see it. In the circumstances not to notice the difference of one digit on the number plate was perfectly understandable. That it was his van there could be no doubt. Unmistakably down the side was the imperfectly painted-out sign of St Margaret's School. With unusual courtesy the attendant offered to guide Charles Brett whilst he backed the vehicle out of the yard. Had he had any thought to check that its contents were intact, he could hardly have opened the rear door in front of the other man. In any case he was so suffused with relief that he was ready to get on his way. The Euroshuttle beckoned.

'Well, dammit, I really wanted to see that room where the king screwed all those broads.' So said Geraldine Rogers at the completion of what had been a slow-moving tour of the public rooms of Helmerstead Hall. C. Ramsgate Fishburn said that he couldn't see why they couldn't 'kinda double back'. It had only been a rope barrier in the way. Repairs didn't sound exactly life-threatening. It was persuasive talk. Always game for a bit of initiative and enterprise Geraldine Rogers and Margaret Hamersteen said that they would try it. The infiltration began.

The tea interval had long been over for Gregory Braine and Lloyd Hart. They had collected the Reverend Maxwell Clover. Whilst Lloyd Hart, drove Gregory Braine did his best in the back of the ambulance to bring some relief to the vicar's pain. He too had decided not to remove the stump, preferring that to be a doctor's decision. Lloyd Hart was a strong man, but he could not help but wince at the Reverend Clover's injuries.

Having got him to hospital there was further embarrassment when a crowd of youths leaving the Accident and Emergency Department found the sight of a patient with an undisguised cricket stump protruding worth a hearty laugh and some very uncouth remarks. The Reverend Clover was sufficiently aware of his surroundings to pray that they did not come from his parish. Job done, the paramedics adopted what seemed the wisest course and that was to take up station once again close to Helmerstead Hall. It was to prove a shrewd move and there would be no time for a brew.

The umpires, having consumed brandy and burgers whilst exchanging pleasantries (Syd Breakwell was a fan of Figg and Fagge), began to think about a resumption of play. They realised that nothing about the length of the tea interval had been laid down. They had assumed twenty minutes, but already they were beyond that point. Yet there was no sign of the teams getting ready for action when Billy and Syd returned to the pavilion. They decided to go back – with caution – to the tea tent. As they drew near strange sounds could be heard. Billy Fagg knew his Gilbert and Sullivan. This at least provided him with a clue. He recognised that the cricket match in which he was participating was meant to be a light-hearted occasion, but he had not thought (nor had he been warned) that pranks were to be extended to every aspect of it. From what he was hearing he doubted whether either W. S. Gilbert or Arthur Sullivan would have appreciated the joke. Sadly, as Billy Figg and Syd Breakwell were about to discover, it was no joke.

The tea tent had caught the attention of the Randall boys a little earlier. Having seen the cricketers troop in there and being not put off by the sight of a few early withdrawals, Craig and Danny had edged closer. The tent, they discovered, had a covered area at the rear designed essentially for the accumulation of waste and scraps. It had an easily openable flap. The modus operandi of the Social Women had already given rise to an appreciable collection. Hacked off pieces of bread and cheese were very welcome to two growing lads, who had discharged a lot of energy since their aborted family picnic. They were not disturbed in their repast. Access to the main part of the tent was blocked by a walking-frame and the back of a chair occupied by an elderly lady with a harmonica. On something which might approximately be described as a chord a chorus (again a loose description) began. Of this the boys were spared the sight, if not the sound. What they could see – Danny nudged Craig – was a bag resting by the feet of the walking-frame. From the bag protruded a set of keys. The boys' eyes met. And the scooter out front had looked tempting.

'This is it', exclaimed Geraldine Rogers. The three Americans had edged their way back counter to the flow and reached the spot where the diversion had been put in place. A sign stating 'Room closed to visitors' was sufficient instruction to the average Briton to keep out, but totally insufficient to repel inquisitive American tourists. It was perhaps also thought to be sufficient barrier, for the door when tried was found to be unlocked. The words 'Well, let's see what the hell this is all about' were slow to have an effect on what was happening inside the room of supposed historical significance. It proved to be not so much the furniture and fittings which caught the visitors' attention as the motion in the bed itself. With the awareness of the wonders of animatronics and a dash of naivety the Americans marvelled at the boldness of the British in apparently representing the scene of intimacy which must have taken place centuries earlier. It slowly penetrated into the consciousness of Suzy Waterbeach and Richard Furness that they were no longer alone. At this point they froze. The Americans waited wondering how the tableau would develop. After a while it became evident that it would not. 'The machinery's obviously broken', Geraldine Rogers concluded. 'That's probably why they put the damned place out of bounds. Nice furniture though.' She and her companions moved on. What they had not done was restore the rope barrier and close the door by which they had entered.

Anyone more unlike three little maids from school than Mrs Tester, Mrs Fingle and Mrs Meadows would have been hard to find. The trapped spectators of this extraordinary performance were transfixed, shocked by its wholly unexpected onset and its appalling execution. The feeling that it was some kind of joke held them for a while in anticipation of a denouement. When Mrs Bright wobbled into 'Fair moon to thee I sing' the spell remained unbroken. The return of Mrs Tester as Little Buttercup finally provoked the unkind comment from an unidentified source at the back of the tent, 'You've got to be joking.' This coincided with the entry of Syd Breakwell and Billy Figg to appeal for the resumption of play. Their timing ensured an enthusiastic response.

Craig and Danny Randall bided their time. It was not until the players had rushed from the tent that they reckoned the coast to be clear. The Hertfordshire Social Women were preoccupied with consoling themselves over the abrupt end to their performance and clearing up an unwelcome quantity of left-overs. Starting the scooter was not a problem for the boys and off they set on to the field of play at a speed never previously attained by Lady Foreshaw. Although never intruding on the pitch itself they had managed to complete a couple of circuits before someone, who must clearly have been a cricket lover, in the absence of the umpires decided that the risk of damage could no longer be tolerated. His giving chase to the boys on the scooter was at first thought by other people to be a fresh piece of foolery. The man flapping his arms in pursuit of the scooter did appear faintly ridiculous until he was joined by two more men who had recognised the boys and were certain in their minds that they were most definitely not part of the day's entertainment. The reinforcement had the desired effect, but an unintended consequence.

It required all of Stewart Thorogood's persuasive powers to establish a sales force for the raffle tickets which had been thrust into the Outcasts' lap. Those who were down to bat in the middle order (already minus Harry Northwood and Ray Burrill, who had gone for a drink to recover from the shock of tea) argued that they had to remain padded up in the pavilion in case there was an early collapse. Stewart knew that this was all too real a possibility and so put his greatest pressure on those whom he knew had had an afternoon of greatest inactivity. Phil Cole was not sure whether to be pleased or sorry when he was excluded from selection. The prospect of the elf costume loomed. The only possible consolation was that it would spare him the need to traipse around selling raffle tickets. He bolstered his spirits with the thought that the Celebs would not actually need him. His comfort would be short-lived.

The ability to conduct a spontaneous raffle requires careful pre-planning. There had to be a supply of tickets, but the information they conveyed needed to be of a general nature. They registered no more than that they were in aid of 'Today's Good Cause'. In tiny print there was added 'as announced'. Not too much was said about the prizes. Top prize was 'A Cruise for two people'. Information was withheld as to where and on what. The second prize was 'A Day at the Races'. What type of race meeting and where were unrevealed details. 'A Gourmet Meal for four' was the third prize. 'Plus many more wonderful prizes' left even more to the imagination. The price of a ticket was bold and specific: £1. As to the rest the wording appeared familiar and comprehensive, but was only an approximate reflection of the law. As promoter only a corporate name was shown in the smallest of print.

By this time in the afternoon Mimi Clutterbone was stressed. She had known all along that she had drawn the short straw. She was in her first year of teaching at St Cuthbert's and she could not afford to disoblige the headteacher when it was proposed that it would be 'lovely' for the Year 6 children to have a treat. In reality it had not been the whole year group, but the lower and laggardly end of it. The headteacher's thinking had been to hold out the promise of a trip to Helmerstead Hall as an incentive for good behaviour in the interim. Soon this under-achieving lot would be the responsibility of some unfortunate secondary school. The interval between promise and delivery had been relatively peaceful, with no more than two suspensions and one permanent exclusion. Mimi Clutterbone's nightmare was that a pent-up tide of aggression would pour out once the prospective visit had become a reality. There were twenty children in the care of herself and two parents. Gavin Porter was divorced and it was his turn to have Grenville with him that weekend. Colin Beane had been ordered out by his wife, who said it had been the only day she could get a hair appointment and he needn't think that she was going out with him to the dance at the golf club looking like a scarecrow. But for these circumstances both men would have been at the Royal Oak. Seeing on arrival the capacious refreshment tent in the grounds of Helmerstead Hall they recognised the next best thing. After a hurried 'You'll be OK with these for a bit, love, won't you?', Mimi Clutterbone had found herself in sole charge.

How long a bit was meant to last was unclear. The teacher realised that the time could not be spent parked outside the refreshment tent. In any case the children had wanted ice cream. Then they had wanted a cold drink, having consumed on the journey the one with which they had been equipped by their parents. Next they had wanted something to eat – naturally not the sandwiches and pies in their rucksacks but rather the burgers which they saw on sale at the mobile dispensary. After that they wanted the toilets, for which there was a queue. The delay was too long for Justin Groves, who had an 'accident', much to the merriment of his companions.

The mopping-up operation had scarcely been completed before Darlene Evans emerged from the ladies to announce that Lizzie Simpson had been sick 'all over the place'. This had the perverse effect of keeping the group together as both boys and girls were ghoulishly curious to find out the meaning behind this evocative word picture. As Mimi Clutterbone struggled to clean up the mess a relay of girls fed the waiting audience with ever more lurid descriptions of the scene inside the toilets. Suffice it to say that neither the memory nor the aroma would easily fade.

The American invasion had been a shock from which Richard Furness and Suzy Waterbeach had needed time to recover. Prudence might have dictated retreat using their route of entry. However, prudence was held in check by other feelings. Both partners experienced something special about their situation, something which they wished to exploit. For a while all seemed quiet. The pair became emboldened and, in Geraldine Rogers' earlier phrase, willing to put the machinery back into working order. Then Suzy suddenly remembered. 'The door', she hissed to Richard. 'See if it's shut.' It was a good thought. Wishing to take the minimal risk in his unclothed state, Richard pushed and the solid door snicked into place. What he did not see and could therefore give no thought to was the rope barrier which was far from being in place. Suzy was all he wanted to give thought to, and passion by then was running high.

After the episode around the toilets it was easy to understand why Mimi Clutterbone saw the mansion as a refuge. The opportunity to broaden the minds of her charges was by some distance a secondary consideration. Gaining access was easy and without cost. Mimi had in the past acted as a part-time tour guide. The official attendant on duty at the door when she arrived was known to her, in fact very well known to her. He blushed on mentally recalling their last encounter. He had no difficulty with her embarking on a tour without additional escort or charge. For the first few minutes this desperate diversion seemed to work. The children were over-awed by their surroundings. Not for long. Gradually the feeling wore off and attention drifted. Mimi noticed an outbreak of idle chatter. At the same time she was keeping an eye on Grenville Porter, who was lurking by a bust on a pedestal. Her mounting stress was compounded by shaven-headed Martin Crooke, who punctuated every second sentence of her

184

commentary with questions of utter banality and irrelevance. Kind at heart, she was torn between trying not to discourage the boy (he was the only one who seemed to be listening to her) and maintaining a semblance of control over the group.

With no more than a wobble of the pedestal to unnerve her, Mimi Clutterbone was able to move on. Grenville Porter had been distracted from the pursuit of more dramatic damage by a sharp kick administered to his shins by golden-curled Christine Glazer. Mimi had stepped in to keep them apart and had then turned to find that she and her troupe were outside the door of the Kings' room, which was closed. In her experience it was usually open. Nevertheless she was inclined to a cautious view and she decided to keep moving. Her caution was not shared by Grenville Porter. He hung back and when the rest of the group were at a sufficient distance he tried the handle of the door.

Charles Brett had failed to make much progress towards Folkestone. It had not been for want of trying. In his rear-view mirror he had caught sight of the flashing blue light before he had registered a degree of lumpiness in the van's performance. His first thought was that he had been rumbled, but after he had pulled into a convenient lay-by on the Yarfield by-pass the smiling face of the police officer who came alongside allayed his fear. The smiling face was accompanied by a pleasant-sounding voice. 'I'm sorry to interrupt your journey, sir, but when we came up behind you we couldn't help noticing that your rear off-side tyre looked a bit flat. You can't be too careful, sir, especially if you're doing a long journey.' Charles Brett briefly wondered which police charm school the young man had attended before alighting from the van to examine his rear wheel. It was not a bit flat. It was very flat. Suppressing a desire to kick the defective wheel in a rage, Charles Brett forced a smile and said 'Thank you, officers' (a second policeman had materialised from his car wearing the same gushingly helpful expression), 'that is lucky you spotted it. Well, I'm very grateful. Don't let me delay you. You've no doubt got some criminals to catch, ha, ha. I'll get on with fixing it now.' 'Just a moment, sir,' said the first policeman, his manner undergoing a sudden change, 'that isn't alcohol I can smell on your breath, is it?'

The wreckage of the tea tent drew an appreciable and appreciative crowd. There was nothing like a minor disaster to stimulate public interest. People moved quickly from all parts of the grounds to witness the latest attraction. In fairness it was quite quickly recognised that the collapse of the tent was not a scheduled event. However, it had been spectacular. A Hollywood producer would have been proud of the effect. Even with prior planning the Randall boys probably could not have picked a better point at which to become entangled with the guy ropes. Of course there had not been any prior planning. They had been in flight at high speed when the impact took place. They were lucky. Thrown from the scooter they hit the canvas sides of the tent which, beginning to collapse, broke their fall. Despite being shocked, winded and bruised they had the wit to realise that this was no place to stay. The members of the Hertfordshire Social Women's Saturday Club did not have the luxury of choice as first the front of the tent and then more sedately the rear fell in upon them. In their understandable terror Mrs Tester, Mrs Fingle and Mrs Meadows achieved considerably higher notes than in their earlier rendition of 'Three Little Maids from School'.

The first wave of helpers had conspicuously not included the representatives on earth of St Joan. It was only with great good luck that they were able to attend at all. After giving little more than verbal comfort to the Reverend Maxwell Clover until more practical help had arrived in the shape of the paramedics Gregory Braine and Lloyd Hart, Paul Wyatt and Laurel Rouse had again retreated to their caravan. Paul slammed the door with a little bit too much relief whilst unbuttoning his tunic and the handle broke off in his hand. Without it the door would not open. Torn between attracting attention to effect escape and shunning it in favour of the pursuit of private pleasures they decided that Dame Fortune had smiled upon them. They had been resting when a knock sounded on the door. Their speed of reaction was commendable and reputation-saving. The visitor was the District Inspector, who had come to carry out (arguably too late) a performance check. He seemed satisfied that the short delay before he was bidden to enter was caused by the need to put items away after a stock check. The door could be opened from the outside. Repairs had necessarily to be postponed as all three officers had then to race off to the scene of the Randalls' latest crime.

Unlike the District Inspector, Grenville Porter had been able to carry out his own performance check. Without word to anyone in his group and unnoticed by Mimi Clutterbone he had silently entered the Kings' room. Despite initial surprise at what he beheld Grenville maintained his silence and watched incredulously. When Uncle Jim had stayed with his mother it had never been anything like this. Richard Furness and Suzy Waterbeach were blissfully unaware of the comparison until finally and climactically the intruder had uttered the single sound 'Cor!' The exclamation was sufficient to assist Mimi Clutterbone in relocating her missing charge. In the circumstances her reactions were razor-sharp. At first she took in only an excited Grenville Porter. It was when she next observed the excited and by now agitated couple on the bed that she performed a remarkable feat of back-tracking before too many more young eyes would have a premature bout of education. Equally fearing the inspection of many more eyes Richard and Suzy executed a panic retreat through the door whence they had come. Within seconds the room was empty, although the same could not be said of the minds of some of the Year 6 pupils of St Cuthbert's who had managed for a few seconds to side-step their escort.

After emerging from the Hall Geraldine Rogers and Margaret Hamersteen with their ever attentive companion, C. Ramsgate Fishburn, had wandered almost aimlessly around those parts of the grounds which had not previously received their attention. In so doing they came upon the official caravan which was Caroline Bingley-Adams' base. Seeing someone inside, Geraldine Rogers was not put off by a door which was shut, seemingly locked and displaying a notice 'Keep out'. She struck the door insistently with her stick. It was the will of Caroline Bingley-Adams which broke first. The words she had been inclined to let fly were held back when she saw the age and infirmity of those who had dared to disturb her. 'How may I help you?' she said. 'Where are they?' barked Margaret Hamersteen. 'Where are who?' asked Caroline still smiling, but sensing a degree of tension. 'The cricketers, of course, the Soul of Discretion', Geraldine Rogers answered. At last recognising American accents, Caroline Bingley-Adams recalled that people from the United States knew next to nothing about cricket. Fixing the American trio with what she thought was a kindly expression, she said 'Why, they're having tea. It's what they do in the middle of a match.' From this point the exchange deteriorated.

This had also been Charles Brett's experience on the Yarfield by-pass. Charm had given way to menace in the person of the first police officer. As he marched back to their vehicle to collect a breathalyser kit he instructed his colleague to 'watch him' as the latter approached the white van. Charles Brett sensed serious trouble, but he was not prepared for what followed. 'Why,' said the second policeman, 'it's Mr Brett, isn't it? My wife said you saved her bacon when you got our cooker going again. She'll be really pleased when I tell her I've seen you.' He turned back to meet the first police officer, who was returning with a purposeful stride. Charles Brett could see them engage in discussion. After a couple of minutes he was offered a deal. No breath test, but he must get the van off the road. There was a garage not far away. One of them would drive the van there. It could be left for the tyre to be repaired and they would drive Charles Brett to his home. The electrician was taking all this in as he heard the kindly second police officer say, 'Now, the spare'll be in the back, won't it? We'll give you a hand changing it.'

It was not just Gregory Braine and Lloyd Hart who descended on Helmerstead Hall once again but the whole poker school. Gregory and Lloyd were the first arrivals, but soon there was a fleet of ambulances in their wake with lights flashing and sirens sounding. If Caroline Bingley-Adams had missed the relatively silent collapse of the tea tent, she could not ignore the fearful disturbance which followed. She saw it as a further threat to the serene progress of the hugely successful event she wished to hold. 'No, they are most certainly not phonies', she almost screamed at Margaret Hamersteen. It was preposterous to Caroline's way of thinking that this decrepit American could pretend to tell one cricket team from another. True, she had not thought it necessary to inform the public that the Outcasts had been an eleventh hour substitution for the Soul of Discretion, but if anyone could tell the difference it certainly could not be an old woman from the United States. However, seeing that the Americans were willing to continue to dispute the point, Caroline Bingley-Adams stormed off in the direction of the former tea tent. She wanted this latest mess cleared up quickly so that the game could recommence and the sale of raffle tickets proceed in a settled atmosphere. 'I could use a drink', said Geraldine Rogers. There was no dissent from C. Ramsgate Fishburn and the Americans moved off in another direction.

To her dismay Caroline Bingley-Adams found that the latest mess was not susceptible to being cleared up quickly. The Hertfordshire Social Women were being retrieved slowly and carefully from the wreckage. Remarkably for the most part they did not seem to be seriously damaged. With the sky, as opposed to canvas, above them there were one or two conspicuously early recoveries from shock. It was shock that was now felt by one young paramedic whose muscles bulged beneath his body-hugging green uniform when, after his lifting a victim on to a stretcher, she had clutched at him, winked and murmured 'I'm called Little Buttercup.' Restored to the land of the living, Mrs Tester still nurtured hope. But then the cry went up, 'Has anyone seen Lady Foreshaw?' Gregory Braine and Lloyd Hart tackled the fallen tent from another direction and then they found her. It was not clear how the harmonica had become wedged in her mouth, but it was immediately clear that it would require surgical extraction. The only sounds the poor woman could make took the form of half-formed notes on the instrument. As gradually the stretchers were placed in the ambulances it was clear that many Saturdays would pass before the Hertfordshire Social Women would be at it again.

Normally cool and clear-thinking, Charles Brett had reacted in panic. He could not allow the rear doors of the van to open to reveal what he believed to be inside. 'There isn't one', he blurted out and immediately felt the first police officer moving in for the kill. 'Now that's a very serious offence, sir', he said with considerable exaggeration. 'A second serious offence. You've got a lot of explaining to do.' In a rush and with a fluency that may have been assisted by the whisky Charles Brett launched into his attempt to retrieve the situation. Considering his unpromising situation it was an ingenious concoction of the truth and lies, with the latter prevailing. He told them that he had taken the spare to Martin More Motors for repair. Whilst waiting for the job to be completed he had received an emergency call from the owner of Helmerstead Hall that there had been a power failure and his help was needed. To spice up the story Charles Brett added that the officers would know that there was a major charity event being staged here. So in the circumstances he had felt his duty to be clear. Having spent several hours putting things right he had at last escaped and was on his way to the garage in the hope that it was still open. He paused to see if his words had had any beneficial effect. 'You know,' said the second police officer reflectively whilst prodding the offending tyre, 'I think it might be no worse than a slow puncture.' Without comment to his colleague he collected a foot pump from their vehicle to test out his theory.

It seemed that he was right. The second police officer, feeling smug, then persuaded his doubting colleague that they could revert to the original plan and take the public-spirited electrician to the garage. On arrival at Martin More Motors there was only time for the first police officer, who had driven the van, to issue a warning to Charles Brett that he was on no account to get behind the wheel again for the rest of the day and, just in case, he would see to it that the registration number was circulated to every police car in the county. The second police officer had taken a call requiring them to go immediately to Helmerstead Hall where a major incident had been reported. Charles Brett was left on his own again before it was clear whether the garage was still open for business. On a casual inspection it appeared not. The electrician swore loud and long before calming down to consider his options.

Incident or no incident, play in the match at Helmerstead Hall was about to resume.

The Outcasts' innings

RESUMPTION HAD BECOME A PRIORITY for Caroline Bingley-Adams. The series of accidents was affecting the public mind. The sideshows had lost their appeal. Some of the stalls (incredibly) had sold out, while others were never likely to. The delay in restarting the cricket added to the restlessness. When she noticed that some people were drifting away Caroline Bingley-Adams leapt to the microphone and announced, without any sure evidence to back her claim, that 'This very exciting and amusing cricket game' was about to continue. She also mentioned the 'absolutely super raffle with absolutely super prizes'. Spying Billy Figg, she shot out of her office and instructed him to 'Get the dog on.' With his showbiz sense Billy Figg recognised the need to grab the public's attention and duly obliged.

Sight of the Old English Sheepdog revived the spirits of spectators, and the laughter occasioned by some playful tomfoolery between umpire and dog drew people back to the arena. The encore was reckoned to be a greater success than the debut, climaxing as it did with the dog majestically and copiously relieving itself against the stumps at the Hall end of the pitch. Much the same kind of relief, but without an audience, was being obtained by Syd Breakwell, anxious to ward off any uncomfortable pressures during the Outcasts' innings stint.

Another lavatory cubicle housed the charity organiser. He had told Don Hennelly that something must have disagreed with him – a plausible enough excuse for anyone who had sampled tea. He had then bolted himself into the WC and his captain had gone in search of Phil Cole to press him into service. Phil was too easily found as most of the Outcasts were under instruction from Stewart Thorogood in the opposing dressing-room. There was much encouragement for Phil as, glowering, he was obliged to wear the elf costume. Cries of 'Who's a pretty boy then?' accompanied him as he exited to join the rest of the Celebs XI. (Beaufort Strange, adopting the martyr's mantle, had declared himself fit to field despite his still-throbbing toe.)

As he strode out to bat with Jon Palmer, Stewart Thorogood entertained no real hope that the Outcasts could make 273 runs to win the match. Even at their best the Outcasts would find this a stiff target. And Stewart was sufficiently aware to know that they were not at their best. One or two he feared were at their worst. The absurdity of the whole set-up and the proximity of some fine ales had caused post-match scales of consumption to be approached at a somewhat premature stage of proceedings. True, he told himself, he and his partner had been relatively restrained, but an early fall of wickets could lead to a cascade. Whilst the crowd might be interested in a fun performance it would not appreciate total ineptitude. However, it soon became apparent that if the proceedings were in danger of descending into farce, the Outcasts would not be bearing sole responsibility.

The hurried reconstruction of the Celebs XI had been carried out with an emphasis exclusively on celebrity status rather than cricketing prowess. Even by that test it had hardly been an outstanding success. Yet the team had contained a kernel of batting ability. There were to be early signs that the same claim could not be made about bowling skills. Nor would fielding be made easy for those with the more bizarre costumes. This latter thought passed through Jon Palmer's mind. He had taken guard and was looking round the field before facing the first ball.

Before leaving the pavilion Don Hennelly had carried out an inventory of his bowling resources. The result startled him. There was no one with pretensions to bowling fast, quick, fast-medium, medium-fast, seam or swing. The best he could come up with was an offer of slow medium from Carl Waterbeach. Straight up and down was tentatively volunteered by Wayne Gaine, who had obligingly discarded his chef's apron. One or two put their hands up for slow bowling, but when the captain enquired 'Offers or leggers?' the replies came back 'No, just slow.' The obvious embarrassment of Don Hennelly was relieved by Hugo Crabscote saying that he had been a net bowler, but it was a while back and he was out of practice. Thus armed the Celebs had taken to the field.

The first few overs gave no hint as to how the match might progress. There was no apparent menace in the bowling of Carl Waterbeach, but he was admirably straight and kept a reasonable length. His slow-medium was nearer to medium-slow, but he conceded no early boundaries. At the other end Wayne Gaine's straight up and down proved to be an exaggeration. There was only a hint of wicket-to-wicket bowling, but his variation of direction, length and speed created such an element of surprise that both batsmen elected to bide their time. The product of five overs was 13 runs and the first shout from beyond the midwicket boundary of 'Get on with it.'

For want of volunteers Don Hennelly himself had decided to keep wicket. If he had not been an unusual sight before, he now looked positively bizarre. Strapping pads to his legs above the skirt of the costume gown produced an extraordinary effect. The forced-back skirt widened his figure and helped to make up for his lack of mobility and, bluntly, skill behind the stumps. Balls which passed the batsmen and which might easily have passed the keeper became embedded in the dress from which they could be promptly retrieved by a member of the fielding side and sometimes even by Don Hennelly himself. As hardly any ball was bowled with real pace this turned out to be a cunning way of suppressing a flow of extras. One or two deliveries appearing to be wide of leg stump might well have been judged wides, but Syd Breakwell's concentration was less than exemplary.

Raffle tickets at £1 each or £5 a book were not selling like hot cakes. By this stage of the day money was in short supply. Those males who were not already in the refreshment tent still had designs on a visit or re-visit before final departure. Wives, more conscious of the family budget, inclined to hold back where it was clear that their partners had made unwise inroads. Some groups of ladies without dependents thought that they might splash out on a nice bottle of wine or a few lagers at the close of play and so were disinclined to splash out on raffle tickets. Some people asked awkward questions about the exact nature of the prizes. The answers given by the Outcasts' sales personnel did nothing to assist sales. There was one exception. Charlie Colson's tongue had been considerably loosened by his intake of superior ales. He gave colourful descriptions of the main prizes which regrettably did not remain constant as he moved amongst spectators in his section of the ground. Overall, however, tickets sold in singles rather than in books.

The Americans had found somewhere to sit in what was a very crowded refreshment area. No table had been free, but Margaret Hamersteen's eyes had alighted on a table in one corner occupied by what she thought a likely foursome. Having moved slowly in that direction, she suddenly staggered and clutched the edge of the table. 'Oh my!' she exclaimed, 'I'm so sorry, my legs kinda gave way.' On cue, Geraldine Rogers added, 'It's one of her turns. She suffers from low blood pressure.' It was enough. The two young couples at the table gallantly got to their feet so that the old lady could rest and recover. The question whether she would like a doctor was quickly declined. All she needed, she explained, was a little space and a little rest and she was sure she would be as right as rain. The image she had created was almost spoiled by the advancing figure of C. Ramsgate Fishburn clutching a bottle of champagne and three glasses. The two couples had fortunately moved out of earshot when he cheerily announced 'I guess you can murder this.'

The cubicle door opened. The charity organiser furtively peered out, but quickly satisfied himself that the changing-room was deserted. Better, he thought, to discard his costume and wear blazer and slacks for his renewed attempt to engage with Edward Waterbeach on matters he hoped might be fruitful. He left the pavilion with caution, not wanting to be encountered by anyone connected with the match and especially not Caroline Bingley-Adams. He achieved this aim and was pleased to arrive at the front entrance to the Hall just as the owner appeared from another direction. On this occasion he found him less distracted, welcoming even. Some pleasantries were exchanged as they strolled into the building. A drink was offered. The charity organiser had just broached the subject of interesting and worth-while (he held back from the word 'noble') projects as they reached the study. He was about to warm to his theme when his host suddenly and vio-lently uttered a profanity. His whisky was missing. As became clear to his companion it was not any bottle of whisky. It was a prized bottle of whisky. It was a whisky of rare and antique quality. Edward Waterbeach did not hold back from the word. His whisky was a noble distillation. He was too much of a gentleman to say that it had cost £375, but this was the reason more than anything else for his anger. Deserting his guest with a muttered apology, he set out to alert his staff to the loss and order an investigation.

Any search of Helmerstead Hall and its immediate environs would, of course, have been to no avail. The new custodian of the whisky in question had no idea of its special excellence or what it meant to its erstwhile owner. His possession of it and the pleasure it might yield were not Charles Brett's first considerations at this time. He was wondering why Martin More Motors were shut on a summer Saturday afternoon. The main door leading to the workshop looked to be firmly closed. There was no visible sign of activity. More in desperation than in hope he walked along the side of the building. He peered in through a grimy window, but could see nothing. He reached the back of the building to find another door, also shut, and a window higher than the other. Looking around, he saw an upturned box the size of a beer crate. He carried it over, placed it under the window and once again tried to discover whether anything was happening inside. With a shock he discovered there was. He took in the scene for a few moments and then stepped quietly off the box. A pause for thought was needed to decide how best to turn the revelation to his advantage.

The separate worries of Edward Waterbeach and Charles Brett in no way impinged on the calm progress of the cricket match. It was altogether too calm, as Stewart Thorogood and Jon Palmer were forced to agree when they went into consultation at the end of the fifth over. They were unaware of such other bowling resources the Celebs might have, but on the basis of what they had seen so far they reckoned that they could take a risk or two. 'Let's apply a little pressure and see' was how Stewart summed up the situation. The pressure on Wayne Gaine soon had an effect, not all of which was predictable. The first ball of his third over took a line narrowly outside off stump and was slightly short of a full length. Jon Palmer offered no stroke. In retrospect it was the peak of the bowler's achievement. It was all downhill thereafter. The second ball was wider and shorter. It was cut with some force straight to Carl Waterbeach and straight through Carl Waterbeach to the boundary with scarcely any loss of velocity. It seemed that the Elvis costume impeded its wearer. Applause rang out around the ground, but it was unclear whether this was for the shot or the gyrations of the fielder (Carl Waterbeach had tried to make the best out of his mistake).

On past evidence the odds were that Wayne Gaine's next delivery would not be wide of off stump or indeed anywhere near off stump. The bowler's attempt to compensate sent the ball down the leg side, so wide that not even Don Hennelly's skirt nor any other part of him could stop it. The batsmen ran two wides. Wayne Gaine got a little nearer to the stumps with his next try, but he could have wished for a better length as Jon Palmer swung him one bounce to the deep midwicket boundary. The bowler tried a change of pace. It also produced a change in direction. Jon Palmer stabbed it towards cover and called Stewart Thorogood for what should have been no more than a sharp single. Beaufort Strange in his tutu swooped on the ball and flung it towards the bowler's end. This was an ambitious piece of fielding as from his position on the field he had only one stump at which to aim and neither the bowler nor any other fielder was standing remotely near enough to gather the ball. It travelled on and Fred Fortune's foot, enlarged as it was by his lion outfit, was insufficient to stop it crossing the boundary line. Jon Palmer was credited with five runs.

The yield from Jon Palmer's personal pressure was a total of 13 runs. Then it was Stewart Thorogood's turn. As much to steady himself as anything Wayne thought he would try a distinctly slower ball. It emerged as a full toss. Stewart Thorogood smacked it high over mid-on. Two fielders moved towards it, but the ball bounced between them and there was no further threat to its reaching the boundary. It was returned to the bowler. Wayne Gaine's demeanour did not suggest a happy return. Almost peevishly he flung down a shorter, faster ball which had the merit of taking the batsman by surprise. It also suffered the demerit of being hit for six, for in a hurried move Stewart Thorogood tried a hook. It was not textbook, but the pace of the ball and the edge of the bat took the delivery high and directly behind the stumps. No fielder could get near it. More pressure had added another 10 runs.

In the wake of this one over there was conspicuously less enthusiasm evident in Carl Waterbeach's approach to the resumption of his spell. He waved one or two fielders into more distant positions. His first ball was consistent with those he had already delivered. It was admirably straight and maintained a reasonable length. The similarity ended there. Jon Palmer advanced two paces and hit it on the full. It skimmed past the bowler and its straight path to the boundary bisected the two fielders who had gone back as instructed to positions at deep mid-on and deep mid-off. Carl Waterbeach pursed his lips, altered his grip on the seam of the ball and tried again. Pleasurably for him the ball moved on pitching. Jon Palmer advancing for the second time was beaten and might have been stumped had Don Hennelly not put personal safety before valour and stationed himself some distance behind the wicket. The bowler's pleasure became no more than wry amusement when Jon Palmer, cautious about coming forward to the next ball, failed to take advantage of a half-volley and could do no more than poke it out in the direction of deep point and take a single.

Stewart Thorogood's appetite was whetted. The new tactic of pressure seemed to be having an effect. At the very least he and Jon could enjoy themselves and maybe give the crowd something to cheer. People did in fact react warmly to his next stroke, which was an air shot to an unexpectedly high full toss. Stewart could manage only one off the next ball, because he managed to pick out one of the few fielders who were standing relatively close to the wicket. This brought Carl Waterbeach up against Jon Palmer once again. He produced a passable delivery, but the batsman was in aggressive mode. He swung it towards deep midwicket, but the ball came high off the bat and was clearly not going to cover the distance. Nor it appeared was Beaufort Strange, who had his back to play when the ball was struck, being in animated conversation with a spectator who had asked him the intriguing question 'Didn't I see you in *Twelve Angry Men*?' Never one to shun recognition, Beaufort Strange was drawn to the questioner even though unsure of the answer to give. He had appeared in a stage version some years ago (not as one of the twelve) in East Kilbride. It had not been an extended run. In fact Beaufort Strange had been chased for half a mile from the stage door by a gang of rowdy, unappreciative playgoers. They had only desisted on reaching the Cross Keys saloon. Beaufort Strange doubted whether his current interlocutor could have been one of them. The doubt had nevertheless distracted him and he was slow to react when finally forced to take note of what was happening behind him. The ball fell to earth when he was still well short of it. He threw it back under the glare of ten angry cricketers. The batsmen had run three.

Inside the refreshment tent, discussion amongst the American trio had turned to the wisdom of ordering a second bottle. There was still some champagne left in the original bottle, which C. Ramsgate Fishburn had placed on the ground adjacent to the canvas wall, but, as Margaret Hamersteen had observed, it was better to be safe than sorry: on a hot afternoon demand could very well exceed supply. Before they had reached a conclusion

Geraldine Rogers had observed something quite different. From under the canvas there appeared a hand and it was feeling its way towards the champagne bottle. It failed to make it. Geraldine Rogers brought the point of her stick down on it with a force which very nearly pinned it to the ground. There was a terrible scream from the other side of the tent wall and

the hand withdrew rather faster than it had entered. C. Ramsgate Fishburn went to investigate and that is how he came to meet the hitherto elusive Hamish McTartar. It did not prove to be the intellectual climax for which the American had been hoping.

At first this was not fully clear. Hamish McTartar was writhing in agony, surrounded by a group made up partly of well-wishers and partly of those who obtained vicarious pleasure in observing the pain of others. Fortunately there was a doctor present, although most of his patients would probably have said he was better suited to being a spectator. Hamish McTartar was spared any such thought. Indeed he could be counted lucky that Dr John Crippen was at hand, for the alternative would have been to await the ministrations of Paul Wyatt and Laurel Rouse. It would have been a long wait, by which time much blood might have been lost, not to mention the hand. The St Joan's District Inspector as was his wont had decided to subject his field officers to a routine test. This was carried out inside the caravan after attending the tea tent incident. They could perhaps be forgiven if the scenes they had witnessed made them overlook one small outstanding matter. The door had closed behind them.

Mutual desire between Richard Furness and Suzy Waterbeach had by no means been quenched after their pleasing and at times exciting afternoon together. Amidst promises of future plans Richard slipped away to rejoin the Outcasts, hoping that his absence had not caused problems. It was a little later that Suzy sauntered downstairs with a view to seeing how the event in the grounds was progressing and possibly watching Richard play a part in the match. She first encountered her father and was disappointed when her greeting did not receive the fulsome response she would have expected. He explained that there was a crisis. When he said that there was a thief about she remembered something. 'That's funny,' she said, 'when we, er I mean when I was in my room earlier I thought I heard someone wandering around outside.' She declined to go into detail about the handle of her door being tried in case her father wondered why it had been locked. No more detail was needed. Edward Waterbeach became seized of the idea that he was the victim of a major incident. The missing whisky was serious enough. How much more might have gone with it? He now wanted a full-scale alert.

Such was the reputation of Charles Brett that it never occurred to Edward Waterbeach that the electrician's earlier presence in the house could in any way have a bearing on supposed events. The man of unsullied reputation was at that point engaged in a reconstruction of his exit strategy. Having established that the premises of Martin More Motors were not as deserted as might have first been thought, Charles Brett needed to communicate the presence of a most insistent customer. The scene he had observed inside the workshop led him to be confident which member of staff would be the first to emerge in response to persistent blasts of the horn. At first nothing, but his patience was eventually rewarded when a door opened at the front and a young man's head appeared. It was soon followed by the rest of him as Charles Brett pounced. 'Now look here, young Dayle, I know your parents, right, and I don't think they'd like to know how you've been spending your Saturday afternoons. And they will know, if you don't do exactly what I say.' Charles Brett met no resistance from the pallid youth.

Don Hennelly knew it was a big ask when he threw the ball to Waine Gaine again. To risk another over from him when 25 runs had come from the last was a bold move. Was he being cruel or kind? Waine Gaine took it as an act of kindness without knowing how desperate his captain felt. Even so, a shiver of nervousness went through him as he eyed Jon Palmer, who almost seemed to be licking his lips in anticipation. Nerves must have accounted for the first ball, for it fell away on the leg side. Jon Palmer made no attempt to play a shot, being prepared to accept the gift of a wide. He smiled at the bowler and that sent another shiver down Waine Gaine's spine. To his credit he managed a straight delivery, but with a full swing of the bat Jon Palmer sent it back over his head. This time a fielder in the deep did manage to intercept it before it could reach the boundary, but that was largely because the ball slowed after pitching, having struck a divot. Jon Palmer got two for his efforts, but then managed two easy boundaries after the bowler dropped short. The Outcasts had 50 on the board. Without much intention the fourth ball effectively was a yorker on which Jon Palmer only just got his bat down in time. He recovered his composure by pulling a long-hop for four and followed it with another high and square on the off side. Don Hennelly was left with some hard thinking to do, but at least the crowd was in a good mood.

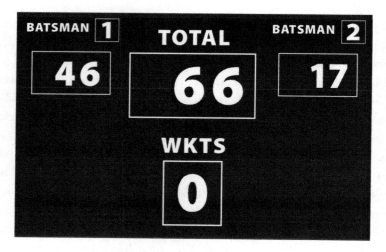

The mood of the Randall boys had improved too. The damage to their fabric had been much less than the damage to the fabric of the tea tent. They had found a quiet corner of the grounds for a retreat from public view. Being tough nuts they had fairly quickly settled themselves down. Some fresh amusement was sought. First wanting an ice cream, they fastened on a young lad (conveniently smaller than themselves) waiting to be served at the ice cream van. He clutched a £10 note and was determinedly trying to remember all the items he had been instructed to buy. Demonstrating that violence was not their only stock-in-trade, Craig and Danny wheedled their way into the company of the bearer of the £10 note. Danny wept as Craig told the tale of their father in hospital and their abandonment without even the money for a drink or an ice cream. With an act which might have qualified them for drama school they came away with two ice creams, two fizzy drinks and a £5 note. They had not extracted these from the seven-year-old, who had told them in a low but firm voice to 'f*** off', but from the lady behind them in the queue, who had been greatly touched by their story. However, when she suggested that she should take them to the event organiser's office to see if they could be looked after until reclaimed by their mother, they had run off. That is when they found the Old English Sheepdog.

Between the ministrations of Dr Crippen and the arrival of the ambulance which someone had had the wit to call, realisation gradually dawned on C. Ramsgate Fishburn. In front of him lay no mine of information about cricket which would enrich his studies. He had travelled across Europe stopping over in countries associated with the International Cricket Council to gather information in anticipation of what he had imagined would be a thorough-going discussion with a repository of knowledge and experience. Possessing like many Americans a skewed understanding of the geographical size and relationship of Scotland and England, he had too readily accepted that a Scot might have more to tell him about cricket than an Englishman. Sight of the man who had fed this misconception was a shock which at first out of old-fashioned courtesy he was reluctant to absorb. Attempts to introduce himself or achieve any kind of recognisable contact were met with cries, moans and a torrent of vile language. It finally became clear that there would be no meeting of minds only when Margaret Hamersteen, slower to reach the scene, pronounced 'He's drunk as a skunk.' When Gregory Braine and Lloyd Hart arrived to cart him away there was no one more relieved than Dr Crippen. C. Ramsgate Fishburn, possibly still in shock, was slowly steered back into the refreshment area by

Margaret Hamersteen. Surprisingly, no one asked how Hamish McTartar had come by his injury, and by the time of their return Geraldine Rogers had carefully wiped the blood from the sharpened point of her stick.

Between the ministrations of Dr Crippen and the arrival of the ambulance, play had gone on undisturbed. This was a source of satisfaction to Caroline Bingley-Adams, whose attention to the latest incident had been attracted by the sound of the ambulance bell. The removal of the turbulent Scot added to her pleasure. As she walked away she realised that there was something puzzling about the scene she had just witnessed, but she could not think what it was. By contrast Don Hennelly knew what was puzzling him. He had felt obliged to give Carl Waterbeach another over in view of the catch that never was and in recognition of the fact that in the context of the innings thus far Carl's bowling had been relatively inexpensive. After that fifth over had been bowled there was cause for reassessment. Sixteen runs came from it. Getting well into his stride, Stewart Thorogood stroked four boundaries, three handsome and the other distinctly streaky when he misjudged the only decent ball that Carl had delivered. Now the captain of the Celebs was unsure whom to bowl at either end.

Don Hennelly had begun to think that his only coherent option was to share the agony by rotating the rest of the bowling amongst the remaining members of his team. Excluding himself and Phil Cole, the substitute fielder, that left seven choices. At least, he told himself, it would provide a spectacle, a forecast which was amply borne out. Without any clear knowledge to guide him in the calibration of the 'talent' available to him, Don Hennelly thought he might try to get the worst over first. On that basis he summoned Fred Fortune. Perhaps, he mused, Fred might be lion-hearted. It was not a thought that lingered for long. The first five balls delivered by Fred Fortune were wides, some by a considerable distance. They were the most economical. The next six which came within reach of Jon Palmer were despatched to all corners. The product of the over was 35 runs, generous applause for the batsman's half-century and gales of laughter. It was hard to judge whether Fred Fortune prancing to the wicket or Don Hennelly diving left or right to try to prevent the wide balls escaping to the boundary earned the greater hilarity.

After one more over opinion amongst the Outcasts in the pavilion shifted. The over in question was in the hands – or, more particularly, the hand – of

George Others. He was attired in a pirate costume, complete with beard, parrot and a hook. Precisely which character this was meant to represent was left to the imagination of the onlooker. Suffice it that the general effect was piratical. It turned out that the hook was affixed to his right hand and he was by nature right-handed. To save time, the hook being not easily detachable, George Others chose to bowl left-handed. His radar was less accurate than Fred Fortune's, with the result that of his six wides three succeeded in eluding the wicket-keeper and reached the boundary without the intervention of any other fielder. His six legitimate deliveries yielded four boundaries, and there might have been more if Stewart Thorogood's power of stroke had not been sapped by his laughter. His final shot did not have the legs to reach the boundary but it brought him to his fifty. By now the crowd seemed to have warmed to the Outcasts' captain as he contributed to their growing entertainment. The Outcasts' total had leapt by 34, and the view in their camp was that the previously unattainable target of 273 had now become 'a piece of piss', as Harry Northwood, after only a few weeks of university education, so eloquently put it. This called for a change of strategy. There was a general drift in the direction of real ale, leaving Dean Faulds and Rashid Ali padded up. A still distracted Kevin Newton offered to hang back as go-between in case a wicket fell and another batsman had to be summoned.

This passage of spectacular cricket had brightened the afternoon of the two police officers who had earlier given Charles Brett a bad time before being called to the tea tent incident at Helmerstead. Although PCs Andrew Bell and Ian Strauss had dutifully taken statements, on learning that the miscreants were minors they were disinclined to make much effort to find them. From the point of view of justice they wearily concluded that there was not much satisfaction in arresting kids when what they really needed was a good smacking, and in any case it would probably be put down as just an accident. They had made a slight show of looking for the Randall boys but were really quite content to take a leisurely break, which could easily be passed off as providing a reassuring police presence at a major event. However, by lingering they were soon to discover that no pretence would ultimately be necessary.

To the intense irritation and frustration of the charity organiser he had had to accept that there was no possibility of having a meaningful conversation with Edward Waterbeach whilst the man was running round demented over the loss of his whisky – and possibly more. Whilst steering clear of the arena where the cricket was taking place he thought that he would seek out Caroline Bingley-Adams, who might have some idea by now about the day's takings. He found her in her caravan office, managed to attract her attention and was admitted to the presence. She was coming to the end of a telephone call. Her demeanour suggested it was not one she had initiated nor one she wished to prolong. She was not doing much listening. Having received a visitor, she made her closing remarks: 'It's no concern of mine that Mr Randall is sitting up and taking nourishment. I don't know where his wretched sons are. I wish they weren't here.' Her voice rose to a crescendo and she slammed the phone down with a flourish. In a complete change of mood she beamed at the charity organiser. 'How are you?' she asked. It turned out to be not as well as he at first claimed once she had revealed the figures to him.

Dayle Chivers, the young trainee mechanic, did exactly as he was told, repairing the suspect tyre. He wondered why Charles Brett would not use the spare, but dared not ask. Once the vehicle was roadworthy Charles Brett ordered Dayle back into the workshop. 'You can loosen some of those ropes and then we'll be on our way.' To a background of foul language from the garage interior Charles Brett hustled Dayle into the driver's seat of the van and off they moved. Despite being thoroughly intimidated Dayle made one or two half-hearted attempts to speak, but each time his passenger snapped 'Just shut up and drive.' After half an hour Charles Brett felt more relaxed. His confidence came back to him as they drove further away from Helmerstead and those harassing policemen. He reached for the whisky bottle. Now he had a driver he could see no harm in having another taste. He silently toasted a better future, but the mistake which would scupper it had already been made.

The large throng which had gathered in the refreshment tent had begun to thin. The change in tempo in the cricket had caused some people to go outside to get a better appreciation of what was going on. Others, who had exceeded their capacity but retained a degree of mobility, had sought fresh air and a grassy bank. A few had had to lie down on the spot, fortunately without obstructing the bar. Some visitors had simply decided that it was time to go home. The Outcasts fell into none of these categories.

The reunification of players with non-players was an event which attracted attention to itself. C. Ramsgate Fishburn immediately took notice. He greeted his pre-match acquaintances and insisted that they meet 'these two charming ladies'. The Outcasts were sufficiently affable and well-oiled to be able to overcome the impostor tag with which, unbeknown to them, they had previously been labelled by Geraldine Rogers and Margaret Hamersteen. Having succumbed very easily to the charms of the Soul of Discretion they found themselves having no difficulty in getting along 'just fine' with this substitute set of young English cricketers. More chairs and tables were commandeered and quite a party developed.

Outside Jon Palmer and Stewart Thorogood were also in something of a party mood. To have almost doubled the score in two, admittedly extended, overs made them realise that the Outcasts were not after all up against it. Against what was plainly rubbish bowling Jon and Stewart felt that they could enjoy themselves and please the crowd. A run feast beckoned. It was now Don Hennelly's turn to feel his festive spirit sink. He remained wedded to his plan and chose Rob Steelback as next in line, reckoning that the man had been a professional. True, as a batsman, but he would surely have had to take his turn to bowl in the nets and should therefore be able to project a ball reasonably straight. Rob was given the nod. When he came up to Don Hennelly from his fielding position on the boundary – where all fielders by now were stationed – he apologised. 'I'm afraid my leg-breaks are a bit rusty.' It was news to Don Hennelly that Rob Steelback had ever bowled leg-breaks and he brightened at the possibility that he had stumbled on some gold amidst the dross.

Rob Steelback's first ball did not confirm his captain's flickering hopes. It was a high full toss which Stewart Thorogood launched even higher to clear the boundary by a comfortable margin. Whether Rob Steelback could actually spin the ball remained an open question. His second delivery did not add to the evidence. It was a low full-toss and Stewart Thorogood did not miss out. He sent it skimming between long-off and deep extra cover without either fielder in those parts getting near it. The third ball had the distinction of pitching, but nothing more. Yet its normality took Stewart Thorogood by surprise and he just succeeded in tucking it off his pad and glancing it for a single to an attentive elf at fine leg. When he reached the non-striker's end he was disappointed to see Syd Breakwell jigging around on one leg, a sign which Simon Crossley in the scorebox acknowledged as a leg bye. With abundant scoring opportunities ahead Stewart decided not to quibble. Yet standing near the portly umpire Stewart thought that he looked uncomfortable.

Jon Palmer looked forward to doing a demolition job on the bowling of Rob Steelback. However, the demolition job was done on his innings. The ball he received was over-pitched and he came forward to meet it and make it into a full toss. It came on to him rather quicker than he was expecting and attack had to be turned into defence. Jon Palmer edged the ball into his pads with a loud thud. With a gentle smile Rob Steelback turned towards Syd Breakwell and asked very politely and resignedly, 'How was that, umpire?' It was not out, of course, because Jon Palmer had hit it and also because he had come so far forward. He smiled too, but not for long. The niceties were seemingly lost on Syd Breakwell, for he dramatically raised his finger before even more dramatically turning on his heel and running towards the pavilion clutching a part of his anatomy. The Outcasts' first wicket had fallen – although it was more of a technical knock-out – at 162. They were comfortably more than half way towards their target.

'It's crap', said Jon Palmer as they passed each other. Dean Faulds, the incoming batsman, thought he meant the bowling, which had been evident to him from a distance. He did not realise that Jon Palmer had the umpire's decision in mind. His mood was not improved when Syd Break-well emerged from the pavilion just as he was entering and made a clean breast of it. 'I'm sorry, old boy, just had to do it. I was in agony, the water-works you know. It won't matter, old boy, you look as though you'll flippin' murder them.' Whether it was the repeat of that notorious expression or the sheer farce of the situation, Jon Palmer's mood broke. 'It'll cost you in the bar later', he shouted after the retreating white-coated figure. Then to Rashid Ali, sitting intently with pads, gloves and bat in place, Jon added, 'If you get in, Rash, I think it could well be flippin' murder.' Laughing, he went into the dressing-room to remove his gear.

Buoyed by taking a wicket Rob Steelback did a few more exercises to loosen himself up. The result was two more dot balls. Dean Faulds thought it wise just to get the feel of ball on bat. The onslaught could wait until he was next on strike. Both he and Stewart Thorogood waited with interest to see who would bowl next. Having had success by calling on the most experienced cricketer in his ranks, although there had been no visible sign of spin, Don Hennelly decided that Hugo Crabscote looked to be the logical successor. Hugo was not so sure. Don Hennelly took his protests for modesty and insisted, 'Give it an over and we'll see.' Chivalry forced Hugo's hand. As to what he might bowl there was complete uncertainty. Right-arm over was the only guide. The fielders scattered and Don Hennelly compromised by standing a few feet back from the stumps. Hugo Crabscote whirled his arm. Stewart Thorogood twirled his bat.

It was obvious from the start that Hugo Crabscote was right to be hesitant in acceding to his captain's request. From the length of his run-up Stewart Thorogood, unlike Don Hennelly, was not expecting any kind of pace. He was right, but this made him unprepared to take advantage of the no-ball which Hugo Crabscote delivered. His foot was so far over the line of the crease that Billy Figg could not fail to notice the error. With a theatrical impulse to reassert his role in proceedings he gave loud voice to the offence and was quite pleased to be called into action again when Hugo Crabscote's second ball was wide of leg stump. On the evidence of these two deliveries Don Hennelly reverted to a position immediately behind the stumps. It was a wise move. After Hugo Crabscote had managed two legitimate deliveries, both of which had been struck for four by Stewart Thorogood, he could perhaps best and most politely be described as a slow trundler. However, that is not to say that there is no place in the game for a slow trundler, a point which Hugo Crabscote was very soon to demonstrate. Having more or less sorted his direction, the bowler concentrated on trying to achieve an optimum length – without quite succeeding. Stewart Thorogood felt sufficiently on top of his game to seek every scoring opportunity. He added 8 more runs off the next three deliveries and his mouth watered when the last ball of the over was short of a length and had 'Hit me' written all over it. Unfortunately for Stewart Thorogood it was an invitation he fluffed and the next human agency making a connection with the ball was Don Hennelly, who broke the stumps.

More theatre followed. Such was the lunge with which Don Hennelly grabbed at the ball that his momentum carried him forward. He broke the stumps not so much with his gloved hands but with his whole body. From a recumbent position he appealed to the world as a whole. The world as represented by the assembled crowd, who thought this a highly amusing spectacle, roared its approval. The umpires appeared to be swept along by this tide of enthusiasm. Both raised their fingers. Billy Figg believed that Stewart had nicked the ball and had been caught behind the wicket. Syd Breakwell thought that Stewart had been out of his ground and was stumped. The crowd did not mind either way and became slightly impatient when Stewart stayed put. This was not lack of sportsmanship on his part. The umpires had decided to confer and he simply awaited the outcome of their deliberations. These were somewhat drawn out as each umpire seemed to want to claim responsibility for the decision as a matter of professional pride. In the end they surreptitiously tossed for it and Stewart was given out stumped. He departed to unseemly chants of 'Out, out'. The harsh fact was that he was not out at all. He had neither hit the ball nor had Don Hennelly control of it when he fell across the stumps. Sadly for Stewart's sake, and for the better education of spectators, camera evidence was not available to prove the point. Yet even so the Outcasts needed fewer than 100 to win, albeit with two new batsmen at the crease. It was only while he waited for the incoming batsman that Billy Figg remembered that he should have allowed Stewart Thorogood a free hit after the no-ball.

The noble distillation stolen from Edward Waterbeach was having a soporific effect on Charles Brett. As the journey had gone on he had not limited himself to a single swig. This had also led to a softening of his attitude towards his driver, Dayle. It has often been observed that a relationship can develop between prisoner and guard. So when the young trainee dared to open his mouth again he was not peremptorily told to shut it. That was despite the blatant stupidity of the question he asked. 'Got any music with you?' There was not even a radio in the van. With a gesture Charles Brett made this plain. 'Got any food then? I ain't 'alf 'ungry.' 'You should have thought of that earlier' was the rejoinder, which brought them uncomfortably back to the circumstances on which Charles Brett had intruded at the garage. 'You won't really tell me mum and dad about what, you know, what you saw at work?' Work, Charles Brett thought drowsily, so that's what he calls it. Dayle persisted, ''E made me. Don't tell 'em for Christ's sake.' He glanced pleadingly at Charles Brett, but he had nodded off. Hungry, without music or even conversation, Dayle was left with no option but to concentrate on driving. So he decided to put all his efforts into that.

Don Hennelly was encouraged by the turn of events. He abandoned the idea of rotating his bowlers. He felt that he could hardly turn his back on

Rob Steelback and Hugo Crabscote after each had taken a wicket. The little matter of 28 runs having been taken from their two overs was something he was prepared to overlook, the two preceding overs having cost 69. He felt strengthened in his decision when the second Steelback over was completed at a cost of two singles and a bye, which Don Hennelly knew was his own fault. Hugo Crabscote also achieved a better line, but could not prevent Dean Faulds easing into his innings with two fluent cover drives earning four and two respectively.

Toby Lederwood was forced to detach himself from the increasingly convivial party in the refreshment tent, but Harry Northwood insisted on downing the pint in front of him before he followed. Kevin Newton snatched a pint himself whilst waiting and watching. Surrounded by voluble cricketers C. Ramsgate Fishburn was on a fast learning curve about the English game. He was being fed some junk by the likes of Charlie Colson and David Pelham, but a few essentials of the recreational game were put across, not least in liquid form. At their part of the expanded circle Geraldine Rogers and Margaret Hamersteen were charmed by the Furness brothers and the Redman twins. The image of young Englishmen was further burnished and was fortunate not to be dented when Harry Northwood rose unsteadily to his feet and announced his departure with a loud burp.

Having played its part in entertaining the crowd, the Old English Sheepdog was resting in a private compound. It had been fed and watered, but responsibility for its welfare had been assigned to Caroline Bingley-Adams. She had failed to check on the dog's water bowl and supply some chew bars at the appropriate time. The dog's sense of wellbeing had begun to ebb by the time Danny and Craig Randall came upon him. They were in a mood to play. The dog wasn't. The boys tried to fool around with the animal, tugging him here and pushing him there. In fairness, before the dog bit Craig he had given an early warning with a snarl which should have been an unambiguous signal to the boys that they were pushing their luck. They failed to heed it. The last straw was when Danny climbed into the dog's kennel. The dog took its revenge on Craig. As the blood spurted the boy screamed. Danny found it harder to get out of the dog's kennel than it had been to get in. He was stuck. He began to yell. The dog barked. The resulting cacophony came first to the ears of the charity organiser and Caroline Bingley-Adams. The interruption came at a critical moment.

Rob Steelback began a third over, which might have seemed improbable at the opening of his spell. A leg bye came from the first ball, putting Dean Faulds back on strike. He played a defensive shot to the next and an aggressive shot to the one which followed – without connecting. Annoyed with himself, he made a special effort to concentrate. The fourth was a poor delivery and he put it away through midwicket for four. The penultimate ball of the over was even worse, and in his stride now Dean Faulds pulled it high and backwards of square on the on side. It came a little too much from the top of the blade and spent a long time in the air, long enough for the substitute figure of Phil Cole to settle beneath it. As the ball descended Phil was lecturing himself severely that he must not drop it. He simply must not drop it. To Dean's dismay he didn't. Dean and Rashid Ali had crossed twice before the catch was made and so Toby Lederwood found himself facing the last ball of the over. It was to be his last as well. It could not be explained why, when the ball pitched, it barely bounced. It was a grubber. It passed under the left-hander's bat and hit off stump. It was an utter freak, but another wicket for Rob Steelback nonetheless. It left him on a hat-trick – and Harry Northwood in a muddle. Unprepared and unfit he made an uncertain and belated approach to the middle. Had anyone been so uncharitable on ostensibly a charitable occasion to appeal, Harry would have been the victim of a 'timed out' decision. However, he had cover.

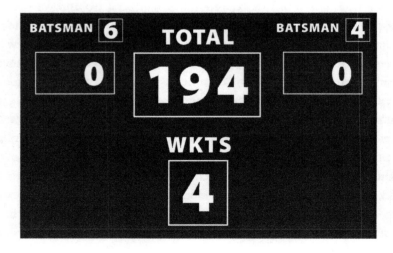

The charity organiser was poring over such figures as Caroline Bingley-Adams was in a position at that stage to provide. The gate receipts were good, but below budget; the fees from stall-holders had raised an adequate amount; bar takings were phenomenal; the major disappointment lay with the raffle. Wanting to squeeze every last penny from the event, the charity organiser pressed Caroline Bingley-Adams to get more tickets sold. Whilst she herself privately felt that her chosen sales force could have injected more effort into selling the tickets, she was straightaway defensive against any implied criticism that her management skills might not have been adequate in relation to the marketing effort. The charity organiser pointed out that there was still time to sell more tickets. He wanted to know why sales had been halted. Caroline Bingley-Adams bridled if for no other reason than that she reckoned (shrewdly) she had more chance of getting the British Cabinet out selling tickets than persuading the Outcasts to take up the role again. The charity organiser could see an awkward quarrel developing and so he decided on a change of tactics. Maybe a gentler approach was called for. A feisty Caroline appealed to him rather more than a feeble, lachrymose Caroline. He looked at her with new eyes. For want of anyone else currently available she might be worth a night out and you never knew. He made a step closer to her and was about to go touchy-feely when some awful cries rent the air. The moment was lost.

They raced outside. Caroline thought the cries came from children. Billy Figg was certain which dog was barking. The three of them tried to restore the situation before the curious began to gather. It suddenly struck Caroline what had been nagging her about the incident involving Hamish McTartar. The St Joan Ambulance officers had not been there. Now they were needed again to deal with these repulsive children. Caroline had needed no persuading about where the fault lay, but she realised that the dog bite would need medical attention. If this meant that the boys could be packed off to hospital, they would be off her hands and reunited with their irresponsible parents. Thus far did Caroline's sympathy extend. She instructed the charity organiser (in a tone which brooked no refusal) to prise the St Joan team out of its caravan, although she put it in more colourful terms than that. This was exactly what the charity organiser had to do, as he found the medical auxiliaries trapped in their mobile operations centre. So painstaking and thorough (nitpicking, Paul Wyatt and Laurel Rouse thought) had the District Inspector been that the trio had been unaware of their imprisonment. The District Inspector was so rigorous in carrying out his routine procedures that he seemed almost reluctant to release his juniors to attend an actual as opposed to a theoretical incident. Interrupted, he finally decided that his job at Helmerstead was probably done and so he thought that he could go home to his wife's steak and kidney pie supper and, as it was Saturday night, maybe more. He had brightened and left, but Paul Wyatt and Laurel Rouse paled when they saw the blood. In his seemingly interminable examination the District Inspector had not covered dog bites. In theory Paul and Laurel should have known what to do; in practice it all looked very unfamiliar. There was a lot of blood and Craig Randall was moaning. Danny had been dragged roughly from the dog kennel by Billy Figg, who automatically (and rightly) knew where the blame lay. Paul and Laurel put into action the only plan they knew and the paramedics were summoned. Gregory Braine and Lloyd Hart had barely completed the transfer of Hamish McTartar when the call came. Their departure was noticed with interest by a furtive figure loitering by the entrance to the A&E department. The words 'It's Helmerstead again' particularly caught his attention.

The best general news reporter affordable to the *North Herts Examiner and Courier* was Lionel McWeasel, known to one and all as Sleazy Weazey. When the *Examiner* had merged with the *Courier* to form the new combined title Lionel McWeasel had come with the deal. The retiring editor of the *Examiner* owed a debt to Lionel's mother for never letting it be known that he was the father. It would have ruined his inheritance from his wife's family. He had had to guarantee employment for the unprepossessing young man, who had acquired his looks and his depraved interests from his mother's side. The former editor of the *Examiner* had thought it best to fulfil his promise in a way that allowed him to keep an eye on the young man. He was rewarded by the discovery that his bastard son could do more than make tea and act as a general dogsbody. He had an uncanny knack for unearthing stories, usually of a disreputable kind. When it was suggested to him that instead of telling tales he should write a proper report he came up with a very readable style. His was usually the prominent and highly contrasting piece in a journal which was otherwise devoted to not much more than the reports of Women's Institutes, Rotary, Round Table and Old People's Clubs.

This particular weekend he was short of a story for the local weekly. He had just filed with his national outlet for an especially large fee a story involving the headmaster of a nearby independent school and members of the first Rugby XV. This had been achieved by dint of hard work and at relatively little cost, if no account was taken of the black eye which had been administered by the back row prop. The satisfaction shown by this thirteen-stone hulk with the long blond hair, mused Lionel McWeasel, would quickly evaporate when he saw what would appear in the national press on Monday. It was the black eye that had brought him to Casualty, where it had taken an inordinate time to get treatment (three stitches were necessary) as priority was given to a succession of ambulance cases. As he waited, fulminating about the National Health Service and what story he might put together on that, he picked up the word that most of these cases appeared to have a common link. Then he remembered seeing an email. There had to be a story at Helmerstead.

The seventeenth over of the match eventually began. The dog was calmed and Billy Figg was back in his place ready to officiate during Hugo Crabscote's third over. Syd Breakwell had taken advantage of the interruption to play to revisit the pavilion for comfort purposes. The batsmen had taken advantage of the break for a tactical discussion. Rashid Ali's beer consumption during the day had, as was his wont, fallen well below that of his comrades, and therefore he was as sharp as a blade in comparison with Harry Northwood. Nevertheless an equation of 79 runs and twenty-four overs did not look too demanding against the quality of bowling they had so far witnessed. The sudden loss of wickets seemed to be a mere blip. 'I think we should finish this off quickly' pronounced Rashid Ali, and Harry Northwood hiccupped his assent.

With Rashid Ali on strike there was the opportunity for his sentiments to be put to the test. Rash was not found wanting. Five handsome attacking shots, three of them piercing the field and the others gaining two apiece, showed him at his best and Hugo Crabscote at his most ordinary. The target shrank by 15 runs, and Don Hennelly was reduced to pinning his faith in Rob Steelback. The man was on a hat-trick and facing him was the new batsman, Harry Northwood. Rashid Ali felt in his bones that this was a perilous scenario. He did not like Harry's pallor or the overly cheerful grin which had spread across his face. He had tried to steal a single off the last ball of Hugo Crabscote's over, but at the critical moment Harry was gazing at the bowler and making no attempt to back up. Rash had a quick word with him before Rob Steelback bowled, but Harry between hiccups assured him that all was well.

The first ball of the new over was met by a very exaggerated forward defensive shot. The hat-trick was avoided. Harry Northwood winked. Then he hiccupped. Rashid Ali watched with continued concern. Harry played the identical shot to the second ball, but made no contact and it floated past his off stump. He winked again. The next ball was short and wide and would have gone past off stump like its predecessor if Harry had not planted a foot in its direction and succeeded in pulling it round over midwicket one bounce into the crowd. It was a remarkable shot and Harry obviously thought so, because he winked yet again. To the fourth ball he played another model defensive shot, but managed only to edge the ball where slip might have been. 'Run', shouted Rashid Ali sensing his opportunity, but before he was too far committed he was met by a stentorian 'No' from his partner, who held up his hand like a policeman on traffic duty to reinforce his intention to stay put. Rob Steelback's next ball was short again and Harry shaped at once to give it destructive treatment. However, this time it pitched on line of middle stump, Harry's swing failed to connect and he was bowled. Somewhat unnecessarily he winked one last time at Rashid Ali and departed. The Outcasts were 214-5.

Lionel McWeasel had tailed the ambulance to Helmerstead Hall and was on hand to witness Gregory Braine and Lloyd Hart attending to the injured Craig Randall and his hysterical brother. He also noticed the presence of the police. Having had a burger apiece the two officers had been debating whether they could get away with having a quick pint despite being on duty. They had discussed whether the combination of onion, gherkin and ketchup would obliterate the smell of beer on their breath. They had reached no conclusion when Craig Randall's cries had pulled them in the direction of the dog compound. These boys, they quickly gathered, were the wreakers of assorted havoc during the afternoon, but the sight of Craig's blood – and the presence of too many witnesses – prevented them administering summary justice. With the arrival of the paramedics they were in any case reduced to the role of bit part players. They concluded that the interrogation of the boys, which might very well prove to be a waste of time, could be deferred until after their treatment in hospital. The thoughts of a nifty pint revived.

The reporter had greater application to his task and a ready mind for scandal, actual or supposed. One line of supposition was prompted by the sight of the St Joan Ambulance team withdrawing in favour of the paramedics. He clearly saw Paul Wyatt fondle Laurel Rouse's bottom (an endearment the said officer had been denied for too long by the presence of the District Inspector) and speculated whether intimacy between the two might have delayed help to the poor, bleeding boy and his wailing sibling. However, this thought was quickly dislodged when he heard someone remark that the little swine had got what he deserved at last. The last two words held particular significance for Lionel McWeasel because they confirmed the occurrence of a series of incidents for which the two lads might have been responsible. When he looked away from the dog compound and noticed the wreckage of the tea tent his pulse quickened.

Movement between the refreshment tent and the players' changing-room had become a relay. With still two full pints in front of them even the Redman twins were having to drain their current glass more hurriedly than they would have liked, just in case they too might be needed to bat. Ray Burrill was padded up and on his way to replace Harry Northwood whilst Richard Furness was in preparation. Rashid Ali was pleased to welcome Ray. His pleasure was not tempered by the aroma of hop which surrounded his new partner because he was confident that his new partner had not consumed the same quantity of ale as Harry. In strictly comparative terms that was true, but Ray's demeanour belied how he felt. He was not at his best, but his confidence improved when he was advised by Rash that the bowling was indifferent bordering on atrocious. He had one ball to face of Rob Steelback's over. It proved to be at the atrocious end of the spectrum and Ray Burrill got off the mark with a square drive which earned him three. The shot itself should have given him great satisfaction. The running did not.

The excellent whisky had helped Charles Brett into a sound sleep. Fright, yet also the thrill of adventure, led his young driver to test the limits of the vehicle. Forced to drive the van Dayle was still excited. He did not expect to come to any harm at the hands of Charles Brett, but he had to hope that helping him out would prevent damaging word getting to his parents about his Saturday afternoon pursuits. If he got into serious trouble with them they would never pay for him to have driving lessons. So far he had been confined to moving vehicles around the yard or in and out of the workshop. He had never been on the road before and so this strange journey was great practice. He hoped one day to have a slick and powerful sports car. As he grew in confidence driving the van he imagined how he would put such a car through its paces. His speed increased and he was surprised how well the van reacted. As he came down the hill the speedometer crept above 70 mph. There was nothing to indicate a left-hand bend at the bottom. In preparation for the erection of a new warning sign with flashing lights on the previous Friday afternoon the old sign without flashing lights had been removed on Friday morning. The highways authority's sub-contractors had then staged a lightning sympathy strike over a disciplined colleague (it was a Friday afternoon for heaven's sake) and motorists were left to work it out for themselves. Those with local knowledge or good road sense coped. Others had difficulty.

Don Hennelly realised that the game had slipped away from the Celebs XI. Despite the little flurry of wickets he knew that only a further 56 runs were needed and there were twenty-two overs left. From what he had seen of Rashid Ali so far he appraised him as someone who was probably capable of knocking off these runs on his own. The one stroke played by Ray Burrill seemed to be evidence of someone else who could handle a bat. To make it as much of a contest as he could he decided he would dispense with Hugo Crabscote and recall Carl Waterbeach to see if he could repeat the economy of his first three overs. If he could spin the game out for a few more overs, he would be giving the spectators their money's worth. This game plan did not coincide with that of Rashid Ali, but Don Hennelly was unexpectedly assisted by Ray Burrill.

Carl Waterbeach's first ball of his new spell erred towards the leg side, Ray Burrill poked at it indeterminedly and looked towards Billy Figg expecting it to be called a wide. The umpire did not move, but someone else did. The ball had brushed Ray Burrill's pad and headed towards fine leg. Rashid Ali had a perfect view and it was his call. 'Run one', he shouted. Ray Burrill had no intention of running any until he had composed himself after the exertion of running three at the end of the previous over. This further exercise did him no favours. He was reluctant to admit to Rash that he was feeling out of sorts and was horrified when his partner called him for a very sharp single off the next ball. This put him back on strike, and it needed all his concentration just to leave the ball and let it pass harmlessly to the keeper. Respite was to be short, because he got an edge to the following delivery. It went wide of an optimistically placed slip fielder, and before Ray could react negatively Rash was charging towards him once again. It took a huge effort to get himself to the other end. Rash then struck a full toss from Carl Waterbeach sweetly past him for four. He was not oblivious to the fact that Ray was not functioning on all four cylinders and so he thought that he should steal the strike. Mid-off had gone deeper after the last stroke and so with a controlled shot he sent the last ball of the over in that direction. It should have been an easy single.

Lionel McWeasel had attached himself to the man who had pronounced satisfaction with what had befallen the Randall boys. It turned out he had been a witness of the bagatelle incident and he was able to confirm that the same 'two little bastards' had caused the collapse of the tea tent and injuries to the ladies inside it. What had happened at the bagatelle became more brutal in the telling and, as he collected eye-witness accounts from others, the story of the tea tent and its victims was greatly embellished. The headline was already forming in the reporter's mind: Charity Event War Zone. He had the impression that the ambulance had been to and fro more often than these events accounted for and so he began to search for other visitors to Helmerstead so that his theory could be further developed. Without too much concern for accuracy he was easily able to encompass both the incident involving the scorer and the injury to the drunken Scot as part of the same pattern. However, when he ran into a group of children who were lolling around on the grass passing sweets amongst themselves, the pattern was disturbed.

Misunderstood communications are commonplace. When Edward Waterbeach instructed his staff to search the house to see if anything was missing it was assumed he meant the public rooms. It seemed obvious. Those were the parts of the house which had been visited by a steady stream of strangers. Edward Waterbeach eventually was told that everything seemed to be in order. There had been disturbance of the Kings' room but nothing was missing. For a moment or two Edward Waterbeach was relieved, although he was still left without an explanation for the missing whisky bottle and, more importantly, without the whisky. It forced him to wonder whether the loss of this one item could have been an inside job. Then he remembered something. Suzy had mentioned a disturbance she had heard upstairs. He called back his chief steward, who had been obliged to admit that the search party had not invaded the family's private quarters. 'I'll come up with you', he said. This put him in the ranks of the first to know that the whisky, however precious, was the least of it.

The Outcasts' sixth wicket had fallen. Ray Burrill had instinctively responded to Rashid Ali's call, but he laboured. The more effort he put into his running the more the stumps at the other end, behind which Don Hennelly loomed, retreated. It was a grossly distorted impression. Lack of puff, a stinging stitch and no lack of ale combined into a formidable handicap. In despair Ray Burrill dived with all the grace of a Premiership footballer, but he was a foot away from the crease when the cleanly fielded ball (by Phil Cole the sub) banged into Don Hennelly's gloves. In one smooth movement the bails were removed. Rashid Ali, part annoyed, part amused, tended advice to his partner. 'I think you should go and lie down – but not here.'

While Ray Burrill was removed amidst general laughter, Richard Furness, his replacement, was talking tactics to Rashid Ali. Fewer than 50 runs were now needed by the Outcasts, but they only had four wickets in hand. However, the two batsmen convinced each other the bowling held no terrors and they should just get on with it, playing their natural game. For the next two overs they did exactly that and to good effect. Don Hennelly had seen no reason to discontinue Rob Steelback's spell, but the rusty leg-spinner, who had not yet shown much propensity to impart spin to the ball, had a bad over. He gave Rashid Ali three good scoring opportunities and the batsman succeeded in taking them to the tune of 10 runs. He could have pinched a single off the last ball, but he assessed Richard Furness to be in better shape than Ray Burrill and thought he could be trusted to do a reliable job. That looked to be a perfectly good call, for Richard Furness, who was feeling pretty good about life, had no trouble in plundering Carl Waterbeach's seventh over for another 10 runs. After he had swung the final ball over midwicket for an effortless six it was high fives for him and Rash. It looked to the Redman brothers as they weaved their way unsteadily from the refreshment tent to the pavilion that they would not be needed after all. Fortunately they did not turn back.

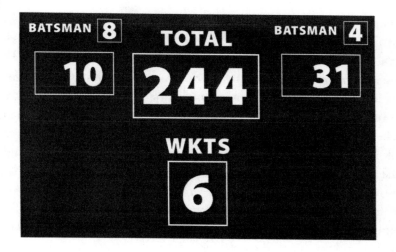

Mimi Clutterbone had spent a miserable afternoon. She had needed all-round vision to keep even a vestige of control over her flock. She hoped that in the end exhaustion would have a taming effect. Having tested to destruction the possibilities the event had on offer, she had gone in search of the accompanying parents, who had ceased to accompany. She found them where she had left them and they at least were of a more cheerful disposition than herself. Too cheerful. They were not ready to go home. 'The cricket's not over yet', said one of them. This was true, but it did not strike Mimi Clutterbone as a material fact, because from where they were (by this time) seated in the refreshment tent they could not see the play. She doubted whether they possessed the capacity of the great Wilfred Rhodes to understand what was happening by sound alone. Neither it seemed were they disposed to share the burden of keeping the children under control. Mimi groaned when the most they could offer was some money 'to buy them some sweets'. This she had dutifully done, though, and when to her pleasant surprise the children had settled down she found herself a cool drink and a vantage point from which to keep them under observation.

On seeing a shabby man in a shabby raincoat approach her charges Mimi Clutterbone was on immediate alert. If this was a sex fiend, he would get away with nothing. Yet when she saw that the exchange was between the man and Grenville Porter, she almost revised her opinion. The encounter did not in fact last long and the man was soon on his way. Mimi was bliss-fully unaware of what had taken place. Grenville Porter had not identified the man as a likely pervert. He had been much closer to the mark when he had accosted Lionel McWeasel. ''Ere mate, you a reporter or a copper?' The answer pleased him. 'Give us a fag and I'll give you a real 'ot story.' This presented no moral dilemma to Sleazy Weazey. When Grenville Porter told him in a couple of coarse sentences what he had seen in the Kings' room the reporter, unseen by the teacher, tossed the remainder of his current packet to him and headed for the mansion in an excited state. His route took him past St Joan Ambulance. On impulse he stopped, thinking this must be a source of information about the day's accidents. Without knocking (he was on official business) he wrenched open the door of the vehicle and found Paul Wyatt giving rather more than the kiss of life to Laurel Rouse. In Lionel McWeasel's book this was ten times better than hearsay evidence and he praised the Lord for camera phones.

After the dismissal of Richard Furness Suzy Waterbeach reckoned that her attention should be redirected towards her father and what might have happened in the house. She did not know a great deal about cricket, but she had enjoyed Richard's brief flurry of an innings. His athleticism, especially as exemplified in the two big hits he had made, had only enhanced his appeal to her. In cricketing terms the twenty-second over had been one of mixed fortunes. Rob Steelback's prowess appeared to be fading as first Rashid Ali and then Richard Furness had tucked in on a series of wayward deliveries. Richard's second six was as glorious as the first. Nineteen runs came from the first five balls of the over as the scoring accelerated. Then something peculiar happened. Rob Steelback discovered his leg-break. With 10 runs only needed to win, Richard Furness was sufficiently fired up that when he saw the ball coming towards him in what seemed a perfect copy of its predecessor, there seemed to be only one thing to do with it. But his footwork was lazy and when the ball turned sharply after pitching nothing was in place to stop it hitting off stump. When they passed on their way to and from the pavilion it was with an entirely nonchalant air that Richard advised brother John: 'Just leave it to Rash.'

Suzy's feeling of wellbeing did not long survive her return to the mansion. She met her father at the foot of the stairs to be told that they had been robbed. As his anger poured out it became clear that this was no petty affair. They had been systematically looted. All their best and most valuable pieces had gone. The police had to be called. Suzy was able to check her father's flow at this juncture: 'But they're here already. I've just passed two police officers.' As soon as she said it she thought it was odd that they had both been eating ice cream, something you would surely not be doing if you were on your way to a crime scene. She was not to know that her father thought it odd that the police had already arrived at Helmerstead before he had called 999. In his excitement he was ready to overlook this detail. All he said was 'Get them in here quickly.' Two careers were thereby saved.

The charity organiser had a visceral dislike of the police. Confident, suave trickster that he might consider himself, he was uneasy when there were police around. He understood that the collapse of the tea tent had brought them to Helmerstead but he was disappointed that their presence at the dog incident meant that they were still hanging around. Once it was clear that the two troublesome boys had been apprehended, if only so far by the Ambulance Service, he had expected the police officers to disappear. He was irritated when he spotted them again later munching burgers, but his anger spilled over when he glanced inside the refreshment tent and saw them with pint glasses in their hands. It took him a while to find the right number to ring (by which time beer had given way to ice cream) but he was eventually able to speak to a station commander, who immediately knew which officers had been sent to the event. The officers in question had just taken a call on their radio to return to base to give an account of themselves when they were accosted by Suzy Waterbeach and the mansion's chief steward with news of a major robbery. They decided that their duty lay with an immediate investigation and ran towards the main entrance with Lionel McWeasel very closely behind them.

The van containing Charles Brett and his coerced driver was unable to take the bend and stay on the road. To Dayle's horror the accelerator froze. How to deal with the situation was way beyond the young man's wit and experience. He hung on to the steering wheel without any clear idea as to how to use it in these circumstances. Luck was on his side when the van was able to cross the carriageway at a point where there were merely cones and not a metal barrier. His luck held when the crossing coincided with a gap in the oncoming traffic. Again luck was with him when no more than a hedge stood between the van and a grassy stretch of recreational land. Good fortune persisted, because this area, popular with children, picnickers and joggers, was relatively deserted and no innocent party was put at risk by the van's progress. The moment at which it could be said the luck ran out was when the van plunged into the Rendon Boating Lake and disappeared beneath its waters.

'Kevin!' The familiar voice hit the disconsolate Outcast like a thunderbolt. The reunion of Gloria Lockwood and Kevin Newton was wondrous to behold. The physical recapture of past pleasures took priority over explanation, but eventually Gloria was able to relate the bizarre chain of events which had first made her a victim of the airlines and then of her mobile phone supplier. She had finally made up for lost time by getting a taxi to bring her to Helmerstead, or at least that had been the intention. Unfortunately the taxi driver had poor English, no satellite navigation system and a broken mobile. The land journey had proved more trying than her eventual flight between the West Indies and London. 'But it was worth it', she quickly assured Kevin and he had no argument with that. 'You could probably do with a drink', he said and Gloria had no argument with that. They headed to the refreshment marquee with Kevin keen to introduce Gloria to the rest of his friends. By that stage of the day it was arguably a bold gamble. The mood was already boisterous.

John Furness could perhaps most accurately be described as a social cricketer. As such he was a stalwart and much valued member of the Outcasts. He was not a batsman of any great note and he was not in the side for his bowling. The advice of his younger brother that matters should be left to Rashid Ali seemed very sound. The same message was delivered by Rash himself once John had joined him. Privately Rash thought that with the quality of bowling on display even John might have no difficulty notching up the 10 runs they needed to win the match. Nevertheless they had contrived to lose seven wickets and so Rash had concluded that they had best play it safe. He had the strike and the plan was to make sure he kept it. The plan failed.

Carl Waterbeach had one over left to bowl before his allocation was complete. Don Hennelly was not confident that he could contain the left-handed Rashid Ali, but amidst the general carnage Carl's figures had a glimmer of respectability. The glimmer threatened to be extinguished when Carl's second ball was swept to the leg-side boundary for four. When Rash played the same stroke to the next ball his placement was not quite so perfect and he got two. This was followed by another two when a straight drive was deflected and slowed by the bowler's boot. Carl rallied from both these indignities to send down a testing length ball which Rash merely blocked and waited for the next. As Rash said, he could probably have got the single had he not hesitated. Having got his side within one run of the Celebs' total, Rash did hesitate. He was self-effacing by nature. It did not bother him that he was two runs short of a personal fifty. Generously he felt that he should allow John Furness to apply the coup de grace. Unfortunately John had not followed this thought process and was still operating in accordance with Plan A. Rash's booming 'No' gave him too-short notice to adjust. He had hurled himself down the pitch so fast that it was useless for Rash to change his mind again and so he decided that he must not make a bad situation worse by sacrificing his own wicket. There were mutual apologies and John Furness was on his way without facing a ball.

The charity organiser was keenly aware that he still needed to pin down Edward Waterbeach if the trip to Helmerstead was to show a real dividend. He made a move in the direction of the mansion, but stopped when he caught sight of the police officers entering. This was all wrong. He thought that he had got them out of the way. What on earth had happened now? He cursed this unexpected development, but calculated wisely that this might not be the moment for a productive meeting with his target. Whilst he generally believed in thinking big there was a petty streak in the charity organiser's character. He could not shake off the belief that there was still more money to be made out of the present event. Obsessively he was convinced that more raffle tickets could be sold. He determined to have another go at persuading Caroline Bingley-Adams to launch another sales drive. When he reached her office she was not there. More surprisingly the door, when he had tried it, was unlocked. In the absence of Caroline the first thing he saw was a pile of unsold raffle tickets. He assumed that the day's takings were in the safe in the corner. The second thing he saw was the scoreboard indicating that the match was almost over. He idly wondered why someone had started a fire, because he could see some smoke appearing from behind it. There was already a drift of people away from the arena in the direction of the refreshment marquee. That looked a promising sales location. With about half an hour to go before the raffle was due to be drawn there was no time to be lost. Shoving the tickets into a plastic bag and grabbing a bucket, the charity organiser realised he would have to do the job himself.

When the chief steward stood in the way of Lionel McWeasel, stating that the house was now closed to visitors, the reporter was just close enough to the uniformed officers to lend weight to his claim. 'I'm with them', and just far enough behind for them not to hear him. 'CID', he muttered, and to a chief steward, who was a devotee of *Columbo*, he looked the part. 'Very well, sir', he responded, and Sleazy Weazey was in. The uniformed police had followed Edward Waterbeach to the study, but the reporter, ostentatiously brandishing a note-book, made for the stairs. He brushed at speed past the one or two members of staff he met with a wave of his press card. 'Police', he barked with growing confidence and, being aware of a crisis, the staff thought better than to stop him. He found the Kings' room, circumnavigated the barrier and closed the door behind him. In less than five minutes he found the two clues to back up the story which was already half-completed in his warped mind. The bed bore the mark of its recent occupants' activity and in the rushed retreat a carton had fallen from the pocket of Richard Furness' borrowed dressing gown. With the evidence recorded on his camera phone Lionel McWeasel made assumptions which avoided the need to look anywhere else. All he needed to do was get out of the house unhindered. An interview with whoever was behind the day's event might be rewarding.

The person behind the day's event was leaving the refreshment marquee as the charity organiser arrived. Thinking ahead, he had no wish to be unkind to her, but he felt it necessary to mention that she had left her office unlocked. 'Oh how silly of me,' she said with only a partly suppressed giggle, 'that's most unlike me. I'll get back straightaway. See you later.' And with another light laugh she shot away. Interesting, thought the charity organiser, but he could not dwell on it, because there was a job to be done with only limited time left. 'Did he see me blush?' Caroline was asking herself as she continued on her way. She had sensed something when they had last been in the office together. Maybe their relationship was about to take a more informal direction. She felt quite excited about the prospect, but also nervous. The excitement explained her omission in failing to lock the door, the nervousness, and the desire for a drink to bolster her courage.

The charity organiser was no mean salesman, and his visit to the refreshment marquee gave the takings a significant boost. Sales resistance had been appreciably eroded by alcohol. He finally came to the corner of the enclosure occupied by most of the Outcasts with their recently acquired American friends. Here the incidence of sales resistance was rather greater despite the amount of alcohol consumed. The black lady with them was stunning and the charity organiser had no difficulty in concentrating his attention on her. It was more for the purpose of dismissal than interest in the raffle that persuaded Gloria Lockwood to flash a £20 note in his direction. This prompted C. Ramsgate Fishburn to ask what it was all about, and he then succumbed to the extent of a £50 note. 'We'll have some of that', Geraldine Rogers piped up. 'Wickets for waifs, you say. Sounds a goodie to me.' More £50 notes appeared from herself and Margaret Hamersteen. That was about as good as it was going to get, the charity organiser decided. If the decision needed any underlining, it was provided by a roar from outside signalling that the match was over. The raffle draw would soon have to begin. The charity organiser withdrew with thanks and Charlie Colson resumed his explanation to a somewhat bemused C. Ramsgate Fishburn of how English cricket spirits had been lifted in 1966 when Brian Close had assumed the captaincy and inflicted an innings defeat on the mighty West Indians.

The police investigation into what was now known to be a major heist at Helmerstead Hall had not made rapid strides. One officer was painstakingly assembling a list of what was missing. The arrival of additional information punctuated the process as further discoveries were made. The second officer had set about interviewing staff. This exercise was carried out under protest from Edward Waterbeach, who tried to convince the policeman that all his staff, in whom he had complete trust, could be accounted for, and that being the case they could not have made off with what they had allegedly seized. Even the policeman's reproof that one of them might have an accomplice did not shake Edward Waterbeach in his belief that this had to be an outside job. 'There have been hundreds of people through this house today', he said, but after a while, as the list of losses continued to grow, he was forced to recognise that it would have taken a small army of visitors to have spirited them from the premises. His electrician was so far beyond reproach that even when Edward Waterbeach recalled his busy presence earlier in the day he thought no more of it. Charles Brett never once came under suspicion.

The roar from the crowd woke Mimi Clutterbone. She did not know how long she had dozed. It could not have been long, she reckoned, but it showed what a trying day she had had and how exhausted she must have become. Anyway, she told herself, there was no harm done. How pleasant it was to be out in the countryside enjoying the warm sunshine. She looked around her and was content with what she saw. It took her a few moments longer to realise what she could not see: the children supposedly in her charge. The space they had previously occupied was vacant apart from a few sweet wrappers. Panic swept over her. She could see her teaching career coming to an ignominious end. Those who up to a short while ago she would willingly have cast into outer darkness suddenly became objects of endearment. How she longed for a sight of their cherubic faces. Her wish once granted proved to be one of rapidly passing pleasure.

The teacher ran about in distracted fashion. She kept clear of the refreshment marquee. Much as she had wanted their help earlier this was not the moment for a parent/teacher colloquium. There was no obvious sign of her pupils. They could not have just vanished. She tried to collect her thoughts and work out what part of the grounds they might have favoured. The back of the scorebox would not have occurred to her. In her panic she had not even noticed the wisps of smoke which were in evidence around it. Not even this would have alerted her had not little Leanne Pettigrew suddenly rushed into view crying and coughing in equal measure. Mimi Clutterbone moved swiftly in the poor child's direction and was thus brought to terms with the full scenario. Several of the cherubic faces now had de luxe filter tips protruding from them. Clearly the experience was producing varying degrees of satisfaction. The manufacturers would doubtless have been pained, but not half so much as Mimi Clutterbone. The pain was not long in turning to fury when Grenville Porter thrust the packet in her direction and said 'Ave a fag, Miss, there's just one left.'

The invitation was declined. Mimi Clutterbone's prime concern was for Leanne Pettigrew, whose normally pretty face was acquiring a tinge of green. One or two others also looked the worse for wear, being evidently not the practised smoker that was Grenville Porter. She needed help but was keen to put off as long as possible looking in the obvious direction. In any case she was stuck, because she could hardly let any of this lot out of her sight whilst she enlisted the aid of St Joan Ambulance. However, at that moment the door at the back of the scorebox opened and Simon Crossley came out. 'I heard this noise. I wondered what on earth was going on.' Then as he took in the scene, 'Is there anything I can do?' Mimi Clutterbone showed she was not a teacher for nothing. She peeled off a series of instructions as if she was setting homework. Simon overlooked the imperative. He was just pleased to help a damsel in distress. Minutes later he wished he had been the one to go and summon St Joan Ambulance.

The match would end much earlier than anticipated. It was clear that the raffle draw would have to be brought forward if the crowd was not to have vanished entirely. There were counterfoils from the late sales to be folded and put in the drums which had magically appeared. After consultation with the charity organiser Caroline Bingley-Adams made an announcement over the public address system that the draw would take place in front of the pavilion in twenty minutes' time. Dealing with the counterfoils in close proximity to the charity organiser, Caroline felt her breath coming more irregularly. Meanwhile the charity organiser had appraised her once again. She had obviously applied more make-up and there was definitely something different about her. When she had made the public announcement she had sounded almost lyrical. He thought that she might do for the evening, there being no rivals available. (It had been abundantly clear that the gorgeous Gloria Lockwood was not available). He allowed his hand to brush her arm and their eyes met. There was no time for further niceties. They embraced. The charity organiser had just murmured 'Let's do dinner' when there was a tap on the window. As they both gazed in the direction of the interruption the shutter on Lionel McWeasel's camera clicked.

The message from Caroline Bingley-Adams prompted a steady flow from the refreshment marquee towards the pavilion. Some were less interested in

leaving than others, but the Outcasts felt that they had better get back to the pavilion in view of the game being over. It was only there that they became acquainted with the climax of the contest. At the fall of the eighth wicket the Outcasts had needed only two runs to win the match. In the full traditional spirit of festival cricket and to give the crowd a final laugh, Don Hennelly decided that the occasion called for a joke bowler. The appropriate candidate was Simon Short, who was dressed as a clown. 'But I can't', he protested. 'Get on with it,' he was told, 'it may only take one ball.' With such encouragement Simon Short felt that he had to play along. He went through an elaborate warming-up exercise which produced another bout of mirth in the crowd. He insisted on keeping on his white conical hat and marked out an absurdly long run-up. To add to the fun Don Hennelly set a field reminiscent of body-line. In his approach to the wicket Simon resembled Groucho Marx. At the point of delivery he virtually stopped and the ball looped out of his hand in a high trajectory.

Outcasts batsmen had from time to time gone out to bat in a worse condition than Tom Redman, but more often than not they had at least known how to hold a bat. This expertise was not one of Tom's assets and therefore could not be expected to act as any kind of effective counter-balance to his basic condition, which could best be described as somewhere between intoxication and oblivion. An almost manic look came into Tom's eyes as he saw the ball heading straight towards them. Syd Breakwell was too surprised to consider calling this beamer a no-ball. He shared in the general amazement when Tom one-handed lifted his bat in the air. The ball struck it and it rebounded in a direction which allowed any one of three fielders to catch it. Guy Harper was the chosen one: caught Clergyman, bowled Clown. The latter did a cartwheel to celebrate. The merriment was general.

Tom Redman retreated into the pavilion and Nigel Redman appeared in his place. There were some spectators who either did not know or had forgotten that there were twins in the Outcasts' side. This caused some cries of 'He can't bat twice', which were followed by the riposte, 'Why not? He was bloody funny the first time.' Nigel too was not without liquor. Rashid Ali ventured to say to him 'Just hang on in there', but doubted whether his advice was absorbed. Simon Short began his loping run-up and Nigel Redman for his part began to laugh. His laughter became so much out of control that he had to hold his hand up and step away from the crease. But Simon Short's advance was not to be thwarted. Syd Breakwell was about to fling his arm out to warn the bowler. He glanced behind him and thought better of it. This time there was no pause before releasing the ball. This did not alter the outcome. The ball at greater speed than hitherto had no batsman in its path to obstruct it. Don Hennelly behind the stumps stooped only just in time. The ball had a clear passage to the boundary. This might have been expected to have gifted the match to the Outcasts, but Syd Breakwell had recovered his poise and declared 'dead ball'.

There was a short interval to allow the ball to be recovered, the bowler to get back to his mark and the batsman to control a fit of giggles. The first two conditions for the resumption of play were fulfilled, but Nigel Redman was still struggling to comport himself to face the next delivery. Tears of laughter had exacerbated the blurred vision with which he had set out to bat. His protagonist was rather peeved as he waited. More shouts of 'Get on with it' finally forced Nigel Redman to resume his stance at the crease. Simon Short at his third attempt achieved a delivery that stood some chance of hitting the wicket. It was nevertheless defective in two respects which a knowledgeable observer would have spotted. Neither umpire qualified for this accolade. Syd Breakwell should have noticed that Simon Short's foot cleared the line by several inches, resulting in a no-ball. There was perhaps more excuse for Billy Figg at square leg turning a blind eye to Simon Short's very bent arm as he delivered the ball. Calling the bowler for chucking would not have been the happiest way to end a charity match. In fact no judgement on Billy Figg's part was involved. His eyes had been closed at the critical moment.

As for the ball, it had no chance of hitting the wicket, because Nigel Redman had blundered in front of the stumps and wafted his bat vaguely in its direction. With blurred vision his chance of making contact was a pure lottery. He lost. The ball hit his pads. An over-excited Simon Short appealed. Syd Breakwell got this one right. Up went his finger in his usual theatrical fashion. Even without clear vision Nigel Redman got the message, but just in case 'That's out' boomed round the ground. It was victory for the Celebs XI by one run.

Scorecard

A Celebrity XI

Strange		b. Thorogood	22
Fortune	c. Rashid Ali	b. Redman, T.	4
Steelback	c. Faulds	b. Redman, T.	131
Hennelly	st. Rashid Ali	b. Redman, T.	34
Waterbeach	c. Rashid Ali	b. Redman, T.	0
Crabscote	not out		50
Short	l.b.w.	b. Redman, T.	0
Gaine	c. Burrill	b. Redman, T.	6
The Vicar	hit wicket	b. Thorogood	0
Others		did not bat	
Harper		did not bat	
Large		did not bat	
Extras			25
TOTAL	(for 8 wickets)		272

Bowling	overs	maidens	runs	wickets
Thorogood	8	0	48	2
Redman, N.	7	1	47	0
Redman, T.	7	1	105	6
Furness, R.	8	2	28	0
Burrill	8	0	36	0

Palmer	l.b.w.	b. Steelback	76
Thorogood	st. Hennelly	b. Crabscote	78
Faulds	c. sub	b. Steelback	12
Rashid Ali	not out		48
Lederwood		b. Steelback	0
Northwood		b. Steelback	4
Burrill	run out		4
Furness, R.		b. Steelback	20
Furness, J.	run out		0
Redman, T.	c. Harper	b. Short	0
Redman, N.	l.b.w.	b. Short	0
Extras			29
TOTAL	(all out)		271

Bowling	overs	maidens	runs	wickets
Waterbeach	8	0	59	0
Gaine	4	0	47	0
Fortune	1	0	35	0
Others	1	0	34	0
Steelback	6	0	52	5
Crabscote	3	0	40	1
Short	0.2	0	0	2

Celebs won by 1 run

THE CHARITY ORGANISER REACTED very sharply to the interruption. He was out of Caroline's arms and her office in a trice. Lionel McWeasel had not dallied, but a journalist's life of booze and fags did not make him fleet of foot. He was still capable of thinking straight. Realising that he had little chance of outstripping the man he had enraged, he sought escape in subterfuge. As soon as he could he was into a crowd of people. He divested himself of his conspicuous dirty raincoat whilst fishing a maroon (but dirty) baseball cap from its pocket. With a pair of cheap sunglasses the effect was, Sleazy Weazey hoped, complete. He moved in a mob of spectators to the larger mob that was gathering in front of the pavilion. He breathed again. The ruse had worked. He had lost his pursuer. It was some time later that he became aware that that was not his only loss.

The fight began shortly after Mimi Clutterbone had turned her back and gone in search of first aid. The casus belli was the last cigarette left in the packet. Grenville Porter's initial generosity had by now been tempered by two considerations. These perfectly good cigarettes had been wasted on most of his classmates who, unlike himself, did not appear to be habitual smokers. Various ill effects had gradually occurred. They ranged from coughing through degrees of biliousness to outright vomiting. There was even one case of singed fingers. The second factor in Grenville Porter's possessiveness was the realisation that it was the last fag in the packet. The aggression came from Max Beane, who had been a non-participant in the original share-out, because he had chosen that moment to relieve himself against the side of the scorebox. Over the last two months Max had stolen cigarettes from his mother's bag whenever opportunity had arisen. Last week she had quit smoking and Max had suffered mild withdrawal symptoms. The one which Grenville Porter was brandishing had a particular attraction for him and Max made a grab for it.

Simon Crossley felt obliged to step in to separate the combatants. It was not a situation of which he had as yet acquired experience. His two sons were nowhere near the age when scraps might become a part of daily life. Wanting to be a modern father and already signed up with Sophie's encouragement to a ban on physical chastisement, Simon had an approach which was not conducive to a cessation of hostilities. Words, however sharply uttered, were not enough. Battle continued to rage. Simon moved closer, ever mindful that the law took a highly restrictive view of even so much as the hand of restraint. With the mutual battering showing signs only of intensification, Simon thought he might be in worse trouble if he stood idly by.

His left hand of restraint was swept back by Grenville Porter with a left hook which Simon had not been expecting. Momentarily off-guard he was unable to prevent his right hand of restraint being painfully scratched by Max Beane. Simon stepped back and the boys resumed their fight. Blood had appeared. With a start Simon realised it was his own. His pink cut-away vest had suffered the first spattering. It took Simon five seconds to overcome his beliefs and instincts. Eschewing half-measures he grabbed a flailing arm of each of the two boys and flung them to the ground where they lay temporarily winded. Fortunately for Simon the deed was done seconds before adult reinforcements appeared. He decided not to hang around for explanations. Gathering his leather case from the scorebox where he had left it, he sped away to nurse his wounds. It was a wise move in view of what was to follow.

Mimi Clutterbone had been lucky to find Paul Wyatt and Laurel Rouse in residence and in uniform. She was less lucky in this being the best first aid available to her, but she was encouraged just to have some support. The plight of Leanne Pettigrew was something Laurel Rouse thought she could manage, albeit without applying a textbook solution. She took Leanne aside and persuaded her to stick two fingers down her throat. Obligingly Leanne was promptly sick and after a short bout of tears began to feel better. Paul and Laurel were disheartened by the news that Leanne Pettigrew was not a lone sufferer. They were compelled to follow Mimi Clutterbone back to the vicinity of the scorebox. Much to the teacher's discomfort they were joined on the way by Gavin Porter and Colin Beane, who had finally accepted that they were a bit full. It would be hard to judge which of the parents, ambulance officers or teacher felt the most alarm when confronted by the current status of the school party. Perhaps the adults could have co-operated in remedial and healing works, but this possibility was spoiled when Darlene Evans pointed to the recumbent forms of Grenville Porter and Max Beane and said in a shrill voice, "'E 'it 'im.'

Darlene Evans might, given the chance, have enlarged on this statement and avoided a lot of unpleasantness. Inadvertently she had lit a very short fuse. The camaraderie of the drinking companions quickly switched to hostility. Gavin Porter swung the first punch in mistaken retaliation for what he thought Max Beane had done to his son. Believing the situation to be the reverse of this Colin Beane was not slow to uphold family honour. The two men's capacity for inflicting serious damage on each other was reduced by the extent of their inebriation. However, their recovering offspring saw this as a signal to resume their own conflict. The other children, upset by a situation which appeared to be spinning out of control, either yelled or were sick. Paul Wyatt and Laurel Rouse knew at once that they were out of their depth and thankfully summoned the paramedics. Drawing on what was by now a diminished instinct, Mimi Clutterbone put everything into her command: 'Sit – now.' More by surprise than natural obedience, Grenville Porter and Max Beane sat. The other children fell silent and gradually followed suit. The parents continued to trade blows. It was never going to be a long drawn-out scrap. An afternoon spent imbibing proved to be the curtailing factor. However, their consumption accounted for the degree of madness with which they assailed each other. When they finally sank to the ground to complete the subdued tableau Gavin Porter was bleeding from both mouth and ear whilst Colin Beane's nose looked a mess. Mimi Clutterbone had the nervy and unenviable task of holding the ring until the paramedics could come to the rescue.

Lionel McWeasel might not have succeeded in giving the charity organiser the slip by disappearing into a crowd of people if the latter's pursuit had not been interrupted by a message on his mobile. It was from an associate in Florida asking him to call 'soonest'. With this particular associate it was not a request to be ignored. In any case there was a big project at stake. Cursing the timing, he realised that he needed somewhere reasonably quiet to make the call. He returned to Caroline Bingley-Adams' office to use her land-line in preference to his mobile. When she stressed that she did not want the time of the raffle draw to be delayed, he asked her to get the prizes from his van and lay them out on a table in the pavilion. He assumed that, such as they were, the boxes containing them were still in the van. He had forgotten that he had not been precise in his instructions to Kevin Newton when he had earlier enlisted his help. He had seen the boxes of promotional material parked in the pavilion, but nothing else. Kevin, for his part, believing the prizes to be valuable, had put them under a cover in the dressing-room. For the charity organiser his lack of attention to detail would prove costly.

Whatever the belated attraction which had grown up between Caroline Bingley-Adams and the charity organiser she had absolutely no intention of dirtying her hands in extracting the prizes from the van. She marched into the pavilion intent on finding someone else to do the fetching and carrying. The first people she encountered were half a dozen of the Outcasts, who had not yet begun to change out of their whites (one or two of them by this time would need to steady themselves before trying). In response to what was more a command than a request they duly co-operated. The opening of the rear doors of the van and the revelation of the hoard within produced some 'Bloody hells' and 'Christ Almighties' laced with a few more expressive reactions from those who had sold tickets and could now see that they had been a better bargain than they or anyone else had supposed. The wording on the tickets 'Plus many more wonderful prizes' was a massive understatement. Some raffle this promised to be. Toby Lederwood wondered whether there was still time to buy tickets. The transfer began.

'I think that's all we can do for the moment, sir', said PC Andrew Bell. 'We've got all the details. It's a matter for CID now. As it's you, sir, I think the DCI himself will be along very shortly to see you.' He kept to himself the knowledge that this would be as soon as he had sobered up. The DCI's Saturday habit was no secret to junior ranks in the force, who had protected him on many an occasion in return for assurances that he would 'see them right'. Edward Waterbeach would have preferred the Chief Constable, but realised that the ordinary constable was probably right. There was little more that could be done here as it was evident to him that his possessions were by now in rapid transit to the continent (he would never have imagined slow transit into his own cricket pavilion). He did not pin the greatest faith on the promised police roadblocks. Until the DCI arrived he thought that he should put in an appearance at what now looked like the rapidly approaching finale of the entertainment.

Feeling that their account had swung into credit with HQ, the two police officers were in no great hurry to leave Helmerstead. They were still debating how they might most enjoyably kill some time when a leather-clad youth ran up to them and with a smirk announced that there was 'a helluva fight' going on behind the scorebox. This was not the optimal way in which they had thought to engage themselves, but duty called. It had similarly summoned Gregory Braine and Lloyd Hart, who had shown great prescience in steering once again towards Helmerstead after depositing their most recent patients at the hospital. The paramedics and police officers reached the battlefield together. The order which Mimi Clutterbone had amazingly managed to bestow was starting to break down. The children remained morose, but still. The two fathers, belying their condition, were limbering up for round two. 'Now then, what's all this?' questioned PC Ian Strauss, in time to take the first blow. The immediate reaction to this was a burst of applause. The police officers had not been the first recipients of the leather-clad youth's news, and quite a few people had walked across to get sight of the action at this latest and unexpected sideshow. 'Punch and Judy for adults', remarked one as PC Andrew Bell grabbed his truncheon.

The young Dayle might not have had a driving licence but he did possess a life-saving certificate. Charles Brett would never have escaped from the submerged van on his own. Nor, having been extricated, would he have survived without the basic first-aid techniques which Dayle was able to employ. Obviously in a confused and semi-conscious state Charles Brett's first reality on seeing Dayle's mouth hovering above his own was one of horror and not gratitude. He did not know then as he lay by the side of the Rendon Boating Lake how lucky he was. Nor later when he found himself in a hospital bed did he appreciate his second piece of luck, for had his accident occurred a week later the Rendon Community Hospital would have been closed in the cause of improving health in the community. Once Charles Brett's brain had begun to re-engage he was in no mood to look on the bright side. Against his basic instinct he realised that he had an urgent need to see Dayle. Where was he?

A nurse told Dayle that the gentleman in the ward was asking for him. He was offered and accepted a wheelchair. Matron decided that she herself would accompany him. Charles Brett may still have been weak in body, but he was by now sharp of mind. 'This young man saved your life', announced Matron. 'Having bloody well tried to kill me', was the response which flashed into Charles Brett's head, but he said nothing. 'Aren't you going to thank him?' asked Matron. Charles Brett forced himself into a perfunctory expression of gratitude. 'I can see you're still feeling the ill effects', said Matron, being relentlessly cheerful. 'I think you need your rest. You can talk to your friend tomorrow.' But Charles Brett desperately wanted to talk to him now. Before Dayle's wheelchair could be swung round for departure the electrician almost shouted 'What's happened to the van, Dayle?' 'Oh. You don't worry about your van at a time like this.' The answer was from Matron. 'Just be grateful he got you out.' But there was nothing that Charles Brett needed to know more than the fate of his van. Dayle caught the imploring look in his eyes, and just before he was wheeled away he managed to blurt out 'It's OK, the police are fishing it out.' Charles Brett emitted a strangulated cry and a nurse closed in on him wielding a syringe.

Wearing no more than a towel, Greg Roberts, whilst waiting for a spare shower cubicle, had wandered into the main part of the pavilion as the objets d'art were being carried in by his friends. He retreated into the changing-room and came back with a box. 'I think you'll be needing this. Hang on, there's more to come.' It had not taken Greg long to realise that the boxes which Kevin Newton had placed discreetly in the changing-room belonged to the raffle. This was largely because the word 'Prizes' had been written on the side of each with a black marker pen. Apart from three envelopes relating to the first, second and third prizes there were assorted bottles (all of them bearing the distinctive mark indicating likely discounted purchase in Calais), chocolates (of a source of manufacture well outside the top group of names) and some tins of biscuits from which the sell-by date had been obliterated.

Caroline Bingley-Adams took charge of arranging the prizes on a trestle table. The envelopes were propped up at the front with the bottles, chocolates and biscuits behind. Then came the array of ornaments, jewellery and paintings which a bunch of the Outcasts were bringing from the charity organiser's van. In his absence Caroline Bingley-Adams felt that she had to make a decision. She knew quality when she saw it. In need of no convincing that the charity organiser was a man of class and distinction the quality of the items being brought before her caused no surprise. He had said to her 'just a few things', and so when she saw them her first reaction was to put it down to the kind of understatement to be expected of such a man. Then, as the table filled, she was beset by second thoughts. Perhaps the emphasis should be on the word 'few'. When Dean Faulds came in with an engraved silver tray of palpable antiquity Caroline called a halt. 'No, I think that will do.' 'There's plenty left', said Dean. 'No,' she said more firmly, 'we'll leave the rest in the van.' So they did.

In a roped-off area in front of the pavilion the two cricket teams assembled. The Celebs were still in their costumes. The Outcasts were not so uniform. Some had changed, some were partly dressed and the rest were still in their whites – the overall impression was much as one would expect from a modern England Test XI. It was clear that Don Hennelly intended to take the lead. No stranger to microphones, he thanked people for coming, made a number of acknowledgements, hoped everyone had enjoyed themselves and extolled the good cause to which the whole event had been dedicated. In a peroration for which Stewart Thorogood for one was utterly unprepared, Don Hennelly said 'I hope we've raised a huge amount of money and just to show our commitment to providing wickets for waifs, my team has had a whip-round. I now want to present the event organiser with this cheque for £1000.' It had, of course, been pre-arranged, with the original suggestion having come from the charity organiser, who had ostentatiously brandished two £50 notes to put pressure on the others. There had been no similar pre-arrangement on the Outcasts' side. When the cheer which greeted Don Hennelly's words died down eyes turned to Stewart Thorogood. Those belonging to his team-mates fastened on him with special interest. Their captain proved equal to the moment. Great leadership lies in the ability to react to unexpected circumstances. Stewart, whose facial expression was more grimace than smile, took a step forward, arm outstretched to congratulate the winning captain. Suddenly he stumbled, his body twisted and he fell to the ground. It was beautifully done. As he was carried back into the pavilion, Caroline Bingley-Adams, determined that another calamity was not going to ruin her day, rushed to the microphone and said 'Let's get on with the raffle.' This also raised a cheer.

If anyone had felt any worry for the welfare of the Outcasts' captain, it was quickly forgotten.

Caroline Bingley-Adams had pre-determined that the raffle would be drawn by the two original umpires, as she expected they would add some comedic effect. Notwithstanding the absence of Tommy Fagge she stayed with the plan even though she could see nothing funny in Syd Breakwell. At the outset she got more comedy than she wanted. Syd Breakwell turned the handle of the drum in which the tickets had been placed so that a good mix could be achieved. Bill Figg thought his efforts too timid and grasped the handle himself and sent the drum spinning. The clasp securing the lid was insufficiently resistant to this treatment. There was a sudden outpouring of paper. Fortunately there was no wind and so none of the tickets travelled far, but some minutes passed before the drum could be reloaded. The amusement initially caused by the accident soon gave way to irritation amongst those impatiently waiting to see what their luck might be.

Richard Furness had been hanging about hoping that Suzy would soon rejoin him and was slow to return to the fold of his team-mates. Moving towards the pavilion aimlessly with eyes downcast he recognised the object for a mobile phone before he trod on it. He would, of course, hand it in. Its owner would be bound to have reported its loss. He noticed that it was switched on and he failed to control an urge to see any pictures which might be on it. It did not take Richard long to recognise the image of Caroline Bingley-Adams and the charity organiser locked in a physical embrace which looked (and he would know) as though it might be heading in an impure direction. He flicked the switch and frowned, flicked again and the penny dropped. How the hell had those pictures been taken? Who was the snooper behind them? Richard tried again and came across the St Joan Ambulance couple, although he could not recognise them as such. There was no more to view. Without hesitation he deleted the two which came closest to home. After a moment's hesitation he charitably eliminated Paul Wyatt and Laurel Rouse from the record. He thought that the remaining photograph would raise a chuckle or two amongst his friends before he handed in the phone to the lady herself to trace its owner.

This would be no simple task, because Lionel McWeasel had gone. Having looked all around him and seen no sign of the charity organiser and noting that everyone's attention seemed to be directed towards the raffle, he had decided to make an early exit. Before leaving he spotted a stray programme. When he saw the Soul of Discretion listed, his senses quickened. Two and two with him made six. He hurried away turning over in his mind some of the lurid phrases he would employ in filing the story.

Once in the privacy of the Outcasts' changing-room Stewart Thorogood staged a miraculous recovery. Caroline Bingley-Adams did not give him a further thought, and in her anxiety to press on with the raffle she had even overlooked the absence of the charity organiser. The contents of the drum had finally been restored. There was one more cautious rotation and then Billy Figg plunged his hand inside to withdraw the first ticket. The winner was in the front row. Geraldine Rogers hobbled forward to collect her prize and as she stepped back outside clutching the envelope she heard a familiar voice saying 'I guess that's mine.' C. Ramsgate Fishburn had won the second prize. It turned out very shortly afterwards that he had also won the third. Generous to a fault, he graciously suggested that it should be redrawn, narrowly forestalling a call from the crowd to that effect. This time Syd Breakwell's hand went into the drum and came out with a ticket which was found to belong to Margaret Hamersteen.

The news from Florida had not been good. His associate had told the charity organiser that complications had arisen. The police were sniffing round. The client was getting nervous. No amount of assurance had seemed to placate his associate. The charity organiser realised gloomily that he would have to fly to the United States the following day. This looked like scuppering a lingering evening with Caroline Bingley-Adams. He was in a poor mood as he stamped his way towards the pavilion, but he brightened when his path converged with that being taken by Edward Waterbeach. A few minutes with him might be a lot more rewarding than an evening with Caroline. They fell into conversation, but this could not be steered in the direction which the charity organiser desired. Something else entirely was dominating Edward Waterbeach's thoughts. He poured out his anger to the charity organiser, who could only offer the occasional word of sympathy as the losses were recounted. Edward Waterbeach might have been cursing his misfortune, but the charity organiser was quietly fuming that all his chances of getting some business done with the owner of Helmerstead Hall seemed to be stillborn. They joined the crowd in front of the pavilion as a bare-chested and heavily overweight man emerged from the pavilion clutching an ornately decorated porcelain vase which looked to be of some antiquity.

In both speech and movement Edward Waterbeach froze. '2756', called Syd Breakwell. A ginger-haired lady in a white T-shirt and green jeans responded. She did not spend long in the pavilion. Excitedly she waved an emerald necklace towards the crowd. Her excitement was exceeded only by Edward Waterbeach, whose stentorian shout 'Wait a minute' halted proceedings. He rushed into the pavilion and found a tasteful display of some of his family's finest possessions. 'Where the hell did you get these?' he demanded of Caroline Bingley-Adams, who was uncertain how to react to this turn of events. Had the question come from anyone other than Edward Waterbeach she would surely have swept it aside in contemptuous fashion. As it was, she could only say in a weak voice 'From the van.' 'Whose van?' She told him. 'But he's just outside.' The voice trailed away and he began to move in that direction. He checked his stride in time to wave a hand towards the trestle table. 'Don't let anyone touch that stuff.'

The charity organiser was no longer to be seen. He had first of all gone forward in Edward Waterbeach's wake, heard the initial exchange, taken in the array of precious items on the trestle table and decided that something – he did not know what – was terribly wrong. To be on the safe side he thought that a quick exit was indicated. Had he stayed in earshot a moment longer and heard the next exchange between Caroline Bingley-Adams and Edward Waterbeach he might have devised a different strategy. 'Where's the rest of it?' the owner of this treasure had asked. 'Why, in the van of course', he was told. Somewhere in the background he heard an engine fire and in a moment the white van could be seen moving in the direction of the mansion and the back exit. The most unclouded brain amongst the Outcasts belonged at this time to Richard Furness, who, whilst his colleagues had been imbibing, had been otherwise engaged. In a moment of inspiration he used the phone in his hand to make a call.

The two police officers were empty-handed. The paramedics had insisted that the assailants, both young and old, should be seen in hospital and bundled them into their vehicle leaving room for no one else. Mimi Clutterbone was advised to get the rest of the children to their coach and have them back at school in time for parents to collect them. The first duty of the police officers should have been to follow the ambulance. They were discouraged for two reasons. Gregory Braine had told them that there was a queue a mile long at casualty. 'They'll be there for hours.' The police officers had no real appetite for that as their shift was due to end in another hour. Secondly, one of them realised that he had some raffle tickets in his pocket and knew that the draw was happening. Their dilatory attitude was soon corrected. When they were seen approaching the pavilion shouts came in their direction, the loudest from Edward Waterbeach, who knew them not just as police but as the two officers who were supposed to be on his case. They were back on it very quickly indeed, racing over to their car and gunning it towards the retreating ambulance.

Alerted by the obvious altercation, Stewart Thorogood and the main group of Outcasts had decided to rejoin the action. Rashid Ali, whose senses had been only lightly dented by alcohol, was troubled. 'Something very strange is happening here, my friend', he confided to Stewart. What was not happening was the raffle draw. This was causing serious unrest amongst the remaining ticket-holders, who did not understand the recent comings and goings. Stewart Thorogood and Don Hennelly summed up the situation together. As the difference between the prizes provided by the charity organiser and the items identified by Edward Waterbeach was so immense they advised Caroline Bingley-Adams to withdraw the objets d'art and proceed with the raffle. Even in her by now distraught and confused state Caroline could see that Edward Waterbeach would have had no proprietorial interest in the wine, chocolates and biscuits. So the precious items were removed from the table and Billy Figg and Syd Breakwell were told to get on with it. As the crowd outside had not actually seen the full array of supposed prizes the draw was completed with little more than sporadic muttering that the remaining items had not matched the splendour of the earlier ones.

On that subject there were mixed views. The possessors of the eighteenth-century porcelain vase and the emerald necklace had moved away to show off what they had chosen to their friends and family. Their satisfaction was not matched by Geraldine Rogers, who, on opening her envelope, found that she had a voucher entitling her to a cruise on the SS *Pink Lady* (sister ship to the SS *Pink Princess*) from a city she knew not where (Newcastle) to a city she felt she knew too well (Istanbul). C. Ramsgate Fishburn was not a horse-racing man and had received his prize of a day at the races with muted enthusiasm. He needed not have worried. Ascot and Goodwood it was not. 'I didn't know they raced dogs', he mused to his companions. 'Where the hell is Clap-ham?' asked Margaret Hamersteen, who was poring over the contents of her envelope. In any case she had no taste for Chinese food and was unlikely to seek out the Mandarin Continental in Clapham High Street. The three Americans consoled themselves with the thought that their money had gone to a good cause. Their pleasure would be short-lived.

The charity organiser was trapped. Just as he got to within fifty metres of the drive's exit to the road a coach swung in through the gate and stopped. There was no way past it. Furious gesticulation towards the driver made no difference. Arthur was not moving. He had, as it happened, timed his return to perfection. The phone call from Richard Furness had come through when he was almost on top of Helmerstead Hall and so he knew exactly what was required of him. If he could not go forward, the charity organiser's only other option was to go back. This possibility was extinguished almost as soon as he had entertained it. There was a screeching of brakes behind him as the ambulance came to rest. Lloyd Hart, the paramedic, not understanding the reason for the obstruction, resorted to the siren and flashing lights which hitherto he had not considered commensurate to the urgency attached to the patients being carried. Seconds later in similar conspicuous fashion the police car joined the line of vehicles.

Meanwhile most of the occupants of the pavilion stood around awaiting developments. All the Outcasts had by now regrouped. The last to arrive was a wobbly Basil Smith helped along by a sprightly Kevin Newton, eager to introduce Gloria Lockwood to the rest of his friends. There was less interest in hanging about on the part of members of the Celebs XI. They had wasted little time in showering and changing, enough only to rid themselves of what were now uncomfortably incongruous costumes. In the ordinary way they might have been willing to share a post-match drink with the Outcasts, but the feeling had spread that, if some kind of police investigation was to be launched, they could be seriously delayed. That did not suit at all. Anxious to preserve their image, they beat a retreat. Billy Figg muttered something about the need to see his partner, Tommy Fagge, and also took his leave.

The Outcasts were engaged in ribbing their scorer, Simon Crossley, on his soiled and bloodied appearance. His explanation would have been better avoided. Simon being worsted by two kids caused great merriment. However, this died away when the charity organiser was marched back into the assembled company between the two policemen. 'Now let's try and get to the bottom of this, sir', said the first police officer, who, having looked inside the van, actually doubted whether there was much more to learn. Edward Waterbeach had seen sufficient of the charity organiser during the day to believe that he could be implicated in the theft even though he had no idea how it was undertaken. The detail seemed irrelevant after the second police officer had triumphantly announced that the rest of the haul had been found in the van which the charity organiser was driving. He added cautiously 'We just have to check the inventory, sir.' Having been caught in possession, the charity organiser's position was gravely undermined. He protested loudly, but to all intents and purposes it looked an open and shut case. If Edward Waterbeach had not chosen that moment to make the audible comment that the man must have had an accomplice, Richard Furness might have forgotten the camera. 'Hang on,' he said to the police, 'take a look at this.' Shortly afterwards the charity organiser and Caroline Bingley-Adams left under police escort, destined after all to spend the night under the same roof, although not the same cell.

That really did bring the day's outing to Helmerstead to an end. The

Outcasts were relieved to board Arthur's coach. The relief was shared by Geraldine Rogers, Margaret Hamersteen and C. Ramsgate Fishburn, the new-found friends for whom the Outcasts felt some sympathy. There was plenty of room on the coach provided they were not averse to a few suitable stops on the way back to London. 'I'll drink to that', said Geraldine Rogers, and the Americans showed great resilience in keeping pace with the Outcasts at the Cow and Thistle, the Drowsy Doorman and the Pig in Muck, all carefully pre-selected by the great researcher, Charlie Colson. The absent friend to whom they remembered to drink at each pub was Basil Smith. When Jane had finally been reunited with her husband it was plain to her that he was in no condition to drive. It also very quickly became plain that their car was in no condition to be driven. Fortunately for Basil his wife's mood was surprisingly placid, sweetened by the presence in her handbag of a beautiful emerald necklace, the provenance of which was as yet a mystery to her.

It was at the Drowsy Doorman that C. Ramsgate Fishburn in pulling out his wallet scattered some raffle tickets about him. Gloria Lockwood and Kevin Newton helped him to gather them. Gloria was about to put them in the bin when she suddenly stopped. 'Kevin, Toby, look at this.' For the first time she had caught the small print and noticed the word, TRANSECT. 'Don't you remember, I told you about this outfit?' She had and slowly they did remember. 'Yes,' said Kevin loudly, 'TRANSECT, of course.' 'Hello,' said Richard Furness, his attention attracted, 'that sounds familiar.' The name bounced around the bar and was picked up by David Pelham. Although his brain was not in ace condition by that time in the day a vague recollection was stirred. He sought help from his mate and former travelling companion, Charlie Colson.

Embussed between the Drowsy Doorman and the Pig in Muck what they knew was gradually pieced together and Gloria Lockwood made careful notes. Between the Pig in Muck and home all the Outcasts could remember was what a great day's cricket it must have been. To the Americans it remained a puzzle.

Aftermath

ON THE DAY FOLLOWING THE MATCH, but at not too early an hour, the Outcasts assembled at the Sink and Plumber. Gloria Lockwood and the three Americans were in attendance. Gloria assembled what between them they knew about TRANSECT. She had the hardest information, but Richard Furness, Charlie Colson and David Pelham were all able to help her to build a picture. Whereas Gloria had expected that the investigatory authorities in Barbados would be the first to break the case, she now found unexpectedly that she had come face to face with a palpable fraud and the chief fraudster.

The supposed charity organiser was held in custody on a charge of theft whilst the police, armed with the new information, conducted international enquiries. They soon knew enough to realise that they had a far bigger case than theft on their hands. Not even the expensive lawyers her father hired could stop Caroline Bingley-Adams being convicted as an accessory. The photographic evidence from Sleazy Weazey's camera was damning. Her sentence was light, but she would never live it down.

Lionel McWeasel lost not only his camera, but also his job. Failing to capture the really big story at Helmerstead and not even coming up with a juicy sex scandal that held any water would probably have been too much for his current editor, but the end was spelt by the overnight take-over of the title by a dynamic newspaper group which had very different plans for it. The shock was too much for the former editor of the *Examiner*, who promptly died. With him went Sleazy Weazey's second line of income.

The Soul of Discretion cricket team returned to London after its enforced detention in Slovenia. A Metropolitan Police officer had been sent to Ljubljana to talk with the local police on a low-key basis. Once a bicycle and two Croatian girls had been taken out of the equation the case was reduced

247

to its basic simplicity: a drunken cricket team enjoying itself. Apologies were made and passage home for the errant young men arranged. Their only compensation was an onrush of journalists seeking exclusive story rights. Whilst the highly embellished articles caused a further wobble in Anglo-Slovenian relations, the Soul of Discretion never wanted for fixtures thereafter.

If the Soul of Discretion flourished, the same was not true of another body. Without the drive and determination of Lady Foreshaw, from whom the drive and determination had been drained by her experience at Helmerstead, the Hertfordshire Social Women's Saturday Club collapsed. No longer was there this invaluable resource to cater for refined gatherings. If Hertfordshire was the loser there was at least one member of the Club who arguably emerged as a winner from the Helmerstead escapade. Mrs Tester was no stranger to hospitals. The demise of all four of her husbands had been preceded by long spells of hospital treatment. Having been widowed for the fourth time she had put her experience to good use as an official hospital visitor. In the course of waiting for her own treatment she had encountered a much cleaned-up Hamish McTartar. Strangely a bond was struck between them. Putting aside dreams of muscular young men in uniform Mrs Tester told herself that she had always been keen on kilts.

The Randall family's day out proved to be longer than expected. The boys were able to go home with their mother. Maurice Randall would not be discharged for another week. After the initial ups and downs he made a full recovery. He could remember nothing of the day at Helmerstead, but strangely never ate paté again.

Thanking God for his deliverance, Tommy Fagge decided to take holy orders. Joan Malcrow did two last favours for the Figg and Fagge duo. She set up a novelty chat show for Billy Figg and married Tommy Fagge.

Paul Wyatt and Laurel Rouse came to the wise conclusion that first-aid work was not for them. Their other experience at Helmerstead was more to their taste and appeared to hold more exciting possibilities. Paul joined the staff of a holiday camp and Laurel became a high-class escort.

For Henry Moulden it was one odd assignment too many. Edward Waterbeach paid for him to enter a residential home, but he would always become agitated when the communal television set was turned to Test cricket.

Proving that life is indeed a bagatelle, Marion Booth expired.

After her two brief encounters with the charity organiser Carla was cleaned up in hospital and referred to a rehab clinic where she stayed sufficiently long to be spared accounts of his trial and awareness of her lucky escape.

For Charles Brett life had to begin again. He suffered some well-deserved days of purgatory before the fear of the police knocking on his door was removed. Relief was mixed with frustration. The big consolation was that he was alive. The accompanying minor consolation was that when embarking on his farewell project he had left no note for his wife. Much as it pained him to return home he could at least do so without either explanation or recrimination. As the young Dayle had been his saviour, he decided to act as his, offering to train him up as his assistant. What he had failed to do for his own wastrel son, he might succeed in providing for Dayle with the offer of a second chance. He needed a new van, of course, but found himself in an exceptionally strong position to extract a bargain deal out of the proprietor of Martin More Motors.

As the full story emerged Jane Smith realised that she could not hang on to the emerald necklace. Basil was threatened with having somehow to make good her loss. He was helped by a consolatory cheque from Edward Waterbeach to purchase something which came within touching distance of Jane's exacting standards. The porcelain vase never came to light, but that was of no concern to Edward Waterbeach. It had neither monetary nor sentimental value, being itself an actual raffle prize which had come into the house following Edward Waterbeach's obligatory attendance at a local charitable coffee morning. He had spent generously on raffle tickets but had gone before the draw had taken place. The vase was delivered with a note from the organiser to the effect that she had chosen it personally as she was sure that his wife would like it. She had discreetly forborne to mention that when Edward Waterbeach's ticket had come out of the biscuit box it was either the vase, a bag of apples or a pink facecloth.

Whether or not Geraldine Rogers and Margaret Hamersteen would have embarked on the SS *Pink Lady* was never decided. On their return from a shopping expedition in the West End of London at the start of the following week they had been confronted in their hotel lobby by burly agents of the FBI. Some unexplained matters had arisen in connection with the deaths of their husbands. The two widows were wanted for questioning.

Their return journey to the United States contrasted in every way imaginable to their outbound voyage. They would never leave its shores again.

C. Ramsgate Fishburn was left in a confused state. His initial enthusiasm for the great study with which he had been commissioned had declined. If he was honest with himself his journey across Europe moving through one country after another which was either an associate, affiliate or prospective member of the International Cricket Council had not really helped him to build up a clear picture of the game. Then he had been gravely let down by his touching belief that his Scottish contact would be a fount of wisdom. By contrast, encountering the Outcasts had been a pleasure, but his head had been filled with so many anecdotes and snippets of information that he felt that he was no nearer understanding the true nature of cricket. But it did seem that it had a lot to do with drinking. One of the last things Winston Jenkins had said to him as they left the Sink and Plumber was 'You must go to Lord's.' And so he had hailed a cab and done just that. He was met by barred gates and an obstructive official. 'You can't come in here.' When he gave the man his card showing that he was there on behalf of U.S.E.L.E.S.S. he was still refused. At that point C. Ramsgate Fishburn's interest in cricket died. On his return to the United States he was reunited with his old love, baseball, and he set up a training school for that most sought-after player, the left-arm pitcher.

Good fortune attended the North Hertfordshire General Hospital, which had been put on full-scale alert as the casualty toll at Helmerstead had mounted. The decision had been left with Edward Waterbeach over what to do with the money raised by the event for a cause which had been found to be bogus. It happened that he was president of the League of Friends of the said hospital. So the answer seemed obvious, and in view of what had befallen so many people there was a certain symmetry about it.

Postscript

As he languished in prison it was inevitable that the events leading up to his arrest were turned over continually in his mind. Some aspects of the day itself remained a mystery. Yet one thing seemed crystal clear. His undoing must have been the fault of those bloody cricketers. The 'Reverend' Jeremy Large cursed the name of the Outcasts with increased vehemence. If he sought some sign from above, it was not forthcoming. There was no more than an earthly hammering on the cell door, 'Give it a rest, Rev.' The core clientele of the Sink and Plumber carried on blissfully regardless.

The author

ALAN HASELHURST was elected Member of Parliament for Saffron Walden in 1977 and appointed Chairman of Ways and Means and Deputy Speaker of the House of Commons in 1997. He was made a Privy Counsellor in 1999. He has been Hon. Secretary of the All Party Parliamentary Cricket Group since its foundation in 1993.

He is a member (and now an Honorary Vice-President) of Essex County Cricket Club, serving on the Committee for twelve years until 2008. His other clubs are Yorkshire CCC (the county of his birth), Middlesex CCC, Rickling Green, Saffron Walden, Halstead, Audley End and Littlebury as well as MCC. He is an honorary life member of Monton Sports Club in Greater Manchester. He is also a Lord's Taverner and a Chance to Shine ambassador.

He still lives in a part of Essex which he is doing his best to keep rural.